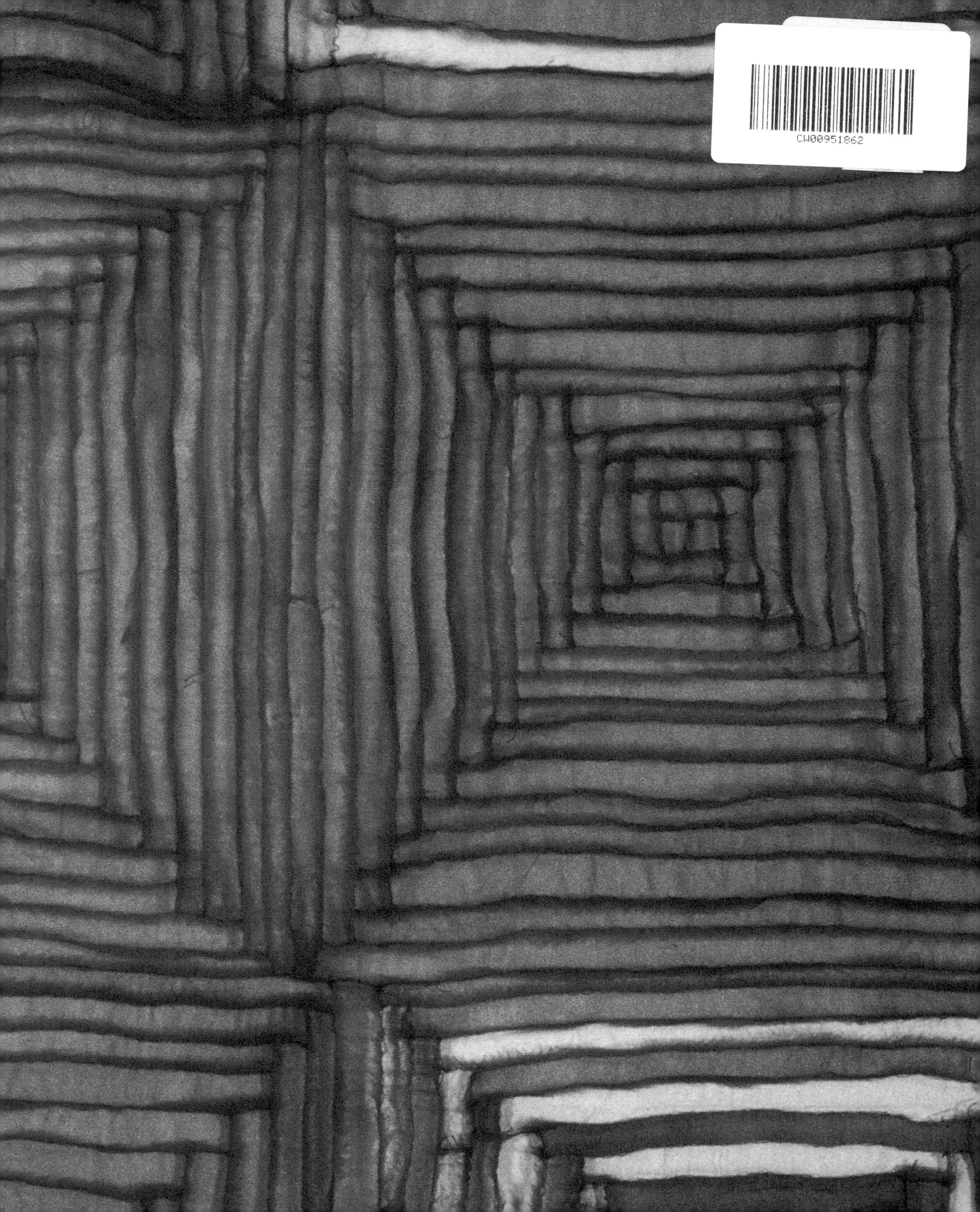
CW00951862

Linda Boddey
Dec 2003
reminder of our trip to
downunder

AUSTRALIA'S QUILTS

A DIRECTORY OF PATCHWORK TREASURES

By Jenny Manning

AQD PRESS

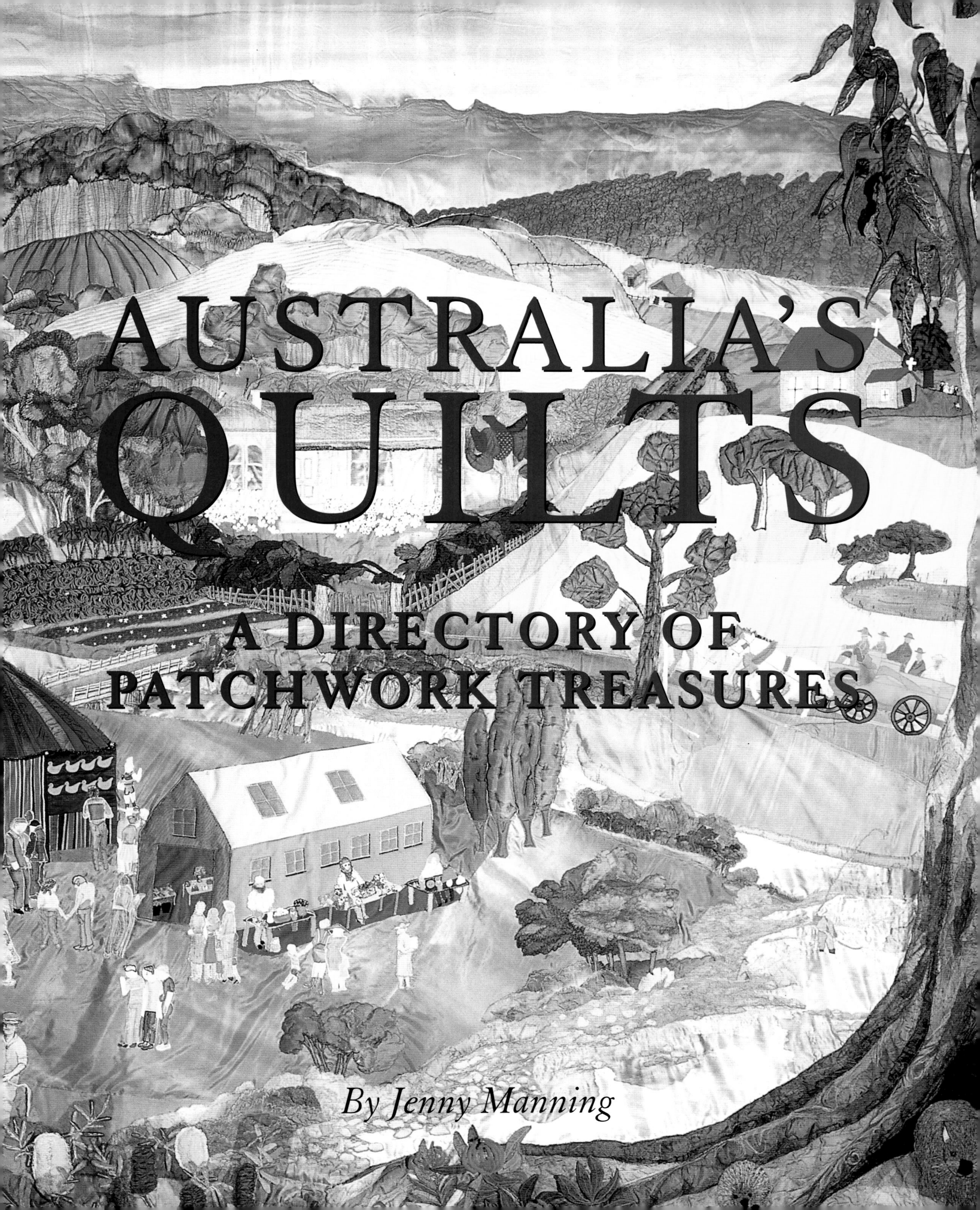

AUSTRALIA'S QUILTS

A DIRECTORY OF PATCHWORK TREASURES

By Jenny Manning

This book is dedicated to my daughters, Polly and Tess, and especially to my husband who learned that quilts, like food and football, become a consuming passion.

ACKNOWLEDGMENTS

Hundreds of people from many different professions and organisations throughout the country have contributed to the writing of this book. There have been quiltmakers, curators of galleries and museums, members of guilds, historical societies and heritage bodies. All have given freely of their time and expertise and I would like to express my gratitude to every one of them.

I am particularly indebted to the following organisations: the Country Women's Association, the Embroiderers' Guilds and Quilters' Guilds in every state and territory, the National Trust, the Historic Houses Trust of New South Wales, the Australian War Memorial, the National Gallery of Australia, the Powerhouse Museum, the National Gallery of Victoria, the Art Gallery of South Australia, the Art Gallery of Western Australia, the Queen Victoria Museum and Art Gallery, the Tasmanian Museum and Art Gallery, the Queensland Art Gallery, the Museum and Art Gallery of the Northern Territory and the many regional galleries in each state.

Several people have supported me from the beginning. They have contributed their knowledge, provided photographs, and encouraged me at times when the project seemed daunting. Jan Marsh read and re-read the manuscript and I am indebted to her for her care, thoughtful advice, and meticulous attention to detail. Any mistakes that remain in the book are entirely my own responsibility. Annette Gero wrote the foreword and spent many hours helping me with countless problems. Barbara Macey contributed her own research on quilts in public places and encouraged support for the project through her newsletter, *Ozquilt.* Dianne Finnegan lent me photographs and shared her extensive knowledge of quilts and quiltmakers. John McPhee provided a great deal of information, particularly during the early months of research. I am especially indebted to Elisa Wood for her brilliant work in designing the book. Several of my greatest helpers lived long distances from my home and became my friends through telephone conversations and letters. In addition to those mentioned above, I would particularly like to thank Jenny Armour, Cynthia Baker, Anne and Roger Bilson, Hilda Bloxham, Jill Cartwright, Lois Densham, Karen Fail, Maureen Hart, Jenny Madden, Jan Morrison, Mary-O Roberts, Alysoun Ryves, Ros Stewart, Shirley Thamm, Dorothy Waide, and Cath Wyatt.

My friends, Bonnie David, Helen Ogg, Jennie Burton, Diana Bryant, Dinky Ure, Jan Bohane and Thea Lessi endured more than two years of my obsession with good humour and interest.

My husband encouraged me constantly from beginning to end, supporting me through the many difficulties encountered and always believing in the worthiness of the project. He will be appliquéd into my next quilt with these words embroidered beneath:

Here's the man behind the quilter
And the treasure of my life.
He says *'Can't you take up cooking?*
You'd be a better wife!

HOW TO USE THIS BOOK

Each quilt entry has been listed under its location. Full address, telephone and fax details have been given along with opening hours. Quilt locations have been grouped by state, each state further divided into the capital city and regions nearby, followed by the country regions. Suburbs within capital cities and towns within regional areas have been grouped according to their proximity to one another. The index at the back of the book provides a listing of every entry in alphabetical order.

A brief locality guide has been included at the beginning of each entry. This is intended to give an indication of the distance and direction of each location in relation to the nearest city centre or country town.

The stories of the quilts and details of their making appear after a ✂ motif.

Specific access conditions are included with each entry and appear after a ✷ motif. They explain how the quilts may be seen and vary significantly from one location to another. Some have very liberal access, others may be restricted to certain hours. Volunteer staff open many historic homes and folk museums and may require notice of your visit in advance. The fascinating experience of viewing the quilts held by major museums and galleries is a great privilege requiring the time of curatorial staff. It is always essential to make an appointment in advance and sometimes it will be necessary to put your request in writing.

CONTENTS

FOREWORD

'Needlework, in all its forms of use, elegance and ornament, has ever been the appropriate occupation of women. From the shades of Eden, when its humble process was but to unite the fig leaf .... down to modern time, when Nature's pencil is rivalled by the most exquisite tissues of embroidery and fancy work.'

Linda Sigourney.
Letters to Young Ladies, 1837.

Over many centuries women, and frequently men, have used a number of different techniques to construct and decorate textiles. For many of us, the most exciting example of such needlework is patchwork and quilting – making use of needle and thread to translate fabrics into a statement of our surroundings and our society.

This wonderful book demonstrates how quilts are becoming part of the journal of Australian history – both the old quilts discovered in collections and museums around Australia, and the on-going tradition of countless communities to celebrate special events throughout this land. Many of the quilts have been created in joyful companionship, some in solitary inspiration. All the quilts in the book, the new as well as those with links to a previous century, have found their way into Australian collections. The continuous generosity of institutions has made it possible for us to view them while at the same time safe-keeping them for future generations.

What a pleasure it is to peruse this book – not only as a guide of where to see quilts, but also as a travel guide of related textile items and historical places. The old, the new, the hessian bags made into bed covers – in churches, museums, community halls, little village cottages, and even lighthouses! There are stories full of warmth and sadness, and also orphan quilts still waiting for their stories to be discovered.

As a quilt historian and collector of both historical and contemporary quilts, I was delighted when Jenny handed me the draft chapter for Tasmania, just as I was heading there on a trip. Armed with a tourist guide book and Jenny's pages, I soon discarded the guide book. *Australia's Quilts: a directory of patchwork treasures* satisfied my every need, not only in finding wonderful quilts to see, but also in directing me to all those other little treasures I would otherwise have missed.

I had a wonderful time. I was inspired by what I saw and impressed by the multitude and variety of quilts. It is wonderful that Australia has such an immensely rich heritage in this art of patchwork and quilting. And I would hope that the awareness caused by the book and the years of labour and love that Jenny has put into it will ensure that our quilting heritage continues to grow and will be viewed with pleasure, not only by us, but by the generations to come.

Dr Annette Gero
Quilt Historian and Collector

INTRODUCTION

Australia's Quilts: a directory of patchwork treasures celebrates the rich heritage of quilts to be seen on public display in galleries, museums, historic properties, churches and many other diverse locations in each state and territory. It has been written for all who love quilts, but especially for those who have the opportunity of travelling throughout Australia and seeing for themselves the patchwork treasures that are to be found in every corner of the country.

The project has involved a nation-wide search, an intriguing peek into the nooks and crannies of fascinating places, and the unearthing of absorbing stories of makers and custodians. Sometimes it has exposed treasures formerly lost, re-discovered in hiding places under mattresses or long forgotten storage trunks. Within each region there has been an attempt to include the quilts created recently as well as those of the past. Covers, wall hangings, patchwork clothing, and other small items of work that have been made using the techniques traditionally associated with the craft have all been included.

There are many articles dating from the late 19th century, often made from silk and embellished with elaborate embroidery, that were originally intended for use on tables, pianos, or the backs of sofas. There are several gowns made from patchwork, quilted petticoats, tea cosies, and a variety of bags designed to hold stockings, nighties and prayer books. There is even a Victorian chair covered in Tumbling Block design, and a three dimensional 'jug' made from velvet patches which is believed to have been used as a needlework case. Many of these items have survived the rigours of time – fire and flood, war and Depression, and the all too common Australian predilection for 'tidying up' which has often been exacerbated by our lack of attics and cellars.

There are contemporary art quilts made by the growing number of textile artists who choose quiltmaking as their medium of expression. These quilts frequently focus on new directions and are often unconventional and highly innovative in style. They have been created with the sole purpose of being hung on a wall and having moved the traditional craft of quiltmaking into the sphere of art, they have now been included in the contemporary collections of many Australian galleries and several corporate headquarters.

The locations included in the book are as diverse as the items themselves. Some are in cities, others in towns and villages spreading from the coast and islands off the mainland to 'beyond the black stump.' There are quilts in wineries, pubs, and lighthouses. A great number of old quilts are to be seen in the folk and historical museums established all over Australia and run by dedicated volunteer staff. Many of these old quilts are of great beauty and were created for pleasure according to the fashions of their era. There are also examples of bush rugs made from suiting samples and waggas filled with recycled clothing, the functional and utilitarian quilts made by thrifty women to keep their families warm. While some were extremely crude, others were cleverly designed with considerable artistic merit. Several on public display, like those at Griffith Pioneer Park Museum in western New South Wales, provide poignant insights into the harsh realities of an earlier life in Australia. History books often tell the stories of men – the convicts, officers, squatters, gold diggers, or the soldiers off to fight the battles of the Great Wars. The stories of women however, are not told as frequently and many of the quilts owned by folk museums provide a wonderful glimpse into women's history – from the clothes and furnishing fashions of the day to the economic circumstances in which their makers lived.

Australia has a rich heritage of quilts brought to the country by immigrants. There are many from England, Ireland and Wales dating from the early and mid 19th century which are now on public display in museums and guild collections. These quilts have survived the years, sometimes under extraordinary circumstances, because they were treasured either for their intrinsic beauty or their association with a far off homeland and loved ones who had owned or made them.

One of the many fine quilts of Irish heritage is a beautiful white embroidered coverlet owned by the Cavalcade of History and Fashion in Sydney. This quilt came to the colony of New South Wales in 1836 as part of the trousseau of Martha Mary Bagot. It had been made by the Sunday School children Martha had taught in Ireland and was given to her as a wedding present upon her marriage to Reverend William Stack. Reverend Stack was to become the first Canon appointed to the Chapter of St Andrew's Cathedral in Sydney.

A frail strippy quilt made in England in 1863 and now owned by the Old Butter Factory Museum in Busselton, came to Western Australia with Clara Staley in 1920. 'Aunt Clara,' as she is remembered, was one of the earliest 'groupies,' – settlers with little or no farming experience who joined the Group Settlement near Busselton. Clara and her husband lived in a hut with hessian walls and bark roof. And yet, through all the great hardships they faced while trying to establish a farm from the virgin bushland, the quilt made by Clara's grandmother survived.

Later migrants from Pakistan, Greece and Italy also brought quilts with them from their home countries. A lovely wholecloth quilt of Italian origin is held by the National Trust Museum of Port Pirie. Such quilts hold a unique place in the Italian heritage of this South Australian town, where they were used as part of street decorations during the Blessing of the Fleet ceremonies of the 1950s.

Old quilts are also displayed in historic buildings owned by the National Trust, the Historic Houses Trust of New South Wales, and other heritage bodies throughout the nation. These diverse locations include century-old inns, former convict gaols, lighthouses, rural homesteads, stately mansions and humble cottages. Historic buildings are usually a delight to visit, not only for the quilts to be seen in them, but for their heritage gardens, collections of antiques, and the light they shed on a way of life now gone. Some of the loveliest old quilts in the country form part of their interiors.

A counterpane which includes the initials of its maker, Elizabeth Leadbeater, and the date of its making, 1798, is displayed at the McCrae Homestead on the Mornington Peninsula of Victoria. One of the oldest quilts in Australia, it is the earliest signed and dated quilt in the Directory. At Woodbridge Historic Home in the picturesque Swan River Valley of Western Australia, there is a beautiful appliquéd quilt made by Sarah Evans in 1806, again with the rare and precious addition of the maker's name and date embroidered on the back. The charming and historic South Australian town of Burra is located north of Adelaide, a drive that allows you to meander through the beautiful countryside of the Clare and Barossa Valleys. Here, in a little Cornish miner's cottage dating from the mid 19th century, there is a fascinating quilt made 170 years ago from pieced squares and naively appliquéd motifs. In one corner the maker has embroidered the initials *'A.N. to S. N.'* and the date *'1829,'* both worked in fine cross stitch. The names and history that belong with these initials remain a mystery.

Quilt collections in the National Gallery of Australia, the state galleries in each capital city, and many smaller city and regional galleries all over the country have been included in the Directory. The curators of each institution were invited to summarise their approach to the acquisition and collection of quilts. Many chose to do so and their comments introduce these entries. Some galleries specialise in contemporary quilts, others in historical examples, and where there are many quilts within a collection, only a representative sample has been described.

The largest individual quilt collections in Australia are held by the National Gallery in Canberra and the Powerhouse Museum in Sydney, and some of the country's most significant quilts are to be found in these institutions. The *Rajah Quilt,* held by the National Gallery, was made by convict women transported to Van Diemens Land in 1841. A work of great beauty as well as historical rarity, it contains a finely embroidered inscription expressing the gratitude of its makers to the British Society of Ladies. This Quaker group worked with Elizabeth Fry to improve conditions for convict women and provide them with an occupation for the long voyage.

The rich and diverse work of many of the country's leading contemporary textile artists is also held within these gallery collections. While some of these quilts are totally contemporary, others combine the traditions of the past with innovative approaches towards design, content and technique. South Australian textile artist Sarah Crowest, whose work is to be seen in both state and regional galleries, has always been inspired by the way in which traditional quilts can document their maker's lives and evoke memories of loved ones. Her fabrics are chosen or printed for their personal meanings and are often associated with significant events in her own life. The salvage art of the wagga tradition, the Crazy quilt and Log Cabin designs have inspired many contemporary quiltmakers including Ruth Stoneley, Barbara Macey, Jocelyn Campbell and Elsje van Keppel, all of whom have work included in gallery collections.

Contemporary quilts often reflect our own unique place in the world and record powerful statements concerning the times we live in. Jan Irvine-Nealie's beautiful airbrush dyed and hand stitched quilts may be seen in several major galleries and are often thought-provoking works inspired by political or social motivations that reflect her thoughts and feelings about our society, its diverse cultural identity and its future.

There are several stories of inspirational wall hangings and murals made by community groups. These hangings are to be found in council chambers, libraries, local halls and theatres and they often tell the stories of their regions and of the proud communities responsible for their creation. Many have been made to commemorate historic anniversaries, particularly the Bicentennial of European settlement in Australia which was celebrated with gusto in 1988. The projects have frequently involved large numbers of people and required hundreds of hours of work. In many cases men have taken active roles as artistic directors, artists, designers or photographers. Sometimes they have built the frame systems on which the quilts have been mounted, sometimes they have kept the home fires burning for the makers.

Community projects tend to assume a special vitality, possibly born of the enthusiasm of their creators – people who have often embarked on the work timidly only to become emboldened by the liberating knowledge that their part is just one piece of the patchwork. Often one project has provided the spring-board for another. When Dorothy Waide saw the huge quilted curtain designed by Cath Wyatt and made by the community of Orange, she determined that her own community of Griffith could also achieve a stunning art work. Ned Terry spent a driving holiday in western New South Wales where he saw the magnificent curtain created by the people of Griffith. It set him on a mission which was to dominate the lives of many people in the northern Tasmanian town of Deloraine for several years. It ended in the creation of a masterpiece of community art – the *Yarns Artwork in Silk*.

Robin Stieger, the artist responsible for the design of a wall hanging in the northern New South Wales town of Narrabri, was moved to comment: *'I am reminded of outback women through time who have always needed to make beautiful things, despite harsh and hard environments, whether in painting, needlecraft, or their gardens and homes. I am so glad that 'our place' has a record of the quality of that ability to create, alive and well in the 1990s.'* And so it seems that the true worth and far reaching value of community quilts is not to be appraised in the tangible and immediate, but in something that continues to evolve over time.

From the early days of our history we have shared with Britain the desire to create beautiful needlework, including quilted hangings, for our churches. In the past, these hangings were often used as the poor man's Bible, and even when education for the poor improved such works continued to play a role in providing inspiration to the congregation. Many ecclesiastical hangings or reredos quilts have been included in the book. A brief description of the church itself mentions the existence of any stained glass windows, tapestry kneelers or other beautiful needlework.

From their inception, the embroiderers' guilds of Australia held strong affiliations with the British Guild and it was from this source that they learnt the value of establishing collections of needlework. Today, quilts form part of the collections of the Embroiderers' Guilds of New South Wales, Victoria, South Australia and Queensland, and all of them have been included in the Directory. The embroiderers' guilds were established almost twenty years before the quilters' guilds and they held the earliest lessons in teaching patchwork. Audrey McMahon, whose work may be seen in the collection of the Embroiderers' Guild of New South Wales, was one of the first teachers in Australia. She conducted classes on behalf of the Guild between 1966 and the early 1980s. Similarly in Victoria, Barbara Macey taught Log Cabin patchwork at the Embroiderers' Guild throughout the 1970s.

The Quilters' Guilds of Western Australia and New South Wales have begun the establishment of collections of quilts and these are also included in the book. From the beginning, each quilters' guild encouraged the formation of local groups, some of which have gone on to make wonderful quilts which are now displayed in public buildings. In particular, the Hamilton Quilters of south western Victoria have created several magnificent quilts which have been described in the Directory and may be seen in local buildings throughout the town.

Long before the arrival of Europeans, Aboriginal women kept their families warm by making cloaks and patchwork rugs from the skins of animals. They stitched them together with needles of bone and thread of sinew, often decorating them with incised motifs. These rugs were purchased by early European settlers who prized them for their warmth. Later they copied the idea and made rugs themselves, several of which may be seen on public display. A rug of chinchilla rabbit skins was made in Sydney by Oscar Bryant during the Depression and is now held by the Childers Historical Complex, north of Brisbane. Oscar had kept the rabbits at his home in Belmore, using them during difficult times as a source of fresh meat for his family. Another rug is now used as a covering for a bed in Montrose Cottage, the first miner's cottage to be constructed on the Ballarat gold fields. This rug, made from the skins of platypus with a lining of blue woollen baize, was in constant use by Colonel Greenfield of the Ballarat Rangers during field exercises in the 1880s.

There are very few patchwork quilts of fabric on public display that have been made by Aboriginal textile workers and it appears that quiltmaking has not become a favoured medium for indigenous Australians. One early quilt c.1840, now owned by the National Library of Australia, was made by Aboriginal children under the guidance of Miss Elizabeth Irwin. More recently, isolated examples of quilts have been made that provide a glimpse of the potential to be realised in the future should indigenous Australians choose to express their traditions and culture through quiltmaking. A quilt entitled *Biri Dancers* was made in 1989 by Coralie Wason, an Aboriginal textile artist from Kurunda, North Queensland, and this work is now part of the collection of the Queensland Art Gallery. Several non-indigenous tutors have worked with Aboriginal groups to produce stunning quilts that reflect the traditions of their makers, combined with the influence of western quilting techniques. One particularly striking wall quilt illustrating Victorian Koori heritage was created by women from the Ballarat and District Aboriginal Co-operative. Students from two TAFE colleges in New South Wales, one at Taree, the other at Cowra, also made vibrant, brightly coloured quilts that now hang on permanent display in the Administration centres of each institution.

Australia is a young country, European settlement spanning just 211 years, and many of our quilts remain within the living memory of the families from which they originated. Wherever possible, the stories of the quilts, their makers and their custodians, have been included in the Directory. Sometimes however, these stories have been lost and occasionally it has been difficult to trace the details of quilts made in quite recent years. The vital message for today's quiltmakers is to sign and date their work and preferably record their stories on the back of the quilt. So much of women's history has been lost. It is up to those with a respect and appreciation for the makers of the past to preserve for future generations the stories of our own lives and times. It can be an emotional experience to examine a quilt and wonder about its maker – ponder the conditions of her life and marvel at how carefully she placed her fabrics and tiny stitches, never dreaming for one moment that years later a stranger would look at her work with admiration and curiosity and wish that she could know more.

It is my hope in presenting this opportunity to enjoy so many of Australia's quilts, hangings and patchwork treasures that it may lead to a greater appreciation of our quilting heritage from colonial days to the present, and that as we approach the 21st century the stories included here may send you in new directions and inspire the creation of new quilts. I look forward to hearing your stories in the future.

Jenny Manning

Pieced Woollen Quilt. Said to have been made by freed Texan slaves, c.1865. 230cm x 165cm. Collection Powerhouse Museum, Ultimo, Sydney.

QUILTS OF SYDNEY AND NEARBY REGIONS

Powerhouse Museum
500 Harris Street
Ultimo, Sydney 2000.
Ph: (02) 9217 0111 Fax: (02) 9217 0355
Hours: 10.00a.m. – 5.00p.m.
every day except Christmas Day.
Approximately 110 quilts.

Ultimo is an inner suburb of Sydney located just a short drive west of the city centre and Darling Harbour.

The Powerhouse Museum, founded in 1880, is Australia's largest museum. It offers a wide range of exhibitions and related public programmes within the areas of science, technology and industry, decorative arts and design, and social history. Its diverse collection features some 30,000 textiles, including fifty historical and contemporary quilts from Australia, Europe, North America and the Pacific. There are also forty miniature Australian contemporary quilts. The quilt collection continues to grow through selective acquisition, by donation and occasionally purchase, of significant examples of the quilter's art.

✷ Viewing of quilts is by appointment only for groups and specialists. Groups may not exceed ten people at a time. Requests are to be made in writing one month in advance to Jennifer Sanders, Associate Director, Collections and Museum Services, Powerhouse Museum, PO Box K346, Haymarket, NSW, 2000.

The Historical Quilt Collection

✄ Some of Australia's most significant historical quilts are held in this collection. Included is a cotton medallion quilt (194cm x 225cm) made by Mrs Brown in Bowning, New South Wales c.1900. It includes a rare example of the use of an unofficial coat of arms. The central block features the emu and kangaroo in Turkey-red cotton, their heads turned backwards to peer at each other over the shield which is sewn upside down. This humorous interpretation of our coat of arms was made before the official version was proclaimed in 1908 and was used by the Quilters' Guild as their logo for the 1988 Quilt Australia activities. (90/732)

A red and white appliquéd coverlet (194cm x 195cm) of unknown maker was probably created in Australia between 1840 and 1860. It features red damask stars, hearts and hexagon rosettes stitched by hand to a white cotton background. The pattern and instructions for making this lovely quilt feature in Dianne Finnegan's book, the *Quilters' Kaleidoscope.* (A9565)

A Crazy Patchwork quilt (227cm x 193cm) was made by Marion Gibson who lived on a property called 'Narringa,' near Hay in western New South Wales. The embroidered initials of the maker and the date *'1892'* were stitched to one corner. Marion described the work as her 'Friendship quilt' because it was made from scraps of fabric collected from family and friends. Included are fragments from wedding dresses, ribbons, pieces from neckties, and even the crown of a man's hat. The quilt provides an important document of one woman's life in rural New South Wales. (90/731)

A patchwork quilt (176cm x 94cm) of embroidered school blazer badges is of unknown maker and dates from the 1950s. Most of the badges originated from New South Wales schools and have been machine pieced together and finished with a dark red binding and backing. (A7441)

A hand pieced quilt (245cm x 235cm) was made in Tasmania in the 1870s. The materials are tiny squares cut from the jackets and trousers of military uniforms worn by the 90th Regiment of Foot of the British Army. This regiment fought with distinction in the Crimea and in recognition of their bravery, were offered land in the Westbury and Deloraine areas of Tasmania. The quilt is said to have been made by the wives of some of the veterans, although the making of quilts from military uniforms has typically been a man's tradition. (98/48/1)

An American quilt c.1865 (230cm x 165cm) is said to have been made by freed Texan slaves shortly after the American Civil War ended. The four year war was the culmination of decades of hostility between the federal government and eleven southern states, including Texas, over trade, tariffs, slavery and states' rights. Slavery ended permanently in America with the passing of the 13th Amendment in 1865. The background of the quilt was pieced from woollen fabrics and the appliquéd flowers and motifs were cut from thick hat felt. (96/379/1)

The Contemporary Quilt Collection

✄ A hand embroidered and appliquéd story quilt was made by Mrs Mai Thoa, a Laotian Hmong woman, while she lived in a refugee camp in Thailand. Story quilts illustrate Hmong history, customs and legends and tell of the war and the escape from Laos after the American defeat in Vietnam. Mrs Mai Thoa's quilt illustrates traditional Hmong and Laotian village life – feeding animals, cutting fire wood and celebrating New Year. Around the border the many animals include two kangaroos. (86/705)

The *Suitcase Quilts* were a Bicentennial initiative of the Quilters' Guild. The forty small quilts, many of them by leading Australian quiltmakers, formed a

PHOTOGRAPH COURTESY DIANNE FINNEGAN

OPPOSITE: *Goodnight, Sleep Tight.* Made by Jocelyn Campbell, 1990. 203cm x 170cm. Collection Powerhouse Museum, Ultimo, Sydney.

upon thine eyes, peace in thy breast, would I were sleep and peace
so subject to rest to sleep perchance to dream for in that sleep what dreams shall come.
Good night good night

PHOTOGRAPHY SOTHA BOURN.

ABOVE: *Pieced Woollen Quilt.* Said to have been made by freed Texan slaves, c.1865. 230cm x 165cm. Collection Powerhouse Museum, Ultimo.

travelling exhibition that toured each state between 1988 and 1993. (96/379/1:40)

Aerodrome was designed and made by textile artist Jan Irvine-Nealie for the Quilt Australia '88 exhibition organised by the Quilters' Guild to commemorate Australia's Bicentenary. While this celebration generally resulted in a great many manifestations of nationalism and patriotic feeling, it also provoked some protest and questioning in relation to Aboriginal issues. Jan's quilt was made as a public and political statement on the struggle of Aboriginal people and was the winner of the 'Political' category. The quilt depicts a deserted landscape under a starry sky. A lighted circle marked by cones represents the structure of society and contains a windsock with the Aboriginal flag inside. The flag represents an integrated society, the windsock blowing in the breeze is a symbol of social trends questioning which way the wind will blow. Made of airbrushed dyed silk, the quilt is wool filled and hand stitched. (89/1607)

Goodnight, Sleep Tight (203cm x 170cm) was made by textile artist Jocelyn Campbell in 1990. It was intended to reflect the Australian wagga tradition of 'making do' and was created from recycled tweed, check and plain woollen fabrics collected by Jocelyn over many years. Some of the pieces were hand knitted. The design features a simple pattern of squares made from four triangles. The stronger colours used were intended to give the design direction. Embroidery was added to enhance the colour and detail on the work, the hand stitched words included for decorative effect and also to give the quilt a context. Buttons were used to tie the layers together and to reflect light. (96/393/1)

The museum has three quilts by South Australian textile artist Sarah Crowest. Included is a hanging entitled *Motherhood* (188cm x 115cm) made in 1993. During this period of her life, the responsibilities and frustrations of motherhood weighed heavily upon Sarah. Love and the desire to nurture her young child was so all-consuming that it diverted her creativity and spirit of adventure. There were simply not enough hours in the day. The distraught face on the quilt belongs to Sarah, her dreadlocks falling out. Her beloved daughter is sitting in the middle of her head with her hands covering her mother's eyes. The quilt was machine pieced using dyed, screen printed and painted cottons and has a cotton border and backing. (94/36/3)

ABOVE: *Ebsworth and Ebsworth Centennial Quilt*. Made by staff and friends, 1996. Ebsworth and Ebsworth, Sydney.

Ebsworth & Ebsworth

135 King Street
Sydney, NSW 2000.
Ph: (02) 9234 2366 Fax: (02) 9235 3606
8.30a.m. – 5.00p.m. Monday to Friday.

✱ The quilt is hung on permanent display in the firm's board room. Visitors may see it by appointment.

✂ This quilt was created in 1996 to celebrate the centenary of legal practice by Ebsworth & Ebsworth. It was made by Ebsworth's staff and friends and illustrates the historical and commercial influences that have shaped the firm's development from its early origins in shipping law to the variety of legal specialties practised today. The firm's logo and the scales of justice have been included at the top. An historical progression begins on the left and moves across the quilt to the present. Sewing techniques follow this same movement in time. Traditional hand appliqué, embroidery and quilting have been used to create the symbols of the early years, while machine techniques reflect the modern world of the law. Fabrics used include cottons, satins, and taffetas with overlays of tulle to provide depth of colour in the ocean. The lower border was created from personal items, ties, and dress remnants obtained from members of the firm. Three dimensional flowers were used to embellish it. The work was finished with hand quilting.

The Quilters' Guild Inc.

Suite 4, Floor 7, 250 Pitt Street
Sydney, NSW 2000.
Ph: (02) 9283 3737 Fax: (02) 9283 3274
10.00a.m. – 3.30p.m. Monday
to Friday.
6 quilts.

The Quilters' Guild Inc. was established in 1982 to promote the art and craft of patchwork and quilting throughout the state. There are now 1200 members who are kept informed of activities and exhibitions through the quarterly magazine, the Template. Meetings are held in Sydney and lectures by local and overseas quilters are included. The Guild offers a teacher accreditation programme, and an annual scholarship is awarded to further the work of an individual. Community quilts are made by members for nominated institutions and quilt valuations are also undertaken. Each year the Guild organises the Sydney Quilt Festival. Activities include an exhibition of member's work, a variety of workshops and a gala dinner.

✱ The collection of quilts is held in conservational storage but visitors are welcome to see them by arrangement with the President.

✂ The Guild collection includes a wholecloth quilt (204cm x 242cm) made

ABOVE: Detail of *Advent Banner.* Made by Barbara Watson, 1997-'98. St Paul's Lutheran Church, Sydney.

in 1916 by Mrs Stephenson of Binchester, near Durham. Mrs Stephenson was one of the last five professional hand quilters in England. The quilt was brought to Australia shortly after it was created and was purchased by the Guild in 1984. It was made from Italian satin in colours of ivory and old gold with a filling of cotton. It was finely hand quilted in an intricate all-over design called Feather which was one of Mrs Stephenson's own patterns.

A quilt of Suffolk Puffs (206cm x 254cm) was made by Mrs W. C. Moodie between the War years of 1942 and '45. A few of the fabrics were purchased specially, some came from friends, but most were remnants from the clothes of her daughter, Mrs Ailsa Daniels, who donated the quilt to the Guild in 1989.

The *Four Seasons Quilt* (122cm x 184cm) was made from entry blocks depicting the various seasons and sent to the Guild for a competition held in 1984. There are also two Signature quilts in the collection which were made to raise money for the Quilt Australia '88 exhibition.

St Paul's Lutheran Church
3 Stanley Street
Sydney, NSW 2000.
Ph: (02) 9419 6586
If the church office is unattended please leave a message and the Pastor will ring you back.
A service is held on Sunday at 10.30a.m.
4 quilted banners.

✷ The banners are hung on permanent display within the Church and can be seen most days. Please telephone the Pastor for daily opening hours.

✂ Four ecclesiastical banners reflecting the different seasons of the church year were designed and created for St Paul's

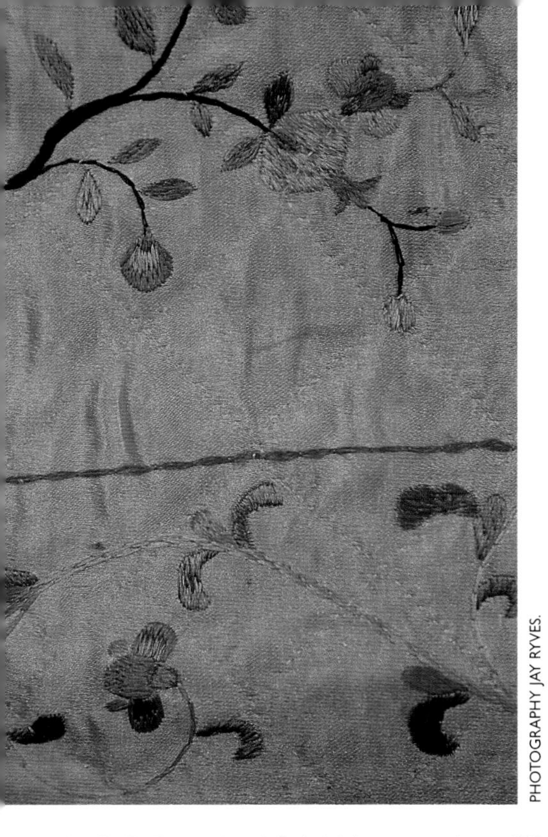

PHOTOGRAPHY JAY RYVES.

ABOVE: *Embroidered Quilt.* Unknown maker, c.1790. 215cm x 216cm. Collection National Trust of Australia (New South Wales) – Lindesay, Darling Point.

Church by Barbara Watson. Made during 1997 and '98, each banner is rich in symbolism and required months of planning and stitching.

The banners represent Advent, Lent, Pentecost and the Sacraments. The *Advent Banner* depicts the people of Sydney against a pieced background of the harbour and the Australian bush. The stormy sky of the *Lenten Banner* reflects the first Good Friday nearly 2000 years ago when the skies darkened and people were afraid of the power of God. The radiating blue circle of the *Pentecost Banner* symbolises the Holy Spirit spreading out to all the world. The traditional symbols of wheat and grapes represent the sacrament of communion, a waterfall the sacrament of baptism.

Each background was created from blocks of strip pieced fabrics which were cut up and then appliquéd in position by hand. Details were added in hand and machine appliqué and embellished with hand embroidery. Much of the work was padded to create dimension. The banners were honoured with a visual art award for outstanding design, symbolism and technical expertise by the Department of Visual Arts, Lutheran Churches of Australia.

Also in the City

There is a large pictorial collage displayed in the foyer of Parliament House, Macquarie Street. The work illustrates the history of New South Wales from the arrival of the First Fleet and was created in 1980 by textile artists Dawn Fitzpatrick and Lee McGoran. It may be seen between 9.30a.m. and 4.00p.m. weekdays.

Dawn also created textile portraits of all the Australian Prime Ministers and they are hung on display in the foyer of Darling Park, 201 Sussex Street. According to legend, every Prime Minister has had a drink at the Sydney Hilton's 'Marble Bar,' so it was in this setting that Dawn chose to depict them. Darling Park is open between 6.00a.m. and 7.00p.m. weekdays.

A commemorative embroidery was created in 1988 for the Australian National Maritime Museum, Darling Harbour, by the Embroiderers' Guild of the Australian Capital Territory. Designed by Sharon Peoples, the work has the theme of migration and of the many faces of Australia today. It may be seen in the 'Tasman Light' section of the Museum (just near the gift shop) between 9.00a.m. and 5.00p.m. daily.

Lindesay

1 Carthona Avenue
Darling Point, NSW 2027.
Ph: 02) 9363 2401 between the hours of
9.30a.m. – 1.30p.m. Monday to Friday
Fax: (02) 9328 2649
There are scheduled Open Days.
Other times by appointment.

The suburb of Darling Point is located 3kms east of the city.

Lindesay was built in 1834 by the Colonial Treasurer, Campbell Drummond Riddell. It was the first house in the colony to be constructed in the picturesque Gothic style of architecture and also the first house built on

Mrs Darling's Point, now known as Darling Point. It holds a fine collection of 19th and 20th century paintings and decorative arts.

✷ The quilt is not always displayed. It may be seen during an Open Day or by appointment. Groups of up to 20 would be preferred. Please telephone a week in advance.

✂ This silk embroidered quilt (215cm x 216cm) is a treasure of unknown maker. It originated in England and is believed to have been made in the late 18th century. Although frail, the colours of the threads and the sheen of the fabric remain unchanged after two hundred years. The top has been pieced from large rectangles of cream silk, finely sewn together by hand. The panels have been embroidered before they have been joined and there are small areas of motifs that have been sewn into the seam lines. The motifs include beautifully worked sprays of flowers interspersed with a variety of birds and insects. Each one is different and there is no repeated design. The stitches include satin and straight, French knots and couching. Very fine black pattern markings are still clearly visible. A myriad of butterflies, moths, dragon flies and other little insects have been created in intricate detail, tiny feelers even stitched in two different colours.

The quilt has been finished with a border enclosed between two rows of couched braid. It features satin stitched flowers embroidered along a curved trail of gold thread. The batting is a thin layer of loose fleece wool and the work has been quilted in a simple design of diagonal lines. The cream satin backing fabric was probably added at a later stage.

SCEGGS Darlinghurst
215 Forbes Street
Darlinghurst, NSW 2010.
Ph: (02) 9332 1133 Fax: (02) 9332 1858
8.30a.m. – 4.00p.m. Monday to
Friday during school terms.
2 quilts.

Darlinghurst is an inner suburb of Sydney located approximately 2 kms east of the city centre.

✷ The quilts are hung on permanent display within the school. Visitors may see them by appointment during school hours. Please contact the Archivist.

✂ SCEGGS Darlinghurst began as a small Anglican school for girls on the 17th July 1895 with one pupil, one teacher and

PHOTOGRAPHY ESTHER RUSSELL.

THIS PAGE AND OPPOSITE: The *SCEGGS Centenary Quilts*. Made by the SCEGGS Community, 1995. SCEGGS Darlinghurst, New South Wales.

one Headmistress. One hundred years later these two quilts were created by the school community to celebrate the SCEGGS Centenary. Every current student, as well as Old Girls, staff and parents were invited to think about what SCEGGS meant to them and to contribute ideas towards the design of the quilts. In this way it was hoped to capture the unique character and spirit of this inner city school with its diverse social mix of girls from all over Sydney.

The central medallion of each quilt depicts school buildings and special features. A huge Moreton Bay Fig tree which has stood in the school grounds from the earliest days has its shady branches extending across both quilts providing continuity. The books along the base were hand appliquéd and embroidered, each one recording a different aspect of school history. The hand-painted background illustrates the school's setting and close proximity to the city. Hundreds of leaves were made from layers of taffeta and organza and much of the work was padded to create dimension. The surrounding border of clasped hands symbolises the lifelong friendships made during school years and was created by transferring photographs of students' hands to fabric.

The quilts took two and a half years to complete and involved the work of more than one hundred members of the school community.

ABOVE: *Hexagon Quilt with Chinoiserie border.* Unknown Maker, c.1840-'50. 257cm x 232cm. Collection Historic Houses Trust of New South Wales – Vaucluse House, Vaucluse. BELOW: Detail of hexagons and border.

Vaucluse House
Wentworth Road
Vaucluse, NSW 2030.
Ph: (02) 9388 7922
10.00a.m. – 4.30p.m. Tuesday to Sunday.
Closed Mondays except Public Holidays.
4 quilts.

The suburb of Vaucluse is located approximately 10 kms east of the city.

Vaucluse House is the oldest house museum in Australia. It was the home of William Charles Wentworth, one of the most influential Australian-born colonists who was instrumental in the making of the Australian Constitution. The grounds surrounding the house and outbuildings overlook Sydney Harbour and research has established the original boundaries of the pleasure gardens, gravelled carriageways and rear service yard. The house is furnished as it would have been between 1827 and 1861 during the Wentworth family's occupation.

✷ The quilts are not usually on display. Please contact the Curator at least one week prior to your planned visit.

✂ The collection includes a beautiful quilt of hexagons (257cm x 232cm) hand made in England between 1840 and 1850 by an unknown maker. It features rosettes cut from pale cotton prints in colours of brown, pink, cream and blue. A Chinoiserie border frames a central square of rosettes as well as the outer edge of the quilt. It features Chinese figures in blues and pinks on a dark brown background. The quilt was purchased by

PHOTOGRAPHY PATRICK GRANT.

ABOVE: *Silk Hexagon Quilt.* Unknown Maker, c.1840-'50. 270cm x 240cm. BELOW: Detail of *Hexagon Quilt.* BELOW, TOP: *Wholecloth Quilt.* Unknown Maker, c.1850. 195cm x 160cm. Collection Historic Houses Trust of New South Wales – Vaucluse House, Vaucluse.

the Historic Houses Trust at auction in 1981. Ref. V81/50

A magnificent silk quilt (270cm x 240cm) of unknown maker originated in England between 1840 and 1850. Single hexagon rosettes have been hand sewn from vibrant silks, satins and brocades in stripes, florals, and plaids. They have been framed by a background of dark hexagons in shades of brown and black. There is a thick filling of wool. The cover is reversible with the back having the appearance of a wholecloth quilt. Made from a plain copper-pink silk, it features hand quilted swags and flowers worked in green silk thread. Ref. V82/71

A mid 19th century wholecloth quilt (195cm x 160cm) is also of unknown maker. The top has been made from a red and white cotton fabric, printed in an elongated chequer-board pattern. Sewn entirely by hand, the work has a backing of heavy calico, a filling of cotton, and no binding. It has been closely quilted in traditional English strippy designs which feature alternating bands of floral and chain patterns. Ref. V89/24

A quilt of random cotton chintz hexagons (194cm x 141cm) was made in England c.1840. It was donated to the Historic Houses Trust in 1981 and the maker is unknown. The fabrics feature floral, striped and geometric designs in the brown, blue, and pink colours of the period. The work has no filling or binding, the cream cotton backing hand sewn to the top around the edges. There are several small holes in the quilt top through which tiny fragments of the original templates cut from letters can be seen. Ref. V81/9

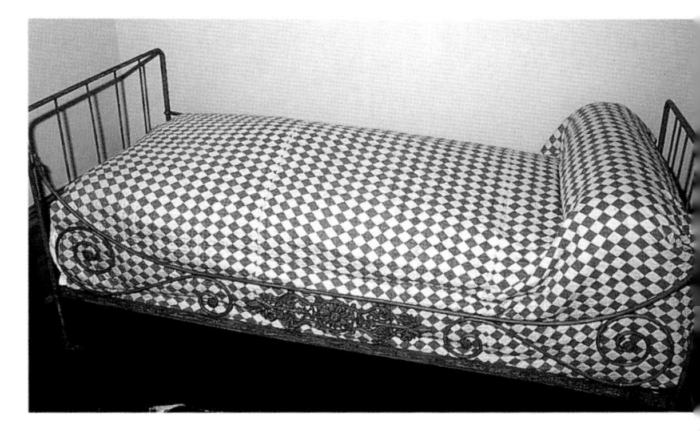

The Historic Houses Trust of NSW

Lyndhurst
61 Dargham Street
Glebe, NSW 2037.
Ph: (02) 9692 8366 Fax: (02) 9660 1426
9.00a.m. – 5.00p.m. Monday to Friday.
3 quilts.

Glebe is an inner suburb of Sydney located approximately 3 kms west of the city centre.

The historic building of Lyndhurst now serves as the Trust's Central Office and the Conservation Resource Centre. It was originally built in 1833 for Dr James Bowman and his wife Mary, the daughter of John and Elizabeth Macarthur. The Trust was established in 1980 and has grown to encompass the management and care of twelve properties within the state. Many contain collections of original and reproduction textiles, including quilts. There are quilts to be seen at Vaucluse House, Elizabeth Farm and Rouse Hill House.

The Conservation Resource Centre was established to record the history of houses, furnishings, and gardens in New South Wales. It also provides the public with access to information, original source material and specialist services relating to domestic design and history. The Centre is comprised of a Research Library and a Reference Collection.

The Research Library contains an important collection of architectural and furnishing pattern books, department store and trade catalogues, journals, pamphlets, charts, and archival material as well as reference books. Also included are original sewing, knitting, and crochet pattern books from the early 19th century to the present day.

The Reference Collection contains original artefacts from New South Wales houses. It includes wallpapers, soft furnishings, floor coverings, photographs, furniture and garden ornaments.

ABOVE: *Log Cabin Cushion Cover.* Made by Ellen Robey, c.1894. OPPOSITE: *Palampore.* Created by an unknown maker, India, c.1820. 198cm x 116cm. Collection Historic Houses Trust of New South Wales – Conservation Resource Centre, Glebe.

✷ The Centre is available to any member of the public wanting access to its specialised resources and materials. It is necessary to make an appointment. Furnishings and other objects from the collection are available for loan to museums and other institutions. Please contact the Collections Management Unit. Telephone (02) 9931 5214

✄ The Reference Collection includes a pair of palampores (198cm x 116cm each) of Indian origin, circa 1820. Palampores were Indian bed covers which featured elaborate painted and printed designs inspired by Persian carpets. The centre of a palampore usually contained either a Tree of Life or an over-all design of flowers. These central motifs were surrounded by wide floral borders and as such were the original medallion quilts. Palampores were enormously popular in England and were imported by the East India Company during the 17th century. They were available in Sydney from the early part of the 19th century, but unfortunately there are none with an Australian provenance that are known to have survived.

The Resource Centre acquired these palampores in London as examples for its collection. They were probably made in Madras or Masulipatam for the export market. The front panel is made of block printed and hand painted cotton in colours of red, blue, cream, brown and beige. The central pattern is a large tear-drop shape and this is surrounded by trailing flowers. At the base of the tear-drop, an onion form surmounts a scale patterned mound and is flanked by peacocks, tigers and rabbits. There are borders of trailing flowers and foliage on all four sides. The works are backed with a cream coloured poplin which has been added at a later stage. Ref. L92/6-1:2

A cushion cover of Log Cabin patchwork was made by Ellen Robey c.1894. It was created in the chequer-board design known as Light and Dark and the following story concerning the work was told in the *Sydney Mail,* November 7, 1934: *'This cushion cover was made forty years ago from strips of velvet in all colours by the late Mrs. Ellen Robey of Wellington, N.Z., for her trousseau. It is now in the possession of her daughter, Miss F. Robey, of Strathfield. The using up of bits and pieces is an art that belongs to the past rather than the present ... the cunning piecing together of patches from the sewing bag seem a tedious means of acquiring a bedspread or cushion cover these days.'* Ref. L91/107

The Trust also owns a bush rug c.1950 (222cm x 147cm) which was retrieved from a derelict building in Mudgee, New South Wales. It consists of rectangular pieces of men's suiting samples in designs of houndstooth, pinstripes, Prince of Wales check, as well as solid colours. The work has been machine sewn in a haphazard composition. Ref. L90/62

PHOTOGRAPHY TONI VALENTINE.

ABOVE: Details of *Irish Quilt of Embroidered Squares.* Made by Sunday school children for Martha Mary Bagot, c.1836. Collection Cavalcade of History and Fashion, Sydney.

Cavalcade of History and Fashion

Locations vary (see below).
Ph: Bonnie McCoy (02)9498 5331
Julie Henning (02)9416 1712
Debbie Thomson (02)9449 7075
Hours vary with the location.
4 quilts.

The Cavalcade of History and Fashion was established in 1962. Today the group has grown to include twenty six members who give their services voluntarily to provide this 'movable historical museum' for the benefit of many charities. They have a wonderful collection of heritage textiles, many of the garments embellished with lace, pin-tucking, insertion and embroidery.

Often historical details and delightful stories from the past accompany the items and are woven into the presentations with great humour, knowledge and understanding of the times. The talks are centred around several different themes. These include Pioneers and Petticoats, Doyleys and Dampers, the Allure of Lace, and a Colonial Wedding. This last talk traces the history of women and their weddings from 1788 until the 1880s and presents a visual feast of trousseau items. There are exquisite wedding dresses, camisoles, petticoats, nighties, and other historical memorabilia, including quilts. The parades are held in the metropolitan area of Sydney as well as many country districts, the location being decided by the organisation sponsoring the charity of the day.

✷ Parades and talks are held once a month from March to October and a programme of dates and venues is available. Information on forthcoming events in which quilts and other items of patchwork will be included can be obtained by contacting one of the listed numbers.

✄ A lovely quilt was made in 1836 and came to Australia as part of the luggage of a young Irish girl, Martha Mary Bagot. The quilt had been made by the Sunday school children Martha had taught and was given to her as a wedding present upon her marriage to Reverend William Stack. The work was made from white cotton squares, each one embroidered in neat buttonhole stitch with a different floral pattern. Baskets of flowers, Tudor roses, thistles and the Irish shamrock are included, some appliquéd as well as embroidered, with all the fabrics and threads in white. Surrounding these squares there is a border of shamrock at the top and bottom and a variety of flowers and leaves at the sides. William and Martha came to Australia in 1837, William becoming the first Canon appointed to the Chapter of St. Andrew's Cathedral, Sydney. Martha must have known that she would never see the children who had made the quilt again. This treasured possession has been carefully looked after and is as white and lovely as the days when it formed part of the trousseau. Ref. 79

A quilt of Log Cabin design was created by the donor's grandmother, Mrs Montgomery c.1870. It was made entirely from ribbons of silk, satin and velvet, some of them plain, others floral, gros-grain and tartan. Ref.187

A fancy dress of Crazy Patchwork is of unknown maker c.1890. The gathered skirt of velvet, silk and brocade has been embroidered with feather stitch. The exquisite jacket of the same Crazy work features tiny prairie points sewn around the waist and beautiful buttons of bone. Ref. 37. There is also a Broderie Perse tablecloth of chintz dating from the 1860s and a Crazy Patchwork tea cosy. Each piece of the cosy has been individually padded and the date *'1899'* has been embroidered in gold thread.

ABOVE: *A Day in the Life of St Joseph's*. Made by mothers of students, 1990. 5.25m x 3.25m. St Joseph's College, Hunters Hill, New South Wales.

St Joseph's College
Mark Street
Hunters Hill, NSW 2110.
Ph: (02) 9816 1044 school office or
0414 266 048 Brother Benet
Bourke's mobile.
8.30a.m. – 4.00p.m. Monday to
Friday during school terms.

✷ The quilt is hung on display in the college hall. Visitors are welcome to see it by appointment. Please contact Brother Benet Bourke.

✂ This pictorial quilt entitled *A Day in the Life of St Joseph's* (5.25m x 3.25m) was created between 1988 and '90 by more than fifty mothers of students. It depicts with incredible detail the myriad activities that make up everyday life at the school. The sandstone facade of the main college building with the statue of Mary above it was used as the focal point of the design. It was made from fabrics of paler tones, deliberately chosen to contrast with those used for surrounding buildings, sporting and musical activities. These were made in brighter colours with darker tones predominating towards the edge of the quilt. The tonal combination created an aura of mystical and spiritual light around the main building.

The project began with the creation of a half-scale drawing of the design. The huge background was then divided into 40cm blocks, each one numbered and coloured to the approximate colour of the fabric required. The curved background strips were pieced by machine and as each appliquéd motif was completed it was pinned into position. Finally, when all the pieces had been returned and their positions determined, they were hand stitched in place. Hundreds of details were added in hand embroidery. The quilt border, made from St Joseph's colours, required almost 170 metres of fabric. The pieced and appliquéd top was quilted by hand with up to ten mothers at a time working around a large frame.

More than 4,000 hours were spent creating this fascinating quilt which now hangs on display in the Brother Emilian Hall, a tribute to all who participated in its making and a magnificent pictorial history of the college.

RIGHT: *Hunters Hill Bicentennial Quilt.* Made by the Hunters Hill Quilters, 1988. 6m x 2.5m. Hunters Hill Council, Hunters Hill, New South Wales.

Hunters Hill Council
Alexandra Street
Hunters Hill, NSW 2110.
Ph: (02) 9816 1555 Fax: (02) 9809 7338
8.30a.m. – 4.30p.m. Monday to Friday.

The suburb of Hunters Hill is located approximately 10 kms west of the city. Australia's oldest suburb, it was established during the 1840s on a distinctive boot shaped peninsula bordered by the Lane Cove and Parramatta Rivers. Much of the 19th century character has been retained and many buildings remain from the earliest days of settlement.

✷ The quilt may be seen any week day during office hours. It is advisable to ring the Council before coming to ensure the Hall is not in use.

✄ The *Hunters Hill Bicentennial Quilt* (6m x 2.5 m) takes the form of a pictorial map of the area and depicts the approximate location of many lovely buildings and local landmarks. The background was made from irregular strips and outlines the boot-shaped peninsula and the rivers that surround so much of it. Yachts with rainbow sails, ferries and rowers are shown on the water.

More than fifty people contributed to the work, making appliquéd houses, churches, trees, boats, wind surfers and even the airship which was frequently seen hovering in the sky at the time. The quilt depicts Hunters Hill in November with the many Jacaranda and Illawarra Flame trees appliquéd in full bloom, just as they appear at this time of year. Dianne Finnegan drew the quilting lines and all the quilting was done by hand, up to eight women at a time working around the large frame.

The finished quilt was so enormous that it proved to be a huge challenge to Council engineers who had to move it from the stage to the foyer where it was to hang. This involved carrying it outside to the front of the Town Hall and removing the entrance doors! Due to excessive light exposure it now hangs on permanent display at the rear of the Town Hall.

Also in Hunters Hill

A museum of local history is located in the Town Hall building and is run by the Hunters Hill Historical Society. Its collection includes clothing dating from the 1880s, a beaded tea cosy and pin cushion, two Signature cloths, and an appliquéd mantel-piece cover. There is also a patchwork draught board made from the uniform of Private Malcolm Biffin who served with the British Army at Waterloo in 1815. The museum is open between 2.00p.m. – 4.00p.m on the 2nd and 4th Sundays of the month or by appointment. Telephone (02) 9817 2212.

There is also a beautifully appliquéd Coat of Arms framed behind glass and hung outside the Mayor's office. Created by Judith Burgess, the work was machine appliquéd and hand quilted.

Ryde City Council Civic Centre
Devlin Street,
Ryde, NSW 2112.
Ph: (02) 9952 8222 Fax: (02) 9952 8339
8.30a.m. – 4.30p.m. Monday to Friday

The suburb of Ryde is approximately 12 kms north west of Sydney. One of the earliest areas to be settled in Australia, many of the historic buildings have been preserved and are featured on the quilt.

✷ The quilt is permanently displayed in the Council Chambers on the 6th floor of the Ryde Civic Centre. Please ring the Mayor's Secretary before visiting to ensure the chambers are not in use.

✂ This quilt (300cm x 200cm) was made in 1992 to celebrate the two hundred years of European settlement of Ryde. Designed by textile artist Judy Hooworth, the work was co-ordinated by Mavis Stuart and made by sixty five community volunteers.

It depicts the history of the district from creation until the present day, the story beginning in the top left corner. The three dimensional sun is the symbol of creation as well as a major influence on the Australian lifestyle. The blocks below it represent the Aboriginal culture of the Wallumede tribe and the birds and animals of the region. These designs were based on Aboriginal rock carvings found in the area. The large central panel illustrates buildings and landmarks from the earliest days to the present. People, flowers, birds and animals are scattered amongst the buildings. During the early days of the colony, the area was found to be highly suitable for farming and a cornucopia of fruits represents the land cultivation and orchards. The Parramatta River flows across the base of the panel towards the embroidered Coat of Arms and the dancing figures. These lively characters were included as symbols of youth, future generations and growth.

The quilt was made in several sections for ease of handling. Each building and motif was created separately. Techniques

ABOVE: *Ryde Bicentenary Quilt.* Made by the Community of Ryde, 1992. 300cm x 200cm. Ryde City Council Civic Centre, Ryde, New South Wales.
OPPOSITE: *The Willoughby Banners.* From left, the *World in Our Hands,* the *Borough of Willoughby,* and *Under the Southern Cross.*
Made by the Community of Willoughby, 1988. Willoughby Civic Centre, Chatswood, New South Wales.

included piecing, hand and machine appliqué, embroidery, and fabric painting. Padding was used extensively to add texture. The work was hand quilted using a large floor frame and finished with green binding to match the zig zag border.

Willoughby Civic Centre
409 Victoria Avenue
Chatswood, NSW 2057.
Ph: (02) 9777 7849 Civic Centre Manager.
8.30a.m. – 5.00p.m. Monday to Friday.
14 quilted banners.

The suburb of Chatswood is located approximately 10 kms north west of the city.

✷ The banners are hung on permanent display and may be seen by appointment. Please contact the Civic Centre Manager one week in advance.

✂ The *Willoughby Bicentennial Banners* reflect the story of Willoughby's past, present, and future. They were created by the community over a four year period culminating in 1988. Local artist Malcolm King designed the banners and textile artist Yvonne Line organised the many volunteers and materials, directing the work from beginning to end. The designs illustrate 200 years of social history and follow a chronological sequence. They depict the Aboriginal domain, the arrival of the First Fleet, pioneer development, the effects of war and depression, change and ethnic diversity, and finally celebration and the future. Each banner was worked in small sections. Pattern duplicates were provided by Malcolm and these were used as templates to cut out the pieces. Fabrics varied from army uniforms to antique lace. Some of the work was appliquéd by hand, some by machine. Hand embroidery, quilting, smocking and weaving were also used. In common with many other community art projects, the banners engendered widespread spirit, co-operation and enthusiasm and the long lasting social and cultural benefits have been as profound as the artwork itself.

1788-1988

BOROUGH
WILLOUGHBY
VICTORIA
STORES
J HAMMOND
BUTCHER

LEFT: *Welsh Wholecloth Quilt.* Made by women at the Pontypridd Centre, South Wales, c.1930. 212cm x 205cm. RIGHT AND OPPOSITE: Details of *Chintz Medallion Quilt.* Unknown maker, c.1810. 177cm x 173cm. Collection Embroiderers' Guild New South Wales Inc., Concord, New South Wales.

St Aidan's Anglican Church
Downing Street
Epping West, NSW 2121.
Ph: (02) 9876 3362 parish office at the sister church, St Alban's, Epping.
Services are held on Sundays at 8.30a.m.

The suburb of Epping is located approximately 20 kms north east of the city.

✷ The quilt is hung on display behind the altar at the front of the Church. It may be seen during services or at other times by contacting Father James Butt.

✂ This quilt (360cm x 180cm) was designed for St Aidan's by Paddy Robinson and made by Evelyn Gray in 1997. In keeping with the Celtic heritage of the Church, the design features eight Celtic crosses. Each one has been created using gold bias appliquéd to a blue or purple background. The crosses have been divided from each other by squares of gold printed cotton which have been heavily quilted. A wide black border of Celtic work surrounds the blocks. The work was appliquéd and quilted entirely by machine.

Also in Epping

Paddy Robinson also designed a contemporary wall hanging for St Alban's, 3 Pembroke Street, Epping. It may be seen between 9.00a.m. and 5.00p.m. weekdays. Telephone (02) 9876 3362.

Banners representing Advent and Lent were made for St Mark's Lutheran Church, 56 Norfolk Road, Epping, by Barbara Watson. They may be seen by appointment. Telephone (02) 9876 2574.

The Embroiderers' Guild New South Wales Inc.
76 Queen Street
Concord West, NSW 2138.
Ph: (02) 9743 2501 Fax: (02) 9743 5320
9.00a.m. – 4.00p.m. Monday to Friday and restricted hours on some weekends.
Approximately 10 quilts plus many small items.

The suburb of Concord West is located approximately 15 kms west of Sydney. The Guild is only a short walk from the Concord Railway Station.

The Embroiderers' Guild New South Wales Inc. was established in 1957 with the aim of encouraging the art of embroidery throughout the state. The Guild conducts regular classes, weekend workshops and summer schools, and also offers a one year certificate course entailing the study of a particular technique. The library has grown to include hundreds of books and there are study boxes that have been compiled on more than twenty techniques. The Guild's collection of embroidery, patchwork and lace is exhibited regularly, both in Sydney and in travelling exhibitions around New South Wales. Guild members have also been responsible for the creation of several lovely items that are now on public display. A tapestry fire screen was made during the 1960s for Eskbank House, Lithgow, and a patchwork quilt was made in 1963 for Experiment Farm, Parramatta.

✷ The quilts are included in regular exhibits but may also be seen by request. Please apply in writing 3 – 4 weeks in advance to the Committee, P.O. Box 109, Concord West, New South Wales 2138.

The Historical Quilt Collection

✂ A beautiful chintz medallion coverlet (177cm x 173cm) is of unknown maker. It is believed to date from the early 19th

ABOVE: *Log Cabin Quilt of Grosgrain Ribbon.* Cornish origin, c.1850-'70. 162cm x 162cm. Collection Embroiderers' Guild New South Wales Inc., Concord, New South Wales.

century and was donated to the Guild by Prue Socha whose family had owned it for many years. It features a central square of Broderie Perse appliqué in which a blue basket of delicate chintz flowers has been surrounded by an oval frame of the same blue fabric. There is a parrot perched on the handle of the basket, butterflies hovering around the flowers, and trails of roses stitched to either side. Each motif has been cut from chintz and applied with a fine button hole stitch. Blue borders of strips, Squares-on-point, and appliquéd chintz circles surround the central medallion.

A lovely quilt of cream silk hexagons was made c.1940 by Miss Roma Fields who was an early member of the Guild and taught embroidery classes over many years. Her book *A Lifetime of Embroidery* includes numerous examples of her beautiful work and some of these are now in the Guild collection. The plain silk hexagons of this quilt have been used as a background for embroidered sprays of flowers, each one finely stitched in woollen crewel work. The quilt was raffled to raise money for the Guild and some years later the country member who had won it donated it back to the Guild collection.

A Log Cabin quilt (162cm x 162cm) of unknown maker was finely hand stitched in Cornwall c.1850-'70. Made in the design known as Straight Furrow, the light and dark areas are reminiscent of the furrows made in the soil during ploughing. Rich multi-coloured velvet and silk grosgrain ribbons have been used for the strips and have been sewn around central squares of black velvet. The quilt has a cream silk lining on which a floral monogram featuring the letter *'M'* has been beautifully embroidered in satin and stem stitch.

A wholecloth quilt of Welsh origin (212cm x 205cm) was sent to the Jenkins family of Gordon, NSW in 1932. It had been made at Pontypridd, a town near the Rhonda Valley in South Wales, by a group of women who worked at the Pontypridd Quilting Centre. This centre had been established during the years of the Depression. It enabled the wives of unemployed miners to earn a little money from their quilting skills and at the same time keep alive one of the fine traditional folk arts of Welsh women. The Duchess of York (now Her Royal Highness, the Queen Mother) came to visit the Pontypridd Centre soon after it opened and ordered a quilt to be made by the women. The quilt now in the Guild's collection is a replica of the Queen Mother's quilt. It was made from rose coloured cotton poplin with a cream backing and wool filling. The beautiful quilting design was worked by hand on a large frame. It is reminiscent of traditional workmen's smocks and features hearts, spirals, leaves, fans and lattice fillings stitched within squares.

The Contemporary Quilt Collection

A framed wall hanging (38cm x 41cm) was made by Audrey McMahon during the late 1970s. Audrey played a vital role in the post 1960s revival of patchwork in Australia. She taught classes in patchwork at the Guild for many years and popularised the use of pieced work made from silk to create op-art effects. This wall hanging was influenced by paintings done by Vasarely and features multi-coloured squares of silk, hand stitched together onto a background of black velvet. Audrey also made many miniature quilts and doll's quilts, all of them pieced in the traditional English method over paper templates.

A contemporary Amish quilt (103cm x 102cm) was made by Leroy Swarey. It was donated to the collection by Heather Joynes, Guild member and author of several books on silk ribbon embroidery. The work features a central diamond of dark red cotton surrounded by strips and triangles of purple and blue cotton. It has been hand quilted in a feather pattern.

A Crazy Patchwork bathing costume was made by Helen Whelan in 1991. The fabric patches of silk and lurex were machine stitched onto a calico base and lined with cerise water-marked taffeta. The costume was embellished with hand and machine stitchery, beads, sequins, and hand-painted pebble beetles.

Hambledon Cottage

63 Hassall Street
Parramatta, NSW 2150.
Ph: (02) 9635 6924
11.00a.m. – 4.00p.m. Wednesday,
Thursday, Saturday and Sunday.
Groups by appointment.

The suburb of Parramatta is located approximately 23 kms west of the city. It is the second oldest area of settlement in Australia, having been founded in November 1788, only ten months after the First Fleet landed at Sydney Cove. Hassall Street is located to the right off James Ruse Drive. Hambledon Cottage is set in parkland on the corner of Gregory Place and is only a short distance from Elizabeth Farm.

Hambledon Cottage is of Georgian colonial design and was built in 1824 by John Macarthur. It was part of his Elizabeth Farm Estate and provided a home for Penelope Lucas for many years. Penelope had been employed as governess to the Macarthur daughters and was also a close friend and companion to Elizabeth Macarthur during the long years of her husband's absence from the colony.

The Parramatta and District Historical Society have meticulously restored the interior of the cottage and furnished it in the colonial style of the 1830s - 1850s. The fine collection of early Australian antiques includes a desk that belonged to Reverend Samuel Marsden, Chaplain of the colony. There is also a lovely inlaid needlework table. In addition to the patchwork quilt, there is a beautifully embroidered Crazy Patchwork tea cosy c.1910.

PHOTOGRAPHY HILDA BLOXHAM.

RIGHT: *Patchwork Wall Hanging.* Made by Mrs Wood, 1865. Collection Hambledon Cottage, Parramatta.

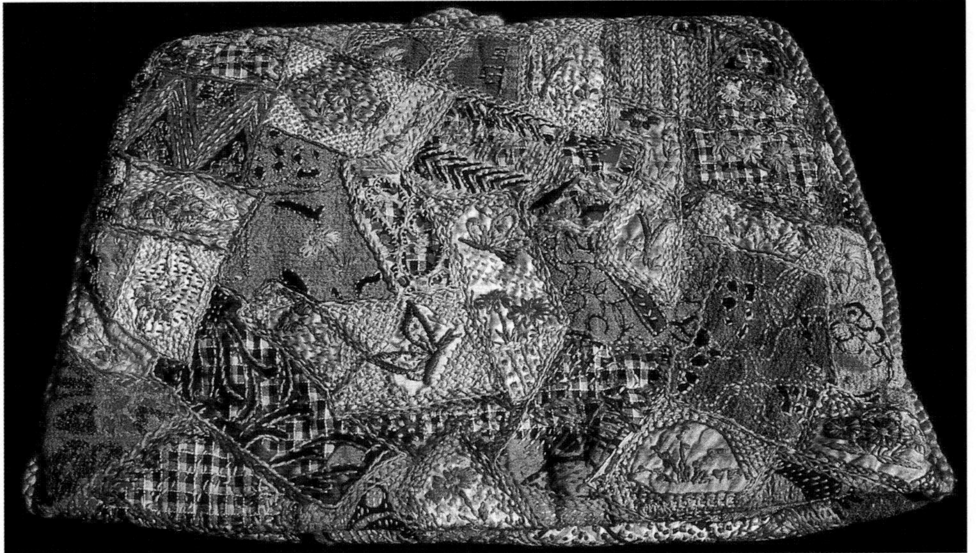

PHOTOGRAPHY HILDA BLOXHAM.

TOP: The maker's family – Miss Muriel Rogers to whom the quilt was given (centre), Mrs Wood's husband, Edgar (left) and daughters, Gertie and Florrie, (right) c.1928. ABOVE: *Crazy Patchwork Tea Cosy*. Unknown Maker, c.1910. Collection Hambledon Cottage, Parramatta, New South Wales. OPPOSITE: *Patchwork Quilt of Tumbling Blocks and Triangles*. Unknown maker. Collection National Trust of Australia (New South Wales) – Old Government House,

✷ The quilt is displayed on the grand four-poster bed and may be seen during opening hours.

✄ This unique wall hanging was made in 1865 by Mrs Wood who lived in St. John's Wood, London. Mrs Wood's husband, Edgar, had worked as a tailor in Queen Victoria's Court and in this role had access to many fine fabrics. The quilt was donated to the Historical Society by Edgar Wood's cousin, Miss Muriel Rogers, who lives in Sydney. A delightful and humorous woman in her 90s, Miss Rogers had travelled to England with her mother in 1928, visiting 'Cousin Edgar' during her stay in London. She had greatly admired the lovely quilt made by Mrs Wood which was hung at the top of the stairs to keep out the cold draught. Some years later Muriel Rogers received a large parcel from England. It contained the quilt which had been left to her following the death of Mr and Mrs Wood.

The work had been made by hand from squares of heavy woollen suitings and worsteds, all of them men's tailoring fabrics and all of very fine quality. Tiny snippets of brilliant satins, brocades, silks and velvets were couched to the background with embroidery stitches. Each square was edged with ribbon, some of velvet, some of grosgrain. Miss Rogers believes that the snippets of colourful silk came from the dresses worn by Mrs Wood and her two daughters, Florrie and Gertie. The quilt was finished with a wide scalloped border on three sides. This had also been made from the woollen suitings and was edged with a gold braid.

Mrs Wood was a skilled needlewoman and her delightful naive stitchery covers almost every centimetre of the top in completely random manner. The work pre-dates the era of the Crazy quilt and does not conform to other traditional styles of its period. Rather it was the creation of an imaginative needlewoman who had been given lovely fabric remnants and created her own unique design. The original curtain tape is still clearly visible, left in place as evidence of its 19th century history. The quilt is displayed on a wonderful four-poster bed. Originally it belonged to the Payten family, pioneers of the Parramatta district who purchased it from Old Government House.

Old Government House

Parramatta Park, O'Connell Street
Parramatta, NSW 2124.
Ph: 02) 9635 8149 Fax: (02) 9891 4102
10.00a.m. – 4.00p.m. Tuesday to Friday.
11.00a.m – 4.00p.m. Saturday,
Sunday, and public holidays.
Approximately 12 quilts.

Old Government House has a picturesque setting in Parramatta Park overlooking the River. It is the oldest remaining public

PHOTOGRAPHY JAY RYVES.

building in Australia and traces its history back to the earliest months of the penal settlement at Sydney Cove. It served as the country residence of all the Governors of New South Wales until the 1850s. The fine Georgian house existing today was built by Governors Hunter and Macquarie between 1799 and 1816. It now contains a wonderful collection of early colonial furniture.

✱ There will always be at least one quilt to see during any visit to Old Government House. The core of the collection is held in storage but the National Trust have organised a rotational display of the quilts. Each one is to be exhibited in an upstairs bedroom for a period of approximately two months at a time.

Quilts belonging to other National Trust properties are also transferred to Old Government House and displayed for several weeks a year. This often co-incides with the annual Sydney Quilt Festival. Information on forthcoming exhibitions is available by fax or telephone.

✂ The National Trust of Australia (New South Wales) has a very significant collection of 19th century quilts. Some were brought to the country from England, others were made here.

One of the quilts is attributed to Elizabeth Macarthur who sailed to Australia with her husband John in 1790. It is a large work (275cm x 285cm) and has been made from hexagons, hand sewn in the Grandmother's Flower Garden pattern. Dated by textile experts to be c.1830-'40, the quilt includes several fabrics, dyes and printing techniques that indicate it may be considerably older. The rosettes have been made from printed cotton dress materials, each one surrounded by a border of plain cream linen hexagons. The work has been finished on three sides with crocheted lace.

PHOTOGRAPHY JAY RYVES.

A quilt with many similarities to Elizabeth Macarthur's was made c.1847 by Lady Mary FitzRoy, wife of the Governor of the Colony of New South Wales and a renowned needlewoman. This work was never to be finished. Lady Mary died in a tragic carriage accident which took place in the grounds of Government House in December, 1847. The patchwork piece and several little rosettes were found in her work bag. She had sewn them by hand in the Grandmother's Flower Garden design over paper templates and the templates still remain behind each hexagon.

A magnificent quilt of Tumbling Blocks originated in England c.1865. Hand pieced from silk, wool and cotton dress fabrics, it was purchased at auction in London and later donated to the Trust. A hexagon star in the centre has been created from pink and yellow silk triangles surrounded by black points. The body of the quilt has been made in the Tumbling Blocks pattern and this has been framed by a wide border of large triangles. The work has been edged with a gold woollen fringing and finely quilted in yellow silk thread.

The oldest quilt in the collection is a large pieced coverlet (220cm x 245cm) of Tumbling Blocks and Hexagon Star pattern. Made in England c.1810, the fabrics include cotton, chintz and linen. There is a wide date range of materials with some as early as the 1780s. The Egyptian motifs that can be seen were very fashionable in furnishing fabrics used around 1800.

A quilt of Lemoyne Star pattern (256cm x 259cm) was made in Ireland c.1880. A cotton patch from a trade label includes part of the word *'Londonderry.'* The work has a filling of cotton, a backing of Turkey-red print, and has been quilted in diagonal lines.

Parramatta Riverside Theatres
Church Street (cnr Market St)
Parramatta, NSW 2150.
Ph: (02) 9683 2511
9.00a.m. – 5.00p.m. Monday to Friday.
9.30a.m. – 1.00p.m. Saturday.

✱ The quilt is hung on permanent display in the foyer of the theatre and may be seen during opening hours

✂ A pictorial quilt (250cm x 250cm) was designed and made between 1987-'88 by the Inner Wheel Club of Parramatta. Co-ordinated by Elaine Turnidge, the work celebrated the Bicentenary of the suburb on the 2nd November, 1988. It depicts many of the buildings from the earliest years of settlement and was appliquéd, embroidered and quilted by hand.

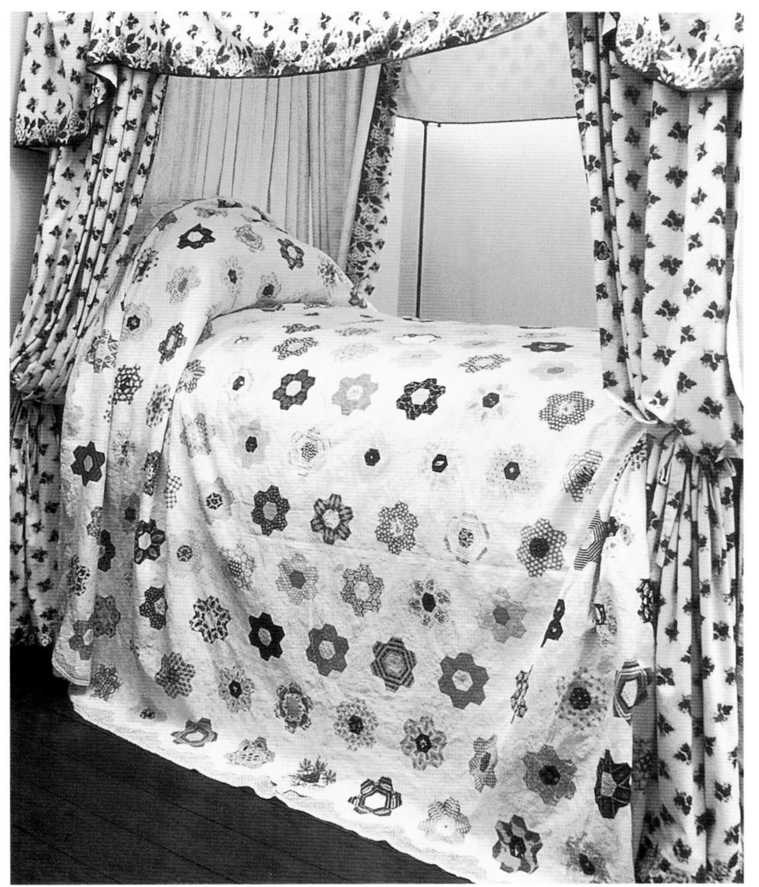

LEFT: *Hexagon Quilt.* Attributed to Elizabeth Macarthur, c.1830-'40. 275cm x 285cm. Collection National Trust of Australia (New South Wales) – Old Government House, Parramatta. RIGHT: *Reproduction of Elizabeth Macarthur's Quilt.* Made by Elizabeth Farm Volunteer Guides, 1986. Collection Historic Houses Trust of New South Wales – Elizabeth Farm, Parramatta. OPPOSITE: Detail of *Patchwork Quilt of Tumbling Blocks and Triangles.*

Elizabeth Farm
70 Alice Street
Rosehill, NSW 2142.
Ph: (02) 9635 9488
10.00a.m. – 4.30p.m. daily.
Closed Good Friday and Christmas Day.

The suburb of Rosehill is located approximately 20 kms west of the city.

Elizabeth Farm was built in 1793 as the home of John and Elizabeth Macarthur, pioneers of the merino wool industry. It was an important social, political, and cultural centre in the early years of the colony. The house has been meticulously conserved, restored and interpreted by the Historic Houses Trust of New South Wales and retains part of the oldest surviving European building in Australia. The interior includes modern replicas of original furniture, portraits and objects belonging to John and Elizabeth Macarthur which impart an awareness and appreciation of the house and its history. There are also reproduction soft furnishings and crafts from the 1830s and '40s.

✷ The quilt is displayed in the Pink Bedroom during the cooler months of the year. It can be viewed daily during opening hours. It is stored on site during summer and inquiries concerning access should be directed to the Curator of the property.

✄ This quilt of hexagons was created by the Elizabeth Farm Volunteer Guides Sewing Group in 1986. The style, fabrics and techniques used in the quilt attributed to Elizabeth Macarthur were replicated as closely as possible. The original quilt was made from hexagon rosettes of cotton and chintz surrounded by a border of plain white. The rosettes for the new quilt were made from remnants of chintz fabrics left over from the reproduction materials used for the house interiors. Like the original, they were surrounded by white cotton hexagons. Many of the guides who contributed to the project are still closely associated with the house. Ref. EF87/30.

Fairfield Regional Heritage Centre
Cnr The Horsley Drive and
Oxford Street
Smithfield, NSW 2164.
Ph: (02) 9609 3993 Fax: (02) 9757 4357
10.00a.m. – 4.00p.m. Monday to Friday.
1.00p.m. – 4.00p.m. Sunday.

The suburb of Smithfield is located 35kms west of Sydney and a 15 minute drive from Parramatta. A '*no right turn*' sign on the museum corner makes it easier to continue along the Cumberland Highway over the Horsley Drive, turning left at Brennan Street and left again at Oxford Street.

The Fairfield Heritage Centre combines the historical collection of a small museum with workshop space and a gallery where changing exhibitions are held. The focus is on social history as well as contemporary and community art. 'Domestic Life' including needlework is one of the strengths of the museum. In addition to the quilt, there is also a lovely embroidered cross stitch sampler made by early pioneer Caroline Stimson and dated 1879.

✷ The quilt is not permanently displayed but may be viewed by appointment. Please contact the Curator by telephone or fax.

✂ This lovely silk patchwork coverlet (143cm x 160cm) was donated to the Museum by the Woods family of Fairfield. It is believed to have been made by a maiden aunt c.1890 and was probably intended for use in the drawing room rather than the bedroom. The striking design of radiant mosaic hexagons and black four-pointed stars was formed by sewing together hundreds of small square blocks. Each block was pieced from four triangular and two diamond shaped segments, a pattern that was published in several needlework books during the 1880s. Miss Woods was a skilled needlewoman with considerable flair in the use of colour. Her coverlet has been meticulously hand stitched using the English method over paper templates and each shape has been outline embroidered in gold silk feather stitch. The myriad of richly glowing fabrics include silk, brocade, moire and taffeta. The work was never completely finished and has no binding or backing.

Rouse Hill House
980 Windsor Road
Rouse Hill, NSW 2153.
Ph: 02) 9627 5108
1 quilt plus other small patchwork items.

Rouse Hill is an outer suburb of Sydney located about an hour's drive north west of the city.

Rouse Hill House was built between 1813 and 1818 by the Parramatta Superintendent of Public Works, Richard Rouse. It was lived in by Rouse and his descendants until it passed into the hands of the New South Wales Government in the 1970s. The house and its wealth of accumulated contents therefore provide a record of the family's daily lives through seven generations.

Rouse Hill House is a 'Museum in the Making' and consequently is not open to the public on a daily basis. Monthly tours are conducted on the alternate first Sunday and first Thursday of each month. Bookings may be made through the Historic Houses Trust of New South Wales. Telephone (02) 9692 8366.

✷ The quilt is held in storage but may be seen by arrangement. Please contact the Curator two weeks in advance.

✂ The collection at Rouse Hill House includes a Crazy quilt (188cm x 150cm) c.1890. The maker is as yet unknown but may be revealed when all the family records have been researched. The patches have been made from velvet, silk, satin, and woollen fabrics and embellished with a variety of embroidery stitches. The border of blue cotton has been edged with large gold star stitches. Sadly some of the patches are beginning to show signs of deterioration. Ref. R81/139.

There are also two cushions of black cotton which have been appliquéd and embroidered with floral motifs. A green silk tea cosy has been decorated with appliquéd pansies, violets and snow drops and finished with an unusual gathered and smocked border. Ref. R97/119, R97/138, and R87/128.

Baulkham Hills Shire Council
129 Showground Road
Castle Hill, NSW 2153.
Ph: 02) 9843 0555
8.30a.m. – 4.30p.m. Monday to Friday.
6 quilted panels.

The suburb of Baulkham Hills is located approximately 25kms north west of Sydney.

✷ The panels are hung on permanent display in the Council Chamber and may be seen any weekday during office hours. Generally the Chamber is only in use on Tuesday nights but it is advisable to ring the Administrative Department before coming to ensure it is free.

ABOVE: *Silk Patchwork Coverlet.* Believed to have been made by a member of the Woods family, c.1890. 143cm x 160cm. Collection Fairfield Regional Heritage Centre, Smithfield, New South Wales.

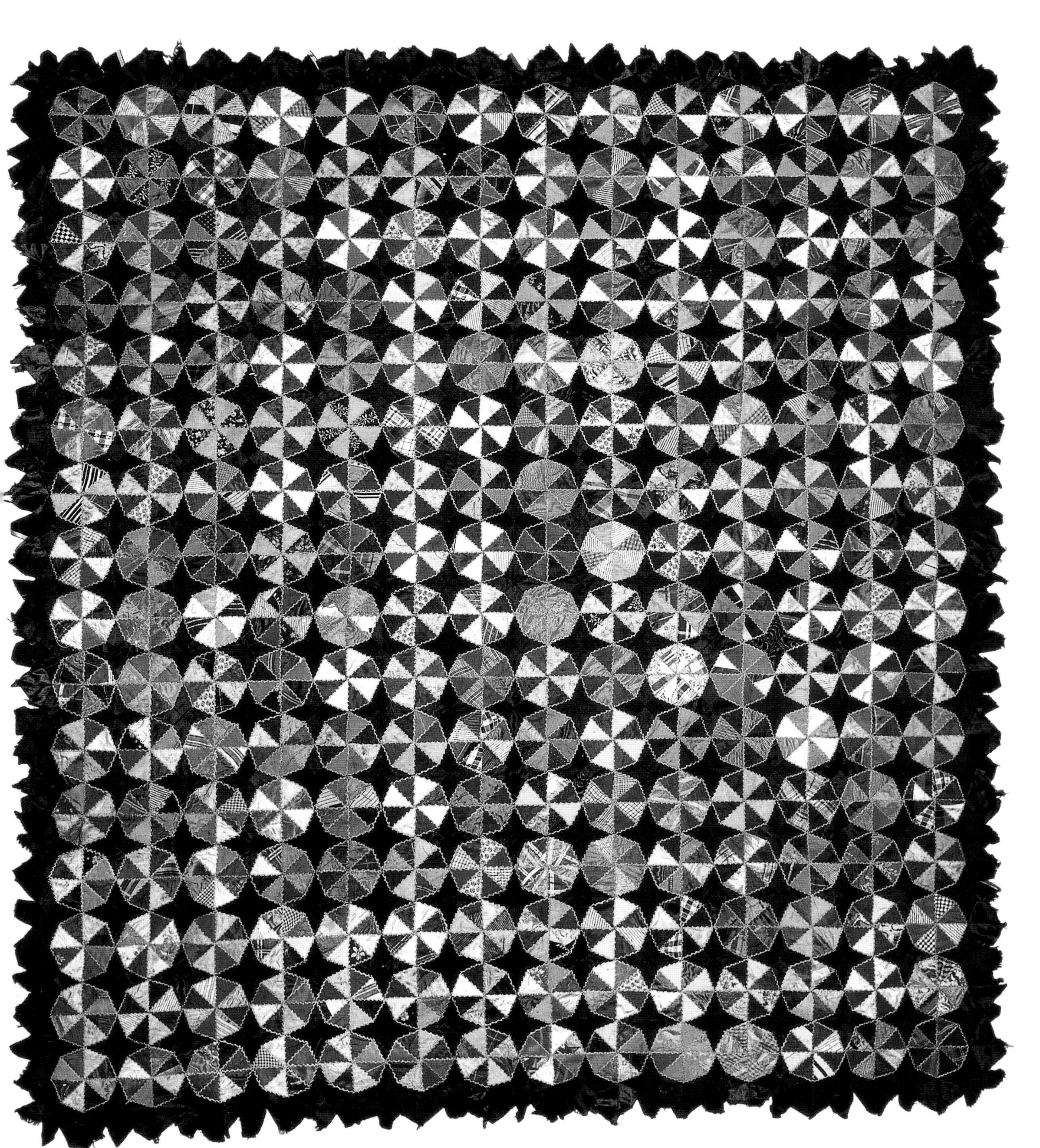

✂ This series of quilted wall hangings was made by the Cherrybrook Quilters between 1985 and '87. The group were commissioned to undertake the project by the Baulkham Hills Shire Council as part of the Bicentennial celebrations. A small committee of quilters led by Val Moore carried out extensive historical research of the Hills area before any stitching began.

The panels were designed by graphic artist Graham Wade, each one focusing on a different aspect of Shire history. The *Architecture Panel* depicts some of the region's historic buildings and includes Aboriginal settlement, early churches, the first public school, and a little worker's cottage. The *People Panel* shows Governor Phillip's first visit to the area in 1791. It also includes the early convicts who were treated extremely harshly with frequent floggings and hangings. There is a hard working farmer with his wife representing the many small mixed farms established during the 1890s. The *Flora* and *Fauna Panels* include remarkably realistic koalas made from fur, kookaburras with feathers, and Australian banksia, bottle-brush and wattle in a variety of three dimensional techniques.

Fabrics of diverse colour and texture were used in the work. They included heavy curtain and upholstery materials as well as silk, taffeta and velvet. Feathers, fur, leather, beads, wool and wire were added for effect and a vast amount of batting was used to achieve the soft sculptured appearance. Techniques included hand and machine appliqué, embroidery, quilting, wiring, crochet, knitting and beading. The hangings were completed by 1987, the Cherrybrook Quilters having spent more than three thousand hours working on their creation.

The Uniting Church
North Rocks Road
North Rocks, NSW 2151.
Ph: 9683 2586 or 9683 2425
Fax: 9630 0461
9.00a.m. – 3.00p.m. Monday to Friday except in school holidays.
Services are held on Sundays at 9.00a.m. and 7.30p.m.

The suburb of North Rocks is part of the Hills District of Baulkham Hills Shire and is located approximately 25 kms north west of Sydney.

✷ The wall hanging is permanently displayed inside the church and may be seen by arrangement with the parish office.

✂ A quilted hanging (300cm x 80cm) was designed and made for the Uniting Church, North Rocks, by Elsie Morrison between 1990 and '91. It features four separate panels, each one representing the new beginnings that are continually taking place in the church: baptism and confirmation, communion, marriage and thanksgiving. The work was made using the Stained Glass technique and is a combination of hand and machine appliqué and embroidery.

Campbelltown

Campbelltown is located about 50kms south west of Sydney. One of the earliest districts to be settled in the new colony, the township was officially founded by Governor Macquarie in 1820. Today the area has grown to become a cosmopolitan city, though it has still retained much of its rural atmosphere.

St David's Presbyterian Church
34 Lithgow Street
Campbelltown, NSW 2560.
Ph:(02) 4625 1037
The church office is open between 9.00a.m. – 5.00p.m. Monday to Friday. Services are held on Sundays at 8.30a.m. and 10.00a.m.

The beautiful St David's Presbyterian Church was built between 1840-'42. It is of Gothic style with pointed arches and tiny obelisks decorating the roof.

✷ The quilt is hung on permanent display and visitors are welcome to see it. Please contact the parish office 24 hours in advance.

✂ A beautiful quilt entitled *In the Beginning* (300cm x 240cm) was made in 1996 by the Embroiderers' Guild, Campbelltown Branch. Designed and co-ordinated by Elaine Balla, the work was based on the seven days of Creation. Each day was depicted within a separate ray emanating from the sun at the top of the quilt. The rays were set against a dark background representing the universe. The sea and sky were portrayed in blue rays, the sea teeming with creatures, the sky filled with birds. Fruit and flowers were shown blooming prolifically in the Garden of Eden and a magnificent Tree of Life and Tree of Knowledge created the focal points in the foreground.

The quilt was appliquéd by hand with many intricate details finely hand embroidered. The title was included along the base using gold padded satin stitch which was then outlined and decorated with stem stitch. The work was finished with hand quilting.

OPPOSITE: Details of the *People Panel* (left) and the *Flora Panel* (right). Made by the Cherrybrook Quilters, 1985-'87. Baulkham Hills Shire Council, Castle Hill, New South Wales.

BAULKHAM HILLS
SHIRE

Camden

The historic township of Camden is set on the banks of the Nepean River, approximately an hour's drive south west of Sydney. The area was originally known as 'Cowpastures,' a name it had been given by Governor Hunter in 1795 because of the small herd of cattle found there. The cows had strayed from the First Fleet Settlement at Sydney Cove in 1788 and although wild, had thrived on the natural pasture land in the region. This same herd went on to form the beginning of the cattle and beef industries in the new colony and were hailed as having saved the fledgling settlement from starvation. Cowpastures was to become the birthplace of many industries and these are commemorated on the quilt for the role they played in the progress of the nation. A walking tour of the town outlines the history of many of the heritage buildings illustrated on the quilt.

Camden Civic Centre
Oxley Street
Camden, NSW 2570.
Ph: (02) 4655 8681 Fax: (02) 4655 3334
8.30a.m. – 5.00p.m. Monday to Friday.
10.00a.m. – 2.00p.m. Saturday.

✷ The quilt is hung on permanent display in the foyer of the Civic Centre and may be seen during the hours listed.

✄ The *Cowpastures Heritage Quilt* (242cm x 242cm) was designed and made by the Camden Country Quilters to celebrate the Bicentenary of the region in 1995. The quilt provides a pictorial history of the area with the large central panel illustrating the story of the Hottentot cows from which it derived its name. Cowpastures was of special significance to Aborigines who used the area as a meeting place to settle differences, to make laws, for marriage rituals as well as for social interaction. Their part in the region's history has been depicted above the map. The natural resources of coal and silver, as well as the vineyards and market gardens that have always thrived in the region's fertile soil, have also been shown. John and Elizabeth Macarthur, pioneers of the Australian wool industry, had extensive land holdings at Cowpastures. Their embroidered portraits as well as their property 'Camden Park Estate' have been included in the top corner. Here too, is St John's Anglican Church, erected on land specially selected and granted by the Macarthurs. Historic John Street which still retains many of the original settler's cottages, has been illustrated in the foreground. More than two years were spent creating this lovely quilt. It was divided into four separate sections for ease of construction and was hand appliquéd, embroidered and quilted.

Gosford

The Central Coast town of Gosford is nestled in a picturesque setting surrounded by hills and overlooking the Brisbane Water. It is a one hour drive north of Sydney and about the same distance from Newcastle. Established during the 1830s, the region was first settled by pioneers attracted to the vast timber resources. The arrival of the railway in 1887 made the area easily accessible from Sydney and it began to develop as a popular tourist destination. Holiday homes, boarding and guest houses were built to cater for the many visitors who came to enjoy the nearby beaches, excellent sailing and fishing. This has continued until the present day with the town developing as the major focal point within the region for shopping and other services.

Henry Kendall Cottage and Historical Museum
27 Henry Kendall Street
West Gosford, NSW 2250.
Ph: 02) 4325 2270
10.00a.m. – 4.00p.m. Wednesday, Saturday, Sunday, all public and school holidays except Good Friday and Christmas Day.
Tours by appointment.

Henry Kendall Cottage was built in 1836 by Irish immigrant, Peter Fagan. The property was constructed by convict labour and for some years was licensed as the 'Red Cow Inn.' The Australian poet, Henry Kendall, lived in the cottage during the early 1870s. The property was purchased by the Brisbane Water Historical Society in 1960 and after extensive renovations it was opened to the public. A new museum was built adjacent to the cottage in 1983 and this houses a wealth of historical memorabilia from Gosford and the surrounding district. There is a changing showcase of period costumes which includes wedding dresses, ball gowns, heirloom underwear and nighties. There is also an extensive collection of embroidered linen, hand made lace, hand knitted and hand crocheted bedspreads, and a Crazy Patchwork tea cosy c.1890.

✷ The quilt is permanently displayed on an old iron bed in the cottage and may be seen during opening hours or by appointment.

✄ This interesting patchwork quilt of squares (225cm x 225cm) was created by an unknown maker c.1945. It has been stitched by hand in a chequer-board

ABOVE: *Cowpastures Heritage Quilt.* Made by the Camden Country Quilters, 1995. 242cm x 242cm. Camden Civic Centre, Camden, New South Wales.

design known as Trip Around the World. Some of the squares have been cut from a cotton print which includes the New Zealand kiwi bird along with the initials *'N.Z.'* and the dates *'1840–1940.'* The fabric commemorates the centenary of the signing of the Treaty of Waitangi on the 5th of February, 1840. On this date, the signatures of more than forty leading Maori chiefs, along with the first Governor of New Zealand, William Hobson, were formally assigned to the document. Initially, the Treaty represented a respect for the rights of the indigenous population by the colonising government.

ABOVE: *Trip Around the World Quilt.* Unknown maker, c.1945. Collection Henry Kendall Cottage, Gosford, New South Wales. RIGHT: Detail showing Treaty of Waitangi Commemorative Print. OPPOSITE: *Medallion Quilt.* Made by Mary Moxey, c.1818-'37. 237cm x 240cm. Collection Grossmann House, Maitland.

In later years it also came to be seen as a symbol of the birth of the nation. The quilt has been lined and edged with fine white cotton lawn. It was donated to the cottage in the 1970s and it is not known if it was made in New Zealand and then brought to Australia or made here using fabric purchased in New Zealand.

Singleton

Singleton is located in the heart of the Hunter Valley. Dairy farms, vineyards, and vegetables have always thrived in this rich countryside and the massive coal resources have made the region the state's largest coal producer.

All Saints Anglican Church
High Street
Singleton, NSW 2330.
Ph/fax: (02) 6571 1414
The church is open everyday from 7.30a.m. Services are held each Saturday at 5.30p.m. and Sunday at 8.00a.m. and 9.30a.m.

The magnificent All Saints Church was built in 1913 on the site of the original Anglican church. The Sunday School built in 1854 still stands in the grounds. In addition to the hanging, there is a beautiful collection of tapestry kneelers made by local embroiderers.

✷ The wall hanging is permanently displayed within the Church and may be seen during the hours listed.

✂ This large hanging (360cm x 375cm) was made in 1983 by three local school teachers, Margaret Beal, Janet Fenwick and Desnie Logan. The idea had come from Reverend Lindsay McLoughlin who believed it would be an inspiring way to celebrate the 70th Anniversary of All Saints. The work depicts the church as the hub of the community surrounded by all the day to day activities of the people in the town and countryside. Grapes frame the top and left side as symbols of the renowned Hunter vineyards. The coal train appears in the foreground, the railway station to its right. There are many touches of local humour. The railway clock indicates a different time of day from the church clock, the quilters being well aware that trains never run on time! The driver of the little car stopped at the railway crossing is Reverend McLoughlin. The beautiful 1870s Gothic rectory is shown beneath the church, the rector's chooks pecking happily around the front garden. Scrap fabrics of diverse textures were used in the creation of the hanging, some specially dyed to achieve a desired colour. Most of the work was appliquéd, some by hand and some by machine.

Maitland

Maitland is only a half hour drive west of Newcastle. Its history dates back to the earliest settlement of the colony and many of the historic buildings remain from the 1820s. Heritage walking tours have been designed to show visitors the three separate towns that originally made up the present city.

Grossmann House
Church Street
Maitland, NSW 2320.
Ph: (02) 4933 6452
1.30p.m. – 4.30p.m. Saturday and
Sunday or by appointment.
2 quilts.

Grossmann House was built in 1870 by Isaac Beckett. It was designed as an architectural mirror of its neighbour, Brough House, in which Beckett's partner Samuel Owen lived. The property has been restored and furnished by the National Trust and contains a superb collection of Victorian furniture and memorabilia.

PHOTOGRAPHY JAY RYVES.

✷ The two quilts are alternated for display so that there will always be one to be seen. The volunteer guides are happy to make the other quilt available for viewing provided they are given sufficient notice. Please telephone the custodian one week in advance between 8.00a.m. and 10.00a.m. or 2.30p.m. and 4.30p.m. week days or weekend hours as listed.

✂ This lovely medallion quilt (237cm x 240cm) was made by Mary Moxey, a member of an early pioneering family from Williamstown in the Hunter Valley. Mary's name and the date *'1818'* have been embroidered in cross stitch using gold silk thread. The central square contains a printed octagonal motif of Broderie Perse appliqué and has been bordered with rounded triangles and flowers. Some of the fabrics have been dated c.1815-'20. The name *'Emma Tremlett'* and the information *'Born Decr 16th 1837'* has been added at a later stage. Borders of diamonds, hexagons, hexagon rosettes and sashes of printed cotton have been added around the medallion. The quilt has been finished with a dog tooth edge of striped cotton. It has a backing of cream linen and no filling. (ref 84.749)

A white coverlet of Suffolk Puffs (238cm x 257cm) was created c.1900 by an unknown maker. It is known as the *'Bluebag Quilt'* because the fabrics used in its making came from the cotton squares containing Reckett's Blue, a laundering agent used for whitening linens in the days before bleach was introduced. The squares were collected, cut into circles, gathered around the outside edge and then sewn together by hand. This coverlet has been finished with a deep crochet fringe and has a white lining on which the only clue to its maker appears. The names *'C. Bleagard'* and *Baby Ken'* have been written in black ink. (ref 84.275-1:2)

Also in Maitland

The Maitland City Art Gallery has a collection of 17 quilts (100cm x 70cm each) created by the Maitland Patchwork Quilters between 1992-'93. Together they form an Education Kit which illustrates many traditional designs. Each quilt is accompanied by detailed documentation explaining all the processes involved in its making. The pattern, templates, fabric samples and instructions have been recorded, along with a profile of the maker. The quilts are displayed intermittently throughout the year and may also be viewed by appointment with the Curator. The Gallery is located in Brough House, 64 Church Street, Maitland. Telephone (02)4933 1657.

Newcastle

Set on a spectacular harbour, the maritime city of Newcastle is only a ninety minute drive north of Sydney. The area around the foreshore has been re-developed with the charming Queens Wharf as the focal point.

Newcastle Court House
Church Street
Newcastle, NSW 2300.
Ph:(02) 4921 2200
9.30a.m. – 4.00p.m. Monday to Friday.

✷ The quilt is permanently displayed in the foyer of the new Court House (uphill from the original building). It may be seen during the hours listed.

✂ This quilt entitled *Images of Newcastle* (375cm x 186cm) was designed by Mary Beeston. It was made to commemorate the Bicentennial in 1988 by members of the Novocastrian Quilters. The work depicts major landmarks of Newcastle and the surrounding region. Deep red fabrics have been used to illustrate the imposing building of Christ Church Cathedral. Behind it are the soft hues of the ocean and the famous Nobby's Lighthouse, the guiding signal for the many ships that enter and leave the busy port. Also shown are the terrace houses and cottages of Cooks Hill and the towering structure of BHP on the horizon. The work was created almost entirely by piecing. Extensive hand quilting was used to emphasise the waves and breakers on the shoreline, the clouds and wind in the sky, and the details of stone and brickwork on buildings.

Also in Newcastle

The magnificent Christ Church Cathedral which dominates the city skyline has a fascinating collection of treasures. Seriously damaged in the earthquake of 1989, the building has undergone painstaking and meticulous restoration and it is only recently that these treasures have been returned to the Church. Included is a tapestry wall hanging by Mary Beeston and twelve banners appliquéd in Australian wool by Rae Richards. There are guided tours of the restoration, history and treasures every Saturday and Sunday between 2.00p.m and 5.00p.m.

A wall hanging entitled the *Newcastle Embroidery* may be seen displayed in City Hall, King Street. It was created by the Embroiderers' Guild as a Bicentennial gift to the community.

There are two large appliquéd banners to be seen at St John's, the oldest church in Newcastle. This lovely building, located in the charming inner suburb of Cooks Hill, was designed by colonial architect Edmund Blacket and is renowned for its beautiful stained glass windows.

In the Nearby Region

Taree is situated north of Newcastle, about half way between Forster and Port Macquarie. There is a stunning embroidered wall hanging to be seen at the Manning Valley Tourist Information Centre, Pacific Highway, Taree North. Designed by Hazel Slip, the work was made by the Manning Valley Embroidery Group in 1988 as a Bicentennial gift to the community. Framed in a glass case, it presents a pictorial history of the Valley and has been made with hundreds of different stitches and threads.Techniques range from appliqué and overlay work to couching, surface stitchery, stumpwork and crewel embroidery. The Centre is open daily, except Christmas Day and Good Friday. Telephone (02) 6552 1900.

Also in Taree, a quilt was made by Aboriginal students and is now hung on permanent display in the Administration Building of the North Coast Institute of TAFE, Taree Campus, in Montgomery Avenue. The quilt, entitled *Winmarra Wirrama,* was made in 1988 and is an abstract pieced work. It may be seen weekdays, except during school holidays. Telephone (02) 6552 0900.

Windsor

The charming and historic town of Windsor overlooks the river in the upper Hawkesbury Valley, approximately 60 kilometres north west of Sydney. One

PHOTOGRAPHY ROGER HANLON.

ABOVE: *Hawkesbury Bicentennial Quilt.* Made by the Patchworkers and Quilters of the Hawkesbury, 1992-'96. 240cm x 300cm. Hawkesbury City Council, Windsor. OPPOSITE: *Images of Newcastle.* Made by the Novocastrian Quilters, 1988. 375cm x 186cm. Newcastle Court House, Newcastle.

of the oldest towns in Australia, many Georgian and mid Victorian buildings still remain. Several were designed by colonial architect Francis Greenway and built using convict labour.

Hawkesbury City Council

366 George Street
Windsor, NSW 2756.
Ph: (02) 4560 4444 Fax: (02) 4560 4400
8.00a.m. – 4.30p.m. Monday, Tuesday, Wednesday, Friday.
8.00a.m. – 7.30p.m. Thursday.

✷ The *Hawkesbury Bicentennial Quilt* is hung on permanent display in the foyer of the first floor of the Council building. It may be seen during the opening hours listed. Sophia Wilbow's quilt is not permanently displayed but may be seen by arrangement. Please contact the General Manager, Hawkesbury City Council.

✂ The *Hawkesbury Bicentennial Quilt* (240cm x 300cm) was created by the Patchworkers and Quilters of the Hawkesbury to celebrate 200 years of white settlement in 1994. Designed by local artist Greg Hansell and co-ordinated by Sandra Edwards, the quilt takes the form of a pictorial map. It illustrates the first twenty two land grants made by Lieutenant Governor Grose in 1794 and includes events up to the present day. The background was made from white cotton fabrics using forty-eight different block patterns. These were joined together to create an illusion of fields as seen from the air. The predominant feature is the river which is also viewed from above. The houses and other buildings are seen from the side, providing a naive look reminiscent of old maps. All the major features on the quilt were appliquéd by hand and hundreds of details were hand embroidered. Quilting lines were also drawn by hand to complement the varying terrain. Beads, sequins and a variety of fabric textures were used to achieve special effects.

The Hawkesbury Council is also the custodian of a quilt made in Tumbling Block design by Sophia Wilbow c.1890. Sophia had been born in nearby Pitt Town in 1829, the eldest daughter of Mary and William Payton. In 1846 she married Thomas Wilbow who worked as a farmer and hotelier in Windsor. She was a prolific needlewoman and quiltmaker and it is believed that she created a quilt for each of her nine daughters. She did not own a sewing machine and stitched each quilt by hand, cutting her templates from blotting paper. This quilt was made from pastel-coloured dress and shirting fabrics. It has no filling and has been backed with red floral cotton. It was donated to the Friends of the Hawkesbury Art Collection and will eventually be housed in the Hawkesbury Art Gallery. Sophia Wilbow's quilts are also held by the National Gallery of Australia in Canberra, and the Hamilton Hume Museum in Yass, New South Wales.

The Blue Mountains

The magnificent Blue Mountains with their towering cliffs and wooded valleys are approximately 70 kilometres west of Sydney and within a pleasant two hour drive. Picturesque towns and villages are part of the character of the mountains and there is an abundance of cosy tea rooms, galleries, craft and antique shops.

Katoomba Branch Library
Town Centre Arcade
Katoomba, NSW 2780.
Ph: (02) 4780 5750 Fax: (02) 4782 7763
10.00a.m. – 5.30p.m. Monday to Friday.
9.00a.m. – 4.00p.m. Saturday.

✷ The quilt is hung on permanent display in the library and may be seen during opening hours.

✄ A contemporary quilt entitled *Valley Light* (200cm x 210cm) was made by textile artist Sue Wademan in 1998. The project was funded by a grant from the Ministry of Arts as part of a scheme to develop the region as a 'City of Arts.' The work was designed to provide a large screen for the Katoomba Library. It also presented a contemporary work of art that echoed the feel of the Blue Mountains for the enjoyment of the community. Initially the screen was to have been a tapestry or painted image but Sue had lived in the region for many years and her work was well known. Her association with the library was to lead to the vision of a work of art in quilt form.

Valley Light features a myriad of blue and green fabrics, many of them collected by Sue during her travels to Bali, Africa, the United States, New Zealand and Japan. Several were hand dyed and some were printed by Tiwi Islanders. The design was inspired by the ever glowing 'blue' of the mountains and the flickering of light filtering through the trees of the valley floor. The touch of orange included in the foreground is often seen on the cliff faces during sunset. The work was airbrush dyed, machine pieced and quilted. Sue used free-cut or 'bohemian blocks' to give her the freedom of moving the elements around. The quilt resonates from changes in tonal value, capturing perfectly the atmosphere and spirit of this spectacular region.

Glenbrook Tourist Information Centre
Great Western Highway
Glenbrook, NSW 2773.
Ph: (02) 4739 6266 Fax: (02) 4739 6787
9.00a.m. – 5.00p.m. daily.

✷ The quilt is hung on permanent display behind glass and may be seen during opening hours.

✄ A quilt entitled *Patchwork Mountain* was created by local quiltmakers in 1988 to commemorate the Bicentennial. The blocks were designed to capture the history and natural beauty of the region, the large central picture illustrating the most famous landmark of mountain scenery – the rock formation of the Three Sisters. The quilt took more than two years to complete and was pieced, appliquéd, embroidered and quilted by hand.

Lutheran Church of Our Saviour
41 Raymond Road
Springwood, NSW 2777.
Ph: (02) 4751 6502
The Church is open everyday
between 8.30a.m. and 5.30p.m.
A service is held on
Sunday at 9.00a.m.

✷ The banner is hung on permanent display and visitors are welcome to see it during opening hours.

✄ An inspiring banner (212cm x 100cm) was designed and made for the Church of Our Saviour by Barbara Watson in 1986. It features the central figure of the Lord appliquéd to a background of mosaic 'tiles' of fabric. The Blue Mountains are depicted in the foreground. Techniques included hand and reverse appliqué, strip piecing, embroidery and machine quilting.

Valley Light. Made by Sue Wademan, 1998. 200cm x 210cm. Katoomba Branch Library, Katoomba, New South Wales.

Mudgee Valley. Made by Jan Irvine-Nealie, 1996. Mudgee Visitors' Centre, Mudgee, New South Wales

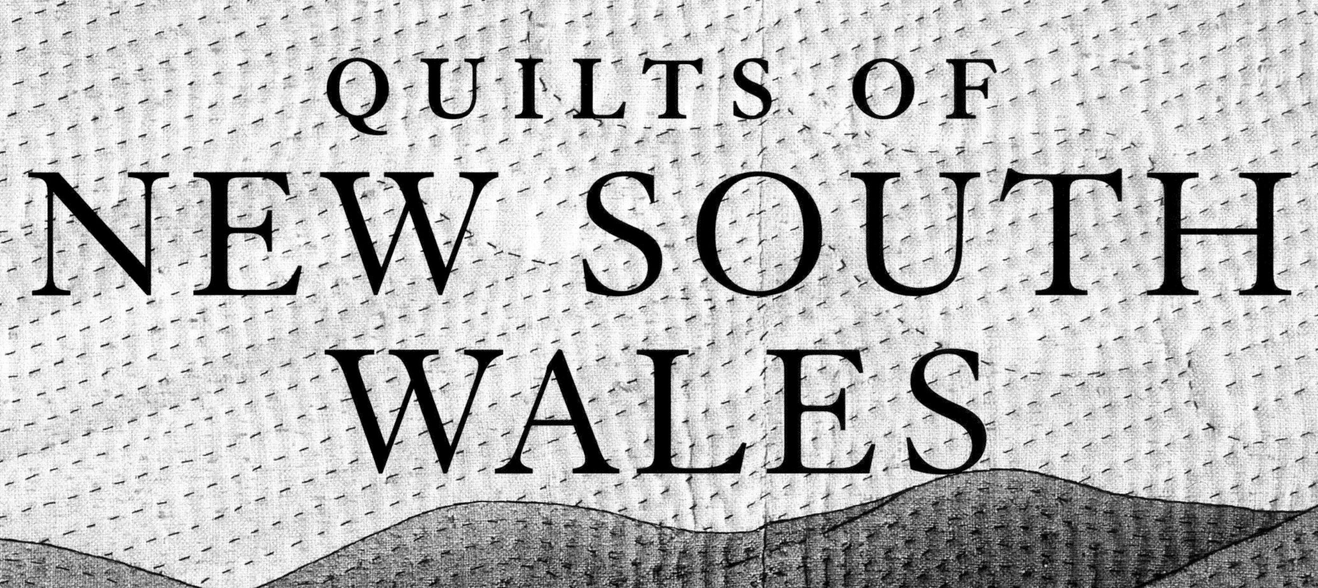
QUILTS OF
NEW SOUTH
WALES

Mudgee

The second oldest town west of the Blue Mountains, Mudgee is nestled in a fertile valley approximately three and a half hour's drive from Sydney. The Cudgegong River winds through the town, and the rich soils of the distant hills provide lush grazing and farmland. Nearby are the quaint villages of Gulgong, Hill End, and Rylstone, all of them established during the gold rush of the 1850s. Many of the fine old buildings in Mudgee also date from this period and a *Town Walks* brochure is available as a guide for visitors. One heritage building, St Mary's Church c.1857 with its graceful tower and spire, has lovely interior stencilled decoration. The region is renowned for its fine wines which are produced by small, friendly, family owned wineries. The Mudgee Wine Festival is held each year in September and many special events are organised, both at individual wineries and throughout the town. There are exhibitions of art, displays of craft work, concerts, dances, and markets.

Mudgee Visitors' Centre
84 Market Street
Mudgee, NSW 2850.
Ph: (02) 6372 5875 Fax: 02) 6372 2853
9.00a.m. – 5.00p.m. Monday to Friday.
9.00a.m. – 3.30p.m. Saturday.
9.30a.m. – 2.00p.m. Sunday and public holidays.

✷ The quilt is hung on permanent display in the Visitors' Centre except for short periods when it is used as a backdrop for regional promotions. Please telephone in advance to check its location.

PHOTOGRAPHY MICHAEL COATES.

ABOVE: *Mudgee Valley*. Made by Jan Irvine-Nealie, 1996. 4.2m x 1.5m. Mudgee Visitors' Centre, Mudgee, New South Wales.

✄ This huge quilt entitled *Mudgee Valley* (4.2m x 1.5m) was made in 1996 by Jan Irvine-Nealie, one of Australia's most respected textile artists. The project was commissioned by the Mudgee Wine Grape Growers' Association whose vision it was to represent the valley landscape and its natural appeal in a quilted wall hanging. The quilt was to form a backdrop to their trade display at the national wine promotion held at Darling Harbour in Sydney, and was to be augmented by the work to two other local artists. Tjenka Murray, a potter and painter, created specially designed spittoon jugs, while Ian Bartholomew, a sculptor, created timber benches. All the work had to be completed in time for the Darling Harbour promotion and this resulted in Jan's own stitching marathon, concurrent with the Atlanta Olympics. Her design, depicting a view of the Mudgee Valley with its vineyards and the township, was drawn and approved within a week. Jan then constructed a moveable pinboard-wall to work on, stretching the silk wholecloth fabric over this surface. Using an overhead projector, she transferred her A4 design onto the 4.5 metre by 1.5 metre stencil card. The card was pasted with a pressure sensitive glue which allowed it to be removed and re-applied indefinitely. It was then cut into hundreds of individual sections and the quilt was airbrushed as a whole, using this giant stencilled jig-saw as a guide. Small bits were continually being

PHOTOGRAPHY MICHAEL COATES.

ABOVE AND OPPOSITE: Details of *Mudgee Valley*. Made by Jan Irvine-Nealie, 1996. 4.2m x 1.5m. Mudgee Visitors' Centre, Mudgee, New South Wales.

lost, so that Jan's husband, Chester, regularly checked her back, arms, and beneath her shoes for the illusive pieces.

Jan and Chester live in picturesque countryside just outside Gulgong. As a potter of international repute, Chester Nealie understood the pressure caused by the deadline. Three weeks and 1500 metres of thread to sew! The twelve hour days began early and Chester cooked the meals and ensured that break times were adhered to. Friends, neighbours, and visitors to the gallery during this marathon were amazed by what they saw. Jan had to cut the huge quilt into three sections in order to handle the stitching, re-joining the pieces at the end. The quilting was done entirely by hand in Jan's unique style, with the direction and length of the stitches varying greatly across the work. Within six weeks the entire project had been completed, and in time for the Darling Harbour promotion. Since then, the quilt has been used regularly as an ambassador for the region, hung at diverse events ranging from wine and tourism shows to local Field days.

Gulgong

One of the best preserved gold mining towns in Australia, Gulgong is set in a picturesque valley about a half hour's drive from Mudgee. Depicted on the original ten dollar note, the town is steeped in history. Its narrow winding streets with their quaint cottages and weatherboard shops remain much as they did during the gold rush of the 1870s. Poet and author Henry Lawson lived in the area during his childhood and he is commemorated at the Henry Lawson Centre. The Gulgong Pioneer Museum, housed in the Old Times Bakery, has a wonderful collection of local history.

St Luke's Anglican Church
Bayly Street
Gulgong, NSW 2852.
Ph: (02) 6374 1421
The church is open between 9.00a.m. and 5.00p.m. daily during Summer, 9.00a.m. and 4.00p.m. during Winter.
1 large reredos quilt, several banners, plus vestments.

The beautiful stone church of St Luke's was designed by colonial architect Edmund Blacket and built in 1876.

✷ Visitors are welcome to see the work during the hours listed.

✂ The *St Luke's Vestment and Banner Project* was a huge undertaking by a small ecumenical group of Gulgong men and women between 1992 and '94. The project entailed people from all walks of life and of many different ages, faiths and abilities. Several workshops were held in silk painting, screen printing, and liturgical design. Jan Irvine-Nealie taught the group airbrush dyeing and quilting. A reredos quilt entitled *A View of Gulgong* is now displayed behind the altar and was made using these techniques. It features three panels depicting the town from Flirtation Hill and includes the church to represent Christian faith, the mill to represent industry, and the main part of town to represent commerce. The colours were carefully co-ordinated to match the three

LEFT: *Appliquéd Vestments.* RIGHT: *Women in Rural Australia.* Made for St Luke's by the community of Gulgong between 1992-'94.
St Luke's Anglican Church, Gulgong, New South Wales.

stained glass windows directly above it. An airbrush dyed and quilted banner entitled *Women in Rural Australia* can also be seen displayed in the church. Vestments for each liturgical season of the Christian calendar have been planned and two of the four sets have been completed. The green set features silk painted and embroidered gum leaves, the white, a segmented star appliquéd over a silk painted background.

Rylstone and Kandos

Rylstone is set on the banks of the Cudgegong River approximately 60 kilometres south of Mudgee. Settlement in the district dates from as early as 1820 and the town is characterised by its charming, historic main street and stone buildings. Many of these buildings are listed on the register of the National Estate. The little town of Kandos, 6 kilometres from Rylstone, has also retained much of its early character and many of the buildings date from the 1920s and '30s.

Rylstone Country Women's Association
Cudgegong Street
Rylstone, NSW 2849.
Ph: (02) 6379 1239 Gwen Nicholson, Rylstone C.W.A.
Hours vary according to functions.

✷ The quilt is hung on permanent display in the C.W.A. Rooms. Visitors are welcome to see it by appointment with Gwen Nicholson.

✂ This lovely quilt (170cm x 170cm) was made by a group of nine women from the towns of Kandos and Rylstone to celebrate the Bicentennial in 1988. Initiated and researched by Gwen Nicholson, it was designed by local school teacher, Chris Herringe. The work featured a large central circle in which the man-made and introduced features of the environment were included. Natural features were placed around the circle, sometimes overlapping the internal images.

Major rural activities including grazing cows, honeycomb and sunflowers were dotted amongst the heritage buildings. A woolly sheep was made from hand spun wool, padded and finished with a nose of chamois. Photographs were used for reference and women were frequently seen standing by walls of buildings, dangling pieces of fabric to match the colours accurately. Many of the fabrics were painted with screen printing inks. Each petal for the huge waratah was created individually from red wool and silk. The kangaroo and frill-neck lizard were painted, embroidered and then quilted. Quilting lines were used to extend the images. The lizard's frills were curved out past the confines of his body, the eucalypt leaves were echoed, and the honeycomb patchwork was extended by quilting a honeycomb pattern to join other images. The quilt took eighteen months to complete and was to inspire the community of Narrabri to create a beautiful hanging for their Shire.

ABOVE: Details of the kangaroo, the Kandos Convent, sunflowers, wattle and bottlebrush from the *Rylstone Kandos Bicentennial Quilt*. Made by women from both towns, 1988. 170cm x 170cm. Rylstone Country Women's Association, Rylstone, New South Wales.

Wellington

The town of Wellington is located in a picturesque valley at the junction of the Bell and Macquarie Rivers, midway between Dubbo and Orange. The second oldest town west of the Blue Mountains, it was discovered by John Oxley in 1817. A convict settlement was established a few years later and many historic buildings dating from early European settlement still remain today. Nearby are the famous Wellington Caves and the Burrendong Arboretum of native flora.

Oxley Museum

Cnr. Warne and Percy Streets
Wellington, NSW 2820.
Ph: (02) 6845 2325 Museum.
(02) 6845 1484 Secretary, Wellington Historical Society.
1.30p.m. – 4.30p.m. Monday to Friday.
Other times by appointment. Closed Christmas Day and Good Friday.

The Oxley Museum occupies a fine two storey building c.1883 which originally served as the Bank of New South Wales. The collection of textiles includes original costumes, wedding gowns, heirloom nighties and underwear. There are also Chinese garments and military uniforms from both World Wars. There are many items of needlework including embroidery, tapestry, beadwork, lace and samplers.

✷ The unfinished patchwork quilt is permanently displayed within the Museum and can be seen anytime during opening hours. Mrs Ling's quilt may be seen by request. Please contact the Museum 24 hours in advance.

✂ A small patchwork quilt dating from the early 20th century was made by Sing Yin Ean Ling. Sing Yin had been born in Melbourne in 1888, her Chinese parents having emigrated to Victoria during the gold rushes. She married William Suey Ling who was the proprietor of Fong Lee & Co. General Store. This shop operated in the main street of Wellington for fifty six years between 1879 and 1935. Mr Ling owned the store from 1889 and it was from sample books held in stock that Sing Yin collected the fabrics for her quilt.

The Depression years of the 1930s were hard and though many people owed Mr Ling large outstanding accounts he was too benevolent to foreclose. Some still remember that he would supply each family with a small packet of boiled lollies, hidden away in their grocery orders for the children. Sadly the store ceased trading in 1935 and Mr Ling died the following year.

Sing Yin had a large family of nine children, seven boys and two girls, and the quilt was made for one of them. It was created from triangular pieces of velvet with a backing of bright yellow cotton sateen. Buttons were used for trim on all four sides. Originally the work had a warm filling which was removed at a later stage.

ABOVE: Sing Yin Ean Ling with her daughter, Alice c.1930 and detail of her patchwork quilt made c.1910. Collection Oxley Museum, Wellington, New South Wales.

Sing Yin taught her daughter, Alice, to sew and they both became prolific needlewomen. There are several other items in the collection made by the pair.

The Museum also has an unfinished quilt of hexagons. It is of unknown provenance c.1890 and features a central diamond surrounded by multi-coloured rosettes of silk and cotton fabrics.

Dubbo

The large regional city of Dubbo is about a 5 hour drive from Sydney. It is the centre of a diverse agricultural region and the home of the renowned Western Plains Zoo.

Dubbo Museum
232 Macquarie Street
Dubbo, NSW 2830.
Ph: (02) 6882 5359
10.00a.m. – 1.00p.m. & 2.00p.m. – 4.30p.m.
every day. Closed Good Friday,
Christmas Eve and Christmas Day.
2 quilts.

The Museum collection includes samplers, embroidered linen and a bed canopy of Carrickmacross lace with muslin appliquéd onto a background of white net.

✷ The quilts are not on display but visitors are welcome to see them. Please contact the museum 24 hours in advance.

✂ A patchwork counterpane was made in England and came to Australia with Susannah Hoath in 1856. The work was pieced by hand using squares of printed cotton of varying sizes. It was hand quilted in a chevron design.

A small and fragile quilt of pieced diamonds is of unknown maker and history. It was made c.1910 and the fabrics include silk, wool, cotton, and velvet.

Gilgandra

The historic town of Gilgandra is approximately 60 kilometres north of Dubbo. The town's famous Coo-ee March of 1915 followed in the wake of the disaster at Gallipoli and a steady decline in recruitment numbers. The march was led by the Hitchen Brothers who set out from Gilgandra with 35 men. The well known bushman's cry for help, *Coo-ee,* was used in every town through which they passed, and upon arrival in Sydney there was a total of 263 recruits.

Gilgandra Museum
Coo-ee March Memorial Park
Newell Highway
Gilgandra, NSW 2827.
Ph: (02) 6847 2045
9.00a.m. – 5.00p.m. everyday except
Christmas Day and Good Friday.

The Museum is housed in the Visitors' Information Centre. Its collection includes a cross stitch wall hanging made by Mrs Gladys Carson during the 1950s and an embroidered hanging made by the Embroiderers' Group to mark the town's centenary in 1988.

✷ The quilt is permanently displayed within the Museum and may be seen during opening hours

✂ This Signature quilt (180cm square) was made between 1937 and '42 by Clara Ward. Clara lived on a property called *Wait-a-While* near the village of Biddon, just north of Gilgandra. She charged sixpence to embroider each name in red thread onto a cream cotton background. From 1700 signatures she raised a total of forty two pounds and ten shillings for the Gilgandra Hospital. Clara continued to add names to the quilt until her death in 1950, embroidering a total of 2,226.

Mendooran

The oldest town on the Castlereagh River, Mendooran is about an hour's drive from Dubbo and Mudgee. It is a measure of the community spirit in this little town of 400 people that there are 38 different clubs and organisations! Murals depicting country life and history have been painted on several buildings by local artist Karin Duce.

Mendooran
Yarn Spinners Craft Shop
Bundulla Street
Mendooran, NSW 2842.
Ph: (02) 6886 1253 Bini Monk.
(02) 6886 1118 Karen Duce.
9.00a.m. – 4.00p.m. Monday to Friday.

✷ The quilt is displayed inside the shop and may be seen during opening hours. The shop is run by volunteers and it is advisable to telephone in advance.

✄ A heritage quilt of appliquéd blocks (210cm x 160cm) was made by the Mendooran Yarn Spinners Group to celebrate the Bicentenary in 1988. The twelve images depict the historic buildings and rural surroundings of the town. The little shop now used by the group has been included at the top. Built in the 1920s, it has served as a fruit shop, bicycle business, station agency, billiard room and doctor's surgery.

Cowra

Cowra is nestled in the Lachlan Valley about an hour and a half drive south of Bathurst and Orange. The establishment of the Prisoner-of-War camp on the outskirts of the town during World War 11 was to have far reaching consequences and lead to a

PHOTOGRAPHY CLIFF DYKES.

ABOVE: *Cowra Bicentennial Wall Hanging*. Made by members of the community, 1988. Cowra Civic Centre, Cowra, New South Wales.

long association with the Japanese. On the 5th August 1944, more than a thousand Japanese prisoners launched a suicidal attack on their Australian guards. Many died during this breakout, and the subsequent care taken of their graves led to Cowra having the only Japanese War Cemetery in the country. All Japanese nationals who died on Australian soil are now buried at this site just north of the town.

Cowra Civic Centre
Darling Street
Cowra, NSW 2794.
Ph: (02) 6341 0100 Fax: (02) 6341 1031
8.30a.m. – 4.30p.m. Monday to Friday.
2 quilts.

The Cowra Civic Centre is located in Civic Square next to the Council, Library and World Peace Bell.

✷ Both quilts are hung on permanent display in the Civic Centre, the *Bicentennial Wall Hanging* in the Auditorium, the *Heritage Quilt* in the foyer. They may be seen during office hours by calling at Waugoola House, directly opposite the Civic Centre. The staff at the Roads, Water and Parks Department will open the Centre for you.

✂ The magnificent *Cowra Bicentennial Wall Hanging* was made as a major community project to celebrate the Bicentennial in 1988. Inspired by the Orange Theatre Curtain, the project was co-ordinated by Rowena Casey and Jan Clements and more than 600 people contributed to its creation. The design was developed following prolonged consultation with the community and final drawings were prepared by local artist Patsy-Ann Flint. The hanging depicts the development of the country between 1788 and 1988 through glimpses of Cowra and the surrounding district. Water, life-blood of the nation, dominates the picture. The giant structure of Wyangala Dam is the focal point with Lake Wyangala above it. The Lachlan River meanders through the valley, weeping willows and poplars shading its banks. The land is shown in all seasons, from parched and brown to the richest green. Most of the fabrics for the project were donated and many different textures were included. The work was appliquéd entirely by hand with details added in hand embroidery.

The *Heritage Quilt* was made by the Cowra Heritage Quilters as a gift to the town for the Bicentennial. It features twelve appliquéd blocks depicting the history, pastoral activities and heritage buildings of the region.

Also in Cowra

The century old Church of St Raphael's in Lachlan Street stands on a hill overlooking the Lachlan River. A quilt was made in 1989 as a celebration of the centenary of the parish. The work was co-ordinated by Sally Delaney and made by a group of needlewomen from the three churches making up the parish. The design by Libby Spackman was based on the journey of faith at St Raphael's and incorporates the sacramental symbols. Plain fabrics of silk, satin, velvet and lamé were used in the liturgical colours of purple, red, gold and black. The work was appliquéd, embroidered and quilted entirely by hand. The church is open every day between 8.00a.m. and 5.30p.m. and visitors are welcome to see the quilt. The parish office may be contacted on (02) 6342 1369.

A small quilt entitled *Life along the River* was designed and made in 1997 by students at the Cowra TAFE college, Carleton Street. Most of the students were Aboriginal and this was their first experience of quiltmaking. The work is hung on permanent display in the Access Education Services Department and may be seen during office hours. Telephone (02) 6342 2466.

In the Nearby Region

The former gold mining town of West Wyalong is located at the junction of the Mid Western and Newell Highways, about an hour and a half's drive west of Cowra. A tapestry wall hanging entitled *Woman of the West* was made for the Bicentenary by the Bland Spinners and Weavers Group. The work pays tribute to the pioneering women of the region and is hung on permanent display in the Bland Shire Council Chambers. Telephone (02) 6972 2266.

The little town of Barmedman is to be found approximately 30 kilometres south east of West Wyalong. To celebrate the Bicentennial, members of the local community made a soft sculptured wall hanging featuring a profusion of native flowers, including among them each state floral emblem. Wool, velvet, cotton, taffeta and satin were used, some flowers being padded and wired, some embellished with crochet and vinyl. The work is hung on permanent display in the Community Hall, Queen Street, Barmedman. To see it please telephone (02) 6976 2088.

Canowindra

The little town of Canowindra is set in beautiful rolling countryside on the banks of the Belubula River. A regional centre for hot air ballooning, it is only a 20 minute drive from Cowra.

Canowindra Historical Museum
Gaskill Street
Canowindra, NSW 2804.
Ph: (02) 6344 1534 Fax: (02) 6344 1602
2.00p.m. – 4.00p.m. Sundays or other times by arrangement.

The Museum collection includes wedding gowns, charleston frocks, examples of lace, needlepoint, crochet and tatting. A glass case houses many delicate glory box items made by Miss Vi Dawes who worked in nearby Finns Drapery Store. This store still stands in Gaskill Street, little changed since the turn of the century.

✷ All items are permanently displayed within the Museum and may be seen during opening hours or by appointment.

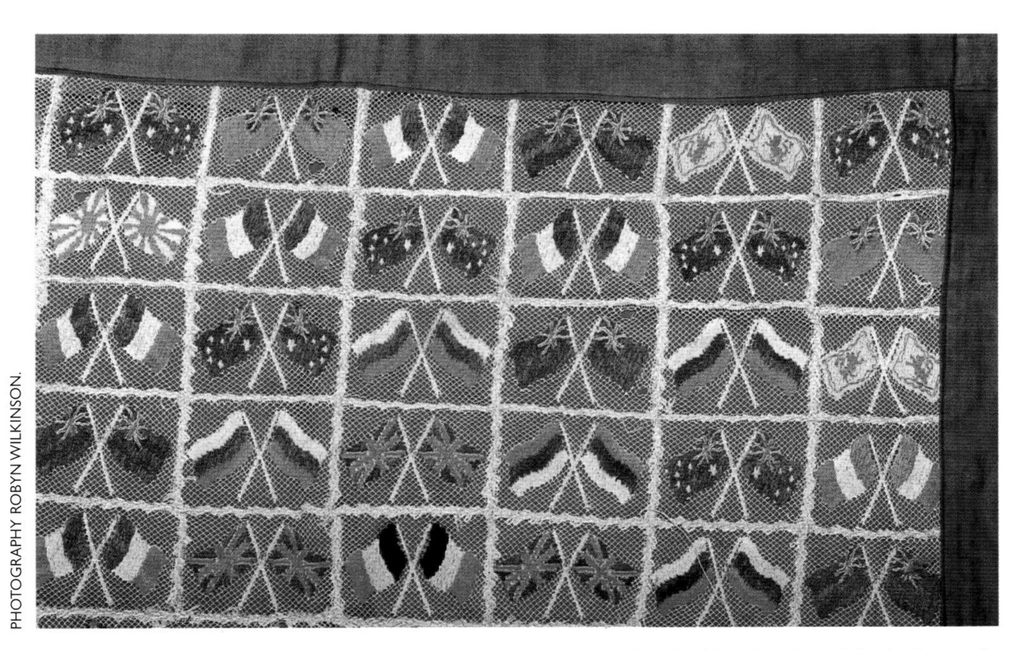
PHOTOGRAPHY ROBYN WILKINSON.

ABOVE: *Cushion Cover of Flags.* Unknown Maker, c.1914-'18. BELOW: *Patchwork Dish Cover of Prairie Points.* Formerly owned by Mrs Charles Whitmee, c.1890.
Collection Canowindra Historical Museum, Canowindra, New South Wales.

✄ A large cushion cover of flags was created by an unknown maker c.1914-'18. These little flags were included within packets of cigarettes during the years of World War I. The maker of this work collected them, stitched them onto net and covered the seams with cream braid.

A patchwork dish cover c.1890 belonged to an early settler of the district, Mrs Charles Whitmee. It resembles a large tea cosy and was used to keep vegetables warm in a porcelain covered dish. It provided a pretty alternative to the costly silver domes that were used by the wealthy. It has been made from hundreds of Prairie Points, each one formed by folding a square of fabric into a triangle and then sewing it to the backing. The fabrics include plain and printed silk, velvet and brocade. The cover has been thickly padded and finished with an edging of braid.

A wagga of unknown maker dates from the 1930s. Made from squares and rectangles of woollen fabrics, it has been backed with floral printed cotton. Typical of such covers, it is very heavy and thickly padded with recycled clothing.

Lithgow

The town of Lithgow lies in a pretty valley on the western fringe of the Blue Mountains. It is approximately 140 kilometres west of Sydney. Once one of the major manufacturing hubs of the state, today it is proud of its beautifully restored heritage architecture. Several former industrial sites are now museums.

Eskbank House
Bennett Street
Lithgow, NSW 2790.
Ph: 02) 6351 3557
10.00a.m. – 4.00p.m. daily, except Tuesday and Wednesday.

Eskbank House was built in 1842 by Scottish emigrants, Thomas and Mary Brown. One of the earliest homes in Lithgow, it was constructed from local sandstone in colonial Georgian style. Its collection of needlework includes an heirloom christening gown, several other children's garments, lace collars and bonnets. A tapestry firescreen was made during the 1960s by the Embroiderers' Guild of New South Wales. There are also several framed cross stitch samplers including one by Sarah Wildgoose made in 1852 when she was aged eleven.

✷ The quilt is displayed within the house and may be seen during the opening hours listed.

ABOVE AND OPPOSITE: *Crazy Patchwork Quilt.* Unknown Maker, c.1893. 200cm x 196cm. Collection Eskbank House, Lithgow, New South Wales.

PHOTOGRAPHY STEVE RAJKOVIC.

✂ This beautiful Crazy Patchwork quilt (200cm x 196cm) of American origin was donated to Eskbank House by Mrs Hutchinson of Lithgow. The maker is unknown but the date *'1893'* has been embroidered onto a velvet patch. The quilt was sent to the Sutton family, early settlers of the Lithgow district, as a gift to celebrate the birth of their new baby.

Made from multi-coloured silks, satins, brocades and velvets, the work has been constructed from nine large blocks. Each one has been stitched around a finely embroidered central motif. A pieced basket design has been worked into the central square and the quilt has been heavily embellished with embroidered motifs.

By coincidence, just a few years before the Sutton's quilt was sent from America, a magnificent Crazy Patchwork quilt of similar design had been made in the Lithgow district. It was created c.1890 by Christina Brown who lived on a property called *Cooerwull* at nearby Bowenfels. This exquisitely embroidered quilt is considered to be one of the finest examples of Crazy Patchwork in this country and is now held in the collection of the National Gallery of Australia.

In the Nearby Region

Australia's oldest inland settlement, Bathurst is situated on the banks of the Macquarie River midway between Lithgow and Orange. Many of the city's historic buildings have been preserved and the main streets are adorned with charming cast iron lamp posts. A wonderful series of banners depicting diverse images of Bathurst is often displayed on these historic lamp posts. The banners were designed by Jan Irvine-Nealie and each one was based on images and ideas contributed by members of the community. The project was initiated by the Bathurst Arts Council and engendered an immense spirit of pride and sense of local identity. The banners are always hung during the Bathurst car racing festival held in October, usually during Easter, as well as for other festivals and special occasions throughout the year.

At Oberon, less than an hour's drive south of Lithgow, a magnificent series of tapestries is displayed at the Cobweb Craft Shop and Tourist Information Centre. The tapestries were designed by local artist Kim Rabbidge and stitched by residents of the town. They depict the landscape and rural industries of the region as well as many of the heritage buildings of Oberon. A wide border of daffodils symbolises the Daffodil Festival held annually during the last weekend of September. On special occasions such as this, the town is decorated with a series of banners representing different organisations and these have also been stitched by the local community. Several banners hang on permanent display in the library. The Tourist Centre is open between 9.00a.m. and 5.00p.m. daily. Telephone: (02) 6336 1895.

Orange

The rural city of Orange is located in the heart of the Central West, a three and a half hour drive from Sydney. Set in rolling hills with Mt Canobolas in the background, the region was first settled by graziers in the early 1800s and grew rapidly when gold was discovered nearby in 1851. Today it is the centre of a rich and diverse farming district renowned for its quality produce, cool climate wines and boutique delicacies. The picturesque countryside is dotted with historic villages and there are numerous galleries, studios, craft and antique shops.

Orange Civic Theatre
Cnr. Byng Street and Lords Place
Orange, NSW 2800.
Ph: 02) 6361 5115 Fax: (02) 6361 5192
9.00a.m. – 5.00p.m. weekdays.

✷ The curtain is often displayed as a backdrop for speakers but cannot always be used during productions. It can usually be seen by arrangement with the Theatre. Please contact the Theatre Manager in advance.

✂ The magnificent *Orange Civic Theatre Curtain* (11m x 6m) was designed and directed by local artist Cath Wyatt. It was undertaken as a major community craft project to celebrate the biennial Orange Festival of Arts in 1983. The work forms a giant backdrop to the stage of the theatre and depicts the rural landscape of Orange. The historic mansion of Duntryleague, once owned by the Dalton family but now part of the golf club, is featured in the foreground. Beyond it can be seen the orchards and pine forests of the surrounding countryside, the undulating hills of the tablelands, and Mt Canobolas in the

distance. Cath began by making a large painting of the curtain. Workshops were held and the design was divided into thirty panels. Each one measured 180cm by 120cm and was completed by a different community group under Cath's direction. Cath selected and cut all the fabrics, often overlaying them to build up a required tone. Strong colours were used to create the distant forests, Duntryleague, the trees and garden. Gauzy overlays were applied to soften shadows and form clouds and mist.

Huge embroidery stitches were used to depict flowers, leaves and other details. Meticulous needlewomen were shocked by the wild nature of these stitches, so different were they from traditional work. Lace, braid, and many metres of black and white cotton tape were incorporated into the design to add depth. Cath's wonderful sense of humour was shown in the soft sculptured figures added here and there. Duntryleague is used as a venue for wedding receptions so it seemed appropriate to add a bride and groom in loving embrace at the window of the bridal suite.

The making of the curtain resulted in the unearthing of some interesting treasures. Maria O'Shea from Molong found some ninety year old linen thread that had been given to her husband by his mother when he first set out jackerooing. This amazing work has inspired the creation of several other projects. They include the *Cowra Bicentennial Wall Hanging* and the *Soft Sculptured Artistic Curtain* at the Griffith Regional Theatre.

Cath Wyatt's innovative talent and wit can be seen in other hangings, as well as in her life size figures. Working under the creative title of *Madame Loose Arts Whacky Works,* Cath has created wizened, apple-faced dolls and soft sculpture figures, many of them local identities. They are displayed regularly at Orange Field Days and Shows and some are accompanied by captions. The caption for her Vicar, outraged by the antisocial behaviour of Mrs McPhee, reads:

'I am the Vicar
I do need some liquor
Mrs McPhee astonishes me.'

In the Nearby Region

The little town of Molong, a short drive from Orange, has been home to a number of artists and craftspeople for many years. The Molong Yarn Market, once an old coach house, is now used by the community as a cultural, craft and exhibition centre. It was at this location that the Orange Theatre Curtain was made. Permanently displayed here is the beautiful *Molong Heritage Screen,* a hand embroidered work comprising four separate panels and depicting fifty years of European settlement of the region. Created by more than seventy local crafts-people, the work was made from hand spun and dyed wool and took more than four years from start to final stitch. The Yarn Market is located in Bank Street and is open between 10.00a.m. and 5.00p.m. everyday. Telephone (02) 6366 8260.

ABOVE: *Orange Civic Theatre Curtain.* Made by the community under the direction of Cath Wyatt (left), 1983. Orange Civic Theatre, New South Wales.

Holbrook

The little town of Holbrook is situated midway between Wagga Wagga and Albury. Originally called Germantown, the name was changed during World War 1.

Woolpack Inn Museum
83 Albury Street
Holbrook, NSW 2644.
Ph: (02) 6036 2131
9.30a.m. – 4.30p.m. everyday. Closed Good Friday and Christmas Day.

The Woolpack Inn Museum is housed in the town's first hotel. It is divided into rooms depicting life as it was for early pioneers during the 19th century. The Sewing Room features a collection of handmade lace, old fabric samples, heirloom underwear, and an appliquéd panel depicting the Three Wise Men. There is also an antique work box with inlaid mother-of-pearl.

✷ The cover is permanently displayed in the Sewing Room and may be seen during opening hours.

✂ A table cover of Crazy Patchwork was created around the turn of the century by Dorothy McLaurin Dalviado. Dorothy made the cover as a gift for aunt Nellie and the names *'Nellie McLaurin'* and *'Ralph C. Bartlet'* have been embroidered onto a patch believed to have been cut from Nellie's wedding dress. Nellie and Ralph lived in Holbrook for many years with their daughter, Sylvia. The cover has been made to fit an oval-shaped table and includes fabrics of velvet, silk, satin, taffeta and brocade. The patches have been outlined with a myriad of embroidery stitches and the work has been edged with a wide gold fringing. The cover remained unfinished until 1972 when it was completed by Mrs Beverley Geddes.

Albury

Albury is set in the foothills of the Australian alps, approximately three hour's drive from Melbourne and six hour's drive from Sydney. It is sited on the New South Wales side of the Murray River, its twin town of Wodonga just across the bridge in the state of Victoria. Nearby are the Victorian snow fields, the wineries of Rutherglen, the gourmet region of Milawa, and many other historic villages established during the gold rush era.

PHOTOGRAPHY TIM ROWSTON.

Albury Regional Museum
Australia Park
Wodonga Place
Albury, NSW 2640.
Ph: (02) 6021 4550 Fax: (02) 6041 3416
10.30a.m. – 4.30p.m. everyday.
2 quilts plus other small items
of patchwork.

The Albury Regional Museum has a lovely setting near the old water-wheel on the banks of the Murray River. It is housed in the former Turk's Head Hotel and its collection includes an extensive range of textiles. There are patchwork tea cosies, unfinished pieces of patchwork, cross stitch samplers, heirloom underwear, and a range of costumes dating from the early 20th century.

✱ The quilts and other items are not permanently displayed but may be seen by appointment. Single visitors are welcome but small groups are preferred. Please contact the Museum one to two weeks in advance.

✂ A beautiful patchwork quilt (170cm x 178cm) dating from the late 19th century was donated to the Museum in 1972 by Betty McIntyre. It originated in England and is believed to have been made by Mrs McIntyre's grandparents.

The work resembles the Military or Soldiers quilts of the era which were frequently created by men during periods of convalescence or to fill in idle hours. It features an intricate star design made by hand from pieced diamonds and hexagons. The plain woollen fabrics in colours of buff, red, black, maroon, dark green and blue, are probably remnants from military service uniforms. The quilt has a lining of red flannelette and its edge has been finished with a red fringe. Ref. ARM985.396

An unfinished coverlet of Log Cabin design dates from the late 19th century. It is of unknown provenance and has been made in the pattern known as Light and Dark. The fabrics include velvet, silk and grosgrain ribbon. Ref. ARM93.160

Jindera

The small rural town of Jindera is located about a half hour's drive from Holbrook. First settled by English and Scottish immigrants, there were also many German pioneers who travelled overland by wagon train from South Australia during the 1860s.

Jindera Pioneer Museum
7 Fallon Street
Jindera, NSW 2642.
Ph: (02) 6026 3622
10.00a.m. – 3.00p.m. Tuesday to Sunday.
2 quilts plus a patchwork tea cosy.

The Jindera Pioneer Museum features rooms in which displays have been designed to depict the everyday life of early pioneers and to reflect the comforts and discomforts of the times. There are examples of ribbon work, several rag rugs, and knitted quilts. There is also a beautiful tea cosy of

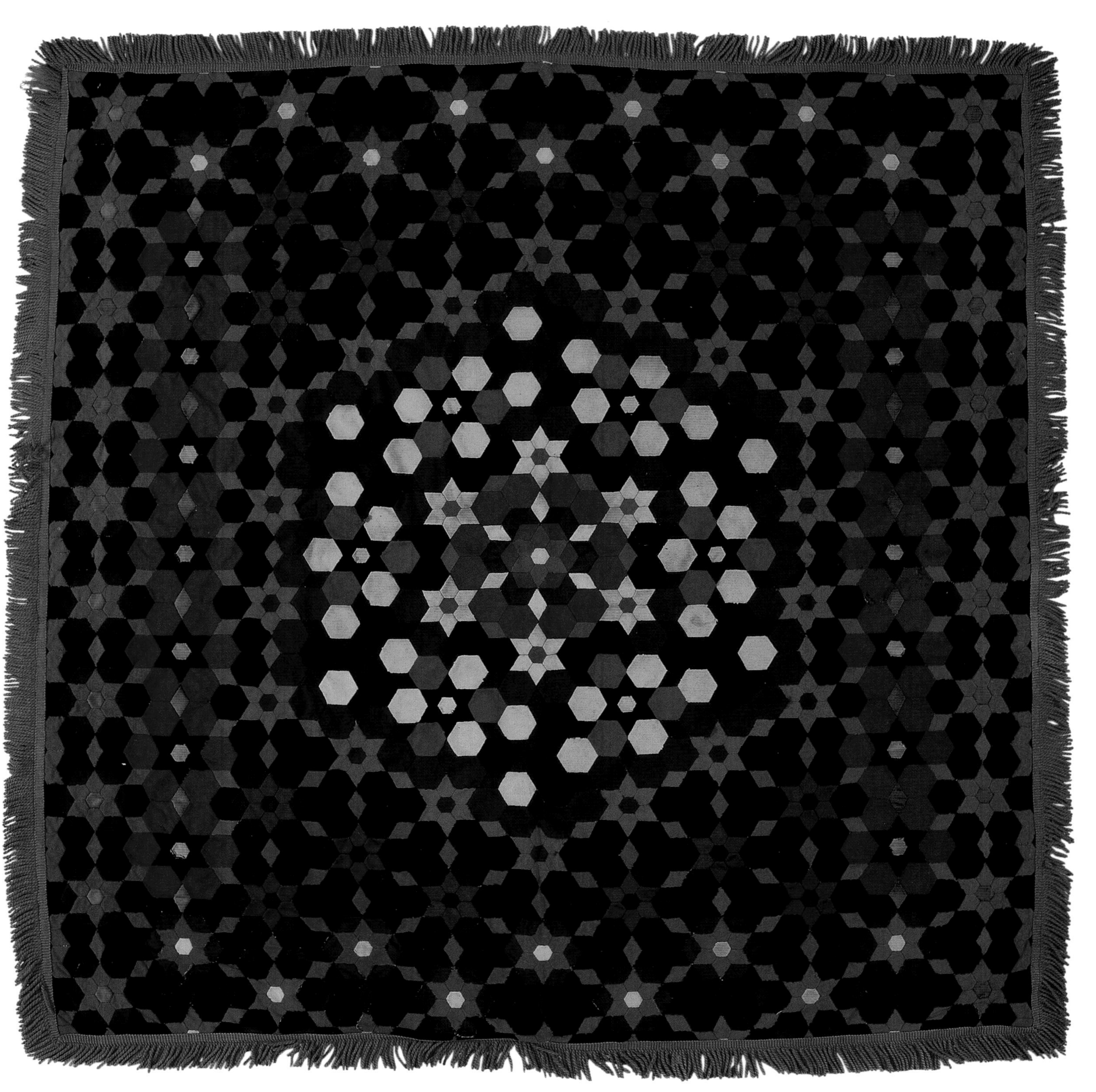

ABOVE AND LEFT: *Patchwork Quilt.* Believed to have been made by Mrs McIntyre's grandparents, late 19th century. 170cm x 178cm. Collection Albury Regional Museum, Albury, New South Wales. FAR LEFT: *Patchwork Quilt of Suiting Samples.* Made by Catherine Anderson, c.1920. 200cm x 182cm. Collection Jindera Pioneer Museum, Jindera, New South Wales.

gold work and a tapestry and beadwork cushion cover. In the words of the Director of the Museum, Catherine Clark, there are 'ingenious forms of decorative art, sometimes primitive and homemade, but frequently showing considerable talent and always striving to make living conditions more comfortable and pleasant.'

✷ The quilts are permanently displayed in the Museum and may be seen during the hours listed.

✂ A patchwork quilt of suiting samples (200cm x 182cm) was made by Catherine Anderson c.1920. Catherine was born in 1866 and lived with her husband, Robert, at Selby Grange, Brocklesby, between 1912 and 1928. The quilt was made from a great variety of tailor's suiting samples with a backing of blue striped flannelette. Catherine's brother-in-law and nephew, both of whom were named William Small, had a tailoring business in Dean Street, Albury. It was almost certainly from this source that she obtained her fabrics. The work is very heavy and is believed to have a blanket as a filling.

A little quilt of unknown maker and date is displayed on an old iron cot in the wattle and daub cottage. It is a simple pieced design of squares, triangles and rectangles and has been machine stitched from cotton fabrics.

A Crazy Patchwork tea cosy c.1890 is of unknown maker. The fabrics are velvets in colours of blue, burgundy and gold and the edge of each piece has been embroidered with gold thread.

Batlow

The little town of Batlow is nestled in the foothills of the Snowy Mountains approximately 30 kilometres south of Tumut. Set in picturesque rolling countryside, it is surrounded by vast forests. The hillsides are covered by the apple, pear, cherry, and stone fruit orchards for which the region has long been renowned. There are four distinct seasons – the trees displaying wonderful colours in Autumn, and masses of blossom heralding the coming of Spring.

Batlow Historical Museum
Tumbarumba Road
Batlow, NSW 2730.
Ph:(02) 6949 1450 or (02) 6949 1451
2.00p.m. – 4.00p.m. Sunday or by appointment at other times.
3 quilts.

The Museum is housed in the original Presbyterian church c.1933. The collection includes a Signature cloth, examples of bead work, a child's nightdress made by Anne Quarmby in 1908 at the Batlow Public School, a beautiful coverlet of Battenburg lace, and a sewing case c.1850 used by Elizabeth Wood.

✷ The quilts are permanently displayed within the Museum and may be seen during opening hours or by arrangement.

✂ A Log Cabin quilt (198cm x 185cm) was created in Ireland c.1870 by Mrs Plunkett, the grandmother of Molly Pursell of Batlow. It was made entirely from pale blue fabric strips. The pattern of Light and Dark was cleverly formed by cutting some of the strips parallel and others at right angles to the selvage, the variance in grain direction governing the light reflection of the fabric. The quilt was stitched by hand from cotton fabric and has a cotton backing.

A Log Cabin quilt (200cm x 158cm) of printed cotton fabrics was hand made in Monkton, Kent, in 1874. It belonged to Elizabeth Simpson (nee Mackett) and was donated to the Museum by Mrs Ethel Clayton of Batlow. It was made in a Light and Dark design, each fabric strip only 6mm wide, plus the turning allowance. The seams were neatened perfectly on the reverse side of the work by folding a tiny hem to the underside and neatly stitching it to the backing. This made the quilt reversible.

A hand pieced mosaic quilt (195cm x 85cm) was created from silk and satin fabrics and dates from the Victorian era. It belonged to Marj Colquhoun of Batlow and is of unknown maker. The work features a repeat design of hexagons created from lozenge-shaped patches. It is a simplified version of a pattern that appeared in Caulfeild's *Dictionary of Needlework* published in 1882.

In the Nearby Region

A short drive from Batlow, the town of Tumut has retained many of the original buildings from the gold rush era. At the Historical Museum, corner of Capper and Merrivale Streets, there is a quilt made in recent years of traditional style displayed on an old iron bed. Telephone (02) 6947 1380. A group of local quiltmakers also created a pictorial quilt to celebrate the Bicentennial in 1988. It is hung on permanent display in the Tumut Library. Telephone (02) 6947 1969.

Tumbarumba

The Pioneer Women's Hut is located 8 kilometres from Tumbarumba in the Glenroy Reserve. It is set in picturesque bushland on the banks of the Mannus Creek with superb views of the Snowy Mountains. Glenroy Cottage Crafts is also located in the Reserve and specialises in quality local craft.

PHOTOGRAPH COURTESY DIANNE FINNEGAN.

LEFT: *Mosaic Quilt.* Formerly belonged to Marj Colquhoun, c1890. 195cm x 85cm. Collection Batlow Historical Museum, Batlow, New South Wales.
RIGHT: *Log Cabin Quilt.* Made by Julia Jeffries, c.1900. Collection Pioneer Women's Hut Museum, Tumbarumba, New South Wales.

The Pioneer Women's Hut
Glenroy Reserve
Tumbarumba, NSW 2653.
Ph: (02) 6948 2635
10.00a.m. – 4.00p.m. Wednesday, Saturday, Sunday and most public holidays. Other times by arrangement.
41 quilts.

The Pioneer Women's Hut is a small, national, free women's museum committed to preserving the heritage of ordinary rural women and their families. The focus of the collection is on everyday life rather than special events and is shown in changing themes. There is also an emphasis on research. The Museum has embarked on a major national project to document quilts made or used in Australia prior to around 1965 for the National Quilt Register.

✷ There are usually several quilts on display and there is easy access to the whole collection during opening hours.

✄ The emphasis of the collection is on functional quilts. Wherever possible, details of the maker's life are recorded and there is information concerning the quiltmaker for all items except three.

The collection includes a bush quilt (144cm x 108cm) made by Agnes Chitty of Tintalda c.1914. This wholecloth work was created from dusty pink cretonne printed with a rose design. The filling is a worn grey blanket and the backing a green floral cretonne.

A Log Cabin quilt was made by Julia Jeffries c.1900. It was stitched by machine from a wide variety of used clothing strips including cottons, men's suitings, wools and pyjama fabrics.

A buggy rug (191cm x 158cm) was made at Carajung, south Gippsland, by two aunts of Sir Murray Tyrrel. It consists of a machine pieced patchwork top of men's suiting samples with a backing of tartan wool.

ABOVE: *Our Part of the Country.* Made by the Wagga Wagga Quilters Group, 1987. 210cm x 145cm. Wagga Wagga Visitors' Centre.

PHOTOGRAPH COURTESY QUILTERS' GUILD INC.

Gundagai

The legendary town of Gundagai is about an hour's drive east of Wagga Wagga. Nestled on the banks of the Murrumbidgee River, surely no other country town has etched a more special place in Australian folklore than Gundagai. From its earliest colonial days in the 1840s it has captured the imagination of song writers and poets including Banjo Paterson and Henry Lawson. Steele Rudd's four memorable characters from the classic radio serial *Dad and Dave* have been enshrined in copper statues opposite the *Dog on the Tuckerbox* a few kilometres north of town. These unique Australian personalities were remarkable for capturing the essence of the pioneer character, indomitable spirit and humour in country towns like Gundagai. Equally famous is the dog, faithful companion to the teamsters of the pioneering days. Today, as in the past, Gundagai is a favourite stopping place for travellers.

Gundagai Historical Museum
Homer Street
Gundagai, NSW 2722.
Ph: (02) 6944 1995 Museum or
(02) 6944 1290 Historical Society.
9.00a.m. – 3.00p.m. Monday to Friday.
9.00a.m. – 4.00p.m. Saturday.
10.00a.m. – 4.00p.m. Sunday.
3 quilts plus small items of patchwork.

The collection of the Museum includes embroidered shawls, handkerchief sachets, night dresses and pillow shams. There are examples of needlepoint, knitted and crochet work, and a wedding gown c.1880 with fine pintucking, lace inserts and embroidery. Many of these lovely items, along with all the patchwork, were donated to the Museum by the pioneering McLean family. John McLean was one of the old teamsters who drove the bullock teams between Sydney and Gundagai before the railway reached the town. He settled on Big Ben Creek and his daughters, Mary and Isobella, were the makers of the quilts.

✷ The quilts are permanently displayed within the Museum and may be seen during opening hours.

✄ Mary McLean was born on the family property in 1877. She lived there all her life and died at the age of ninety four. In addition to patchwork, she was renowned for her beautiful knitting and crochet. Like so many keen needlewomen, Mary also loved gardening and designed and planted the gardens at Big Ben Creek.

A quilt of Tumbling Block design (150cm x 207cm) was made by Mary around 1920. It was created from multi-coloured velvets, the lights and darks carefully arranged to form the cubes. During the 1930s Mary also created a cot quilt of Tumbling Blocks (56cm x 78cm) for her great nephew. This work was made from corduroy velvets with a binding of burgundy velvet. A tea cosy and cushion cover of Crazy work and two cushions of Tumbling Block pattern were also made by this prolific needlewoman.

A quilt of Log Cabin design (110cm x 130cm) was made by Mary's younger sister, Isobella, during the 1920s. The central chimney for each block was cut from black fabric and the arrangement of the strips created of a pattern of stripes. The fabrics are a mixture of cottons and crepes and the backing is a pink cotton sateen. The work has a filling of sheep's fleece.

Wagga Wagga

The large and prosperous city of Wagga Wagga is located midway between Sydney and Melbourne and less than a three hour drive from Canberra. It is a major centre within the region for agriculture, business, education and sport. Nearby, there are several delightful townships. They include Lockhart which is known as the 'verandah town' and Coolamon with its many antique shops and museums.

Wagga Wagga Visitors' Centre
Tarcutta Street
Wagga Wagga, NSW 2650.
Ph: (02) 6926 9621 Fax: (02) 6926 9629
9.00a.m. – 5.00p.m. every day.

✷ The quilt is hung on permanent display in the Visitors' Centre and may be seen any time during opening hours.

✄ *Our part of the country* (210cm x 145cm) was designed and made in 1987 by the Wagga Wagga Quilters Group to celebrate the Bicentenary. A central oval depicts a rural landscape of cultivated paddocks, the undulating hills in the background and the town nestled between them. The Murrumbidgee River flows through the centre of the scene. A wide black border frames the oval and within it there are two large woolly sheep and sheaths of wheat. The quilt was made from cotton, felt, wool and leather. Techniques included hand and machine piecing, hand appliqué, embroidery and quilting.

Also in Wagga Wagga

The Wagga Wagga Historical Museum is located on Lord Baden Powell Drive, adjacent to the Botanic Gardens. Its collection includes a lovely beaded bodice, camisole tops, fans, as well as tiny sewing kits made from beaded velvet. There is an old wedding gown and other period clothing, examples of antique linen, lace and crochet. There is

PHOTOGRAPHY GRAHAM BESLEY.

RIGHT: *Quilt of Tumbling Blocks*. Made by Mary McLean, c.1920. Collection Gundagai Historical Museum, Gundagai, New South Wales.

also a wagga made during the 1930s from serge suiting and cotton twill patches. The work reflects the Australian tradition of 'making do,' its backing of cotton pieces from recycled clothing and its filling from worn out jumpers and old woollies. The Museum is open between 2.00p.m. – 5.00p.m. Tuesday, Wednesday, Saturday, Sunday, school and public holidays. Telephone (02) 6925 2934.

Junee

The small town of Junee is located in the picturesque Riverina region, a half hour drive from Wagga Wagga. The landscape is especially beautiful during Spring when fields of brilliant yellow canola are in full bloom. Junee's main street is dissected by the southern railway line and the beautiful Victorian railway station dates from 1883. Many of the shops and offices have retained the character and charm of a century ago, some still having original verandah posts, awnings, and even hitching rails.

Junee Historical Museum
Peel Street
Junee, NSW 2663.
Ph: 02) 6924 2185 President.
(02) 6924 1372 Curator.
2.00p.m. – 4.30p.m. everyday.

The Museum is housed in an old weather-board cottage. Its diverse collection includes a treasure trove referred to as the Feminine Room and it is here that the quilt is displayed. Glass cases hold a wealth of antique needlework. There are examples of lace, an embroidered antimacassar, smoking cap, and cream shawl c.1850. A small panel of crochet commemorates the 1956 Olympic Games.

✷ The quilt is permanently displayed behind glass and may be seen during opening hours. The Museum is run by volunteers and occasionally the hours may vary from those listed. It is advisable to ring in advance.

✄ This beautiful quilt of Tumbling Blocks belonged to Dr and Mrs Ronald Cuttle. Dr Cuttle lived in Junee for many years and was in charge of the local medical practice. The quilt had been made in England by Dr Cuttle's grandmother, Mrs William Cuttle. She and her husband, Reverend Cuttle, came to live in Australia in 1854 and the quilt was made prior to their journey. It was pieced by hand over paper templates using a wide variety of silk fabrics. They include both plain and printed designs, stripes, florals and plaids, with a backing of delicate striped taffeta.

Monte Cristo Homestead
John Potts Drive (off Anzac Avenue)
Junee, NSW 2663.
Ph/fax: (02) 6924 1637
10.00a.m. – 4.00p.m. every day.

The fine colonial mansion of Monte Cristo was built in 1884 by Christopher Crawley, one of the earliest settlers in the district. Set on a hill overlooking the township, the house has been lovingly restored and furnished with antiques by Mr and Mrs Ryan who have lived in it for more than 30 years. The treasures the family have collected include a beautiful walnut sewing box c.1860, large framed tapestries, and a green velvet tea cosy with beaded flowers and leaves. There are also beaded fire screens and foot stools and a little stitched sampler worked by Mr Ryan's mother early this century. Mr Ryan is an accomplished 'needleman' himself. The house is set in formal grounds and a lovely knot garden of box hedging has been created to one side.

✷ The quilt may be seen during a tour of the house which also includes a fascinating account of the history and restoration of the building and its contents.

✄ This Crazy Patchwork quilt (145cm x 192cm) was created by an unknown maker c.1880. It was purchased by a member of the Ryan family at a South Australian auction and features six blocks of Crazy work separated by dark blue velvet sashing. The sashing has been embellished along both edges with large gold fern stitch. The quilt has a wide border of Crazy work made from beautiful velvets, silks and brocades. There are numerous motifs including Victorian fans, butterflies, stars, dogs, birds, hearts, bows, and horseshoes. One of the motifs is a large three dimensional sunflower with gold velvet petals, each one made separately and then joined to the centre of brown padded velvet. The quilt has been lavishly embroidered in cream thread using a myriad of stitches.

Goulburn

The city of Goulburn is a two hour drive south west of Sydney through the beautiful Southern Highlands. Riversdale Historic Home in Maud Street was built c1840 and is now owned by the National Trust. It is a fine example of a Georgian cottage set in a beautiful garden. Quilts from the Trust collection are on occasional display at the house. To inquire please telephone (02) 9258 0123.

PHOTOGRAPHY GRAHAM BESLEY.

OPPOSITE, TOP: Detail of *Patchwork Quilt of Tumbling Blocks*. Made by Mrs William Cuttle, c.1850. Collection Junee Historical Museum, Junee, New South Wales. BELOW: Details of *Crazy Patchwork Quilt*. Unknown Maker, c.1880. 145cm x 192cm. Collection Monte Cristo Homestead, Junee, New South Wales.

Goulburn Regional Art Gallery
Goulburn Civic Centre
Cnr. Bourke and Church Streets
Goulburn, NSW 2580.
Ph: (02) 4823 0443 Fax: (02) 4823 0456
10.00a.m. – 4.30p.m. Tuesday to Friday.
1.00p.m. – 4.00p.m. Saturday and public holidays. Other times by appointment.
3 quilts.

✷ The quilts are displayed intermittently throughout the year but may also be viewed at other times by appointment. Please contact the Gallery Director by telephone or fax.

✄ The collection includes three quilts by Karen Edin. *Just Below the Surface* (199cm x 201cm) was made from painted, printed and stitched cloth with silk appliqué applied to the background. The work was then surrounded by an over-structure of wood, electronic wires and metals in keeping with its theme of visual reconciliation of technology with the organic world. The two miniature quilts (170mm x 180mm) were made in 1983 and were machine stitched using hand dyed silk and cotton fabrics.

Harden and Murrumburrah

The twin towns of Harden and Murrumburrah are to be found on the south west slopes of the Great Dividing Range, midway between Yass and Young. The undulating green hills of this pretty rural area support wheat and grazing properties, wineries, as well as orchards of cherries and peaches. During Spring and Autumn some of the wonderful private gardens are open to the public.

Harden – Murrumburrah Historical Museum
Albury Street
Murrumburrah, NSW 2587.
Ph: (02) 6386 3354 or (02) 6386 2409
10.30a.m. – 4.30p.m. Saturday.
2.00p.m. – 4.30p.m. Sunday.
Other times by appointment.

The Museum is housed in the old School of Arts building c.1912. Displays include an authentic chemist, blacksmith, colonial kitchen, bathroom and laundry. Upstairs, there is an extensive collection of clothing, heirloom sewn camisoles, nighties, and lace.

✷ The quilt is permanently displayed on an old iron bed and may be seen during the opening hours listed or by appointment.

✄ This red and white quilt of Variable Star design (221cm x 200cm) was made in Victoria by Tamar Borrow during the 1880s. Tamar had been born in 1862 at Mt Clear near Ballarat, the third child of George and Mary Borrow. She inherited her name from her grandmother, Tamar Taylor, who had lived on the Tamar River in Cumberland, England.

After the death of her brother, Harry, the family settled in a house in East St Kilda near Melbourne. Tamar's needlework skills were influenced by her mother and a front room of the house was dedicated to their sewing. Most of the work was done by candle and lamp light.

The quilt was hand pieced from a Nine Patch design of Variable Stars alternated with plain white squares. It was backed with white cotton, finely quilted by hand and finished with a 9cm wide frill. Very few early Australian patchwork quilts were quilted, and in a country with a relatively mild climate and plentiful supply of woollen blankets, quilts tended to be used as decorative items rather than for warmth. Although other Australian quilts of the period feature the Variable Star pattern, Tamar's work remains as a rare example of a 19th century quilt made in the American style of repeating blocks.

Tamar never married. The quilt was donated to the Museum by William J. Mullet and is believed to have came to Murrumburrah with a descendant of the Borrow family.

Also in Murrumburrah

At Whichcraft and Coffee Cottage in Albury Street, just a short walk from the Historical Museum, there is a quilt that was made in 1977 by a community group. Harden had been established in 1877 as a railway centre on the main Sydney to Melbourne line and this work was made to commemorate the centenary. It features hand appliquéd blocks depicting the history of the region with a focus on the railway. Whichcraft is open between 10.00a.m. and 5.00p.m. daily. Telephone (02) 6386 2343.

OPPOSITE: Details of *Variable Star Quilt*. Made by Tamar Borrow, c.1885. 221cm x 200cm. Collection Harden-Murrumburrah Historical Museum, Murrumburrah, New South Wales. ABOVE: Tamar Borrow.

PHOTOGRAPHY MICHELLE PAUL.

Yass

The town of Yass is set in beautiful countryside dotted with sheep, cattle, horse and goat studs, as well as lovely rural homesteads. It is only a 40 minute drive from Canberra. A recent highway bypass has left the town much more quiet and peaceful. Comur Street has been re-paved and many beautiful historic buildings have been painted and restored. Some still have the original hitching rails for horses. There are antique shops, art galleries and craft studios, and in the nearby countryside emu and trout farms, several wineries and a lavender nursery.

Hamilton Hume Museum

Comur Street
Yass, NSW 2582.
Ph: (02) 6226 2167 Marj Wilson or
(02) 6226 2315 Gloria Carlos,
Yass Historical Society.
(02) 6226 2557 Tourist Centre.
10.00a.m. – 4.00p.m. Friday to Sunday
and public holidays.

During school holiday periods the Museum also opens on Wednesdays and Thursdays. Other times by inquiry at the Tourist Information Centre.
2 quilts.

The Hamilton Hume Museum focuses on the colourful history of Yass and the surrounding district. In addition to the two patchwork quilts, there is also an early example of an Australian Marcella quilt with the words 'Australian International Exhibition 1879' woven into its centre. There are period costumes, children's clothing and a Victorian wedding dress. There are also examples of linen and lace insertion work, a little stitched sampler dated 1879 and an antique sewing box complete with contents.

✷ The quilts are not always on display. Please contact the Museum a week or two in advance.

✄ A quilt of Tumbling Block design (192cm x 184cm) was made c.1890 by Sophia Mary Wilbow of Windsor, New South Wales. Mrs Wilbow was a renowned needlewoman and it is believed that she created a quilt for each one of her nine daughters. This quilt belonged to Elizabeth May who married John Thomas Best and lived on a property named 'The Pines' at Tangmangaroo, near Yass. Mrs Wilbow did not own a sewing machine, preferring to stitch her quilts by hand in the traditional English method and cutting her templates from blotting paper. She used printed cotton dress and shirting fabrics in pastel colours, and it is possible that some were tailor's samples as several designs appear in various colour-ways. The quilt has no filling and a backing and outer border of deep red floral cotton.

A quilt of Suffolk Puffs (127cm x 135cm) was created in 1967 by Mrs Florrie McClung (nee Bingley) of Hawthorn, Murrumbateman, near Yass. It was made from plain and printed dress cottons, a central square of pink puffs bordered by a row of blue puffs. The work was edged and backed with tartan printed cotton. It was exhibited at many local shows and it won several prizes.

BELOW, LEFT: *Quilt of Tumbling Blocks.* Made by Sophia Mary Wilbow, c.1890. 192cm x 184cm. BELOW, RIGHT: *Quilt of Suffolk Puffs.* Made by Mrs Florrie McClung, 1967. 127cm x 135cm. Collection Hamilton Hume Museum, Yass, New South Wales.

Cooma

Cooma is located in the Southern Highlands and is the gateway to the Snowy Mountains. Fine examples of early Victorian buildings still remain in historic Lambie Street, the town's oldest thoroughfare. There are also several galleries in which the work of local artists is displayed.

The Travellers' Rest Inn
Snowy Mountains Highway
Cooma West, NSW 2630.
Ph: (02) 6452 4422 Fax: (02) 6452 4523
9.30a.m. – 5.00p.m. daily.
4 quilts and a patchwork screen.

The Travellers' Rest is to be found 5 kilometres from Cooma, just before the turn-off to Adaminaby. Built in 1861, this old coaching inn originally served the bullock teams travelling from Cooma to the gold fields. Today, it has been restored as a living museum and furnished with items from the mid 1860s to the turn of the century. In addition to the quilts, there are many charming examples of women's domestic hand work. Seasonal displays of crafts celebrating Easter, Christmas, and other special occasions are accompanied by explanations of their significance to the various traditions and customs.

✷ The patchwork screen and some of the quilts are displayed permanently and may be seen anytime during opening hours. Others are kept in storage but may be seen by prior arrangement.

✂ An unfinished patchwork coverlet (260cm x 162cm) of Grandmother's Flower Garden design dates from the 1890s and is of unknown maker. It has been hand stitched from printed cotton dress fabrics and shirtings and the original card templates and basting threads are still in place.

Patchwork screens were made in England during the Victorian era, often using hexagon and Tumbling Block designs. This quaint 20th century screen is of unknown maker and has been hand stitched from printed dress cottons c.1960.

There are two striking waggas in the collection. The first of pieced squares (175cm x 210cm) dates from the 1930s and has been made from woollen suiting fabrics. It has been tied with tufted knots using rust coloured cotton thread. The second wagga (155cm x 169cm) has been made from unevenly pieced strips of dark suitings and is believed to have been taken to the war by an Australian soldier. It features his military identification number, *'9752'* embroidered in yellow thread.

Griffith

Griffith is located in the lush Riverina region of South Western New South Wales, approximately 610 kilometres from Sydney. Designed by Walter Burley Griffin, the town has a distinctive radial pattern with wide, tree-lined streets and many areas of parkland. The miracle of irrigation has transformed the countryside surrounding Griffith from a barren waste land into a diverse farming area. It is especially suited to the growing of rice and grapes.

BELOW, LEFT: *Wagga of Suiting Samples.* Unknown Maker, c.1930. 175cm x 210cm. BELOW, RIGHT: *Patchwork Coverlet*, c.1890 and *Screen of Hexagons* c.1960. Unknown Makers. Collection Travellers' Rest Inn, Cooma West, New South Wales.

Soft Sculptured Artistic Curtain. Made by the Community of Griffith, 1987. 12m x 5m. Griffith Regional Theatre, Griffith, New South Wales.

ABOVE: Details of *Patchwork Quilt of Hexagons*. Made by Fanny Elliot, c.1886. Collection Griffith Pioneer Park Museum, Griffith, New South Wales.

Griffith Regional Theatre
Neville Place
Griffith, NSW 2680.
Ph: (02) 6962 7466 Fax: (02) 6962 5726
10.30a.m. and 2.30p.m. weekdays.
Other times by arrangement.

A pictorial record of the transformation of the Griffith region from wilderness to lush farmland may be seen in the photographic collection displayed at the Theatre.

✷ There are two viewing times for the Curtain each weekday as listed above. An audio-tape is available for a small charge and each visitor receives a coloured post card of the work. Weekend access is possible by appointment. Please contact the Theatre administration.

✂ The magnificent *Soft Sculptured Artistic Curtain* (12m x 5m) displayed in the Griffith Theatre was completed in 1987. This huge community project was co-ordinated by Dorothy Waide who had been inspired to initiate the work after seeing the curtain made several years previously for the Orange Civic Theatre.

An original watercolour painting by Griffith artist Robert Barker was chosen for the design. Doug Denham was appointed as artistic director of the project and he began by transferring Bob's painting to thirty canvas drawings. More than 300 women from many different community groups worked on the individual sections. Only non-flammable fabric could be used in the Theatre and Doug travelled to Sydney and Melbourne especially to purchase the colour co-ordinated velvets and wools that were needed.

The achievement of a realistic perspective within the work required considerable planning. The lower section was made heavily three dimensional, the middle section slightly less so, and the top section almost flat. A great deal of time was spent at the top of a ladder to keep the perspective true!

The huge water wheel at the bottom of the curtain was created by three generations of the same family – Nives Piccoli, her mother and her daughter. Weeks were spent washing, dyeing and spinning the wool which was then crocheted into chains to make the rice which is so incredibly realistic. The grapes were hand crocheted and stuffed, their leaves wired and padded. Ploughed fields were made simply from row-upon-row of machine stitching. Freshly planted cabbages were created from pintucking, newly mown grass from pulled-thread work. Reflections and shadows on water were created using different shades of taffeta, cotton, silk, and layered tulle.

ABOVE: Detail of *Wholecloth Quilt.* Believed to have been made by Maria Zilliotto's grandmother, c.1920. Collection Griffith Pioneer Park Museum.

Hand knitted dolls added human life to the picture and Doug Denham was moved to comment that almost every imaginable sewing technique invented had been used, along with a few new ones they had invented themselves!

This wonderful art work has gone on to inspire the creation of many others, both in New South Wales and inter-state. They include the *Heritage Wall Hanging* in the town of Goolgowi, north of Griffith, the *Essence of Maroochy* in Nambour, Queensland, and the *Yarns Artwork in Silk* in Deloraine, Tasmania.

Griffith Pioneer Park Museum

Cnr. Scenic and Remembrance Drive
Griffith, NSW 2680.
Ph: (02) 6962 4196 Fax: (02) 6964 2815
8.30a.m. – 4.30p.m. everyday.
Closed Christmas Day.
6 quilts.

Pioneer Park was established in 1971 with the aim of preserving for future generations memories of some of the struggles endured by the early pioneers. From the 1830s onwards squatters had began to occupy land along the river, but settlement remained sparse throughout the 19th century. There were no towns, drought was a frequent occurrence, and the earliest pioneers tolerated a life of isolation and self sufficiency. Finally, around the turn of the century, a severe drought persuaded the Government to proceed with the irrigation scheme that was to change this semi-arid region into one of the most productive and closely settled rural areas in Australia.

✷ The quilts are displayed on a rotational basis and there will always be at least one on view during any visit. Please contact the Manager one week in advance if you wish to see the entire collection.

✄ Many of the Museum's displays feature the clever innovations of the pioneers. Home-made furniture was built from butter and fruit boxes, flour bags were used for clothes, and farm machinery was often made from the reassembled parts of old equipment. Wagga rugs were very much a part of this tradition. Made from scraps of fabric, they were filled with old clothes or worn out blankets. Once commonplace, these utilitarian covers were designed for thrift and need rather than beauty, though some were not only warm but also decorative.

Two of Pioneer Park's waggas were made by Mrs Edna Richards during the 1950s and donated to the Museum by her daughter, Lorraine. The family had lived on a sheep and wheat property at Merriwagga which was very isolated at the time. There were no roads and no electricity. Mrs Richards made at least a dozen waggas, some for use on the beds of her children, others for shearers and occasional visitors. These two waggas are stuffed with layers of clothing, one with a top of floral cretonne, the other of red and blue check.

Another wagga was donated by Josie Hoare and had been made by her mother, Ellen McRae, during the early 1940s when the family lived at Sunrise, Tabbita, in a house with an earthen floor. There were seven children and like many other rural families of the period, making ends meet was a struggle. Catastrophe struck on the eve of World War II when a fire devastated the McRae home. Friends and neighbours gave clothing and other necessities and it is likely that the material in this wagga came from items donated after the fire. Both sides have been made from a pretty floral chintz with a filling of unpicked clothing tacked to a thin woollen blanket. The wagga was in constant use by the family for more than fifty years.

A quilt of random hexagon rosettes (117cm x 137cm) was made by Mrs Fanny Elliot in Middleton, Stoney, Oxfordshire in 1886. It was donated to the Museum by her daughter, Olive Scott. Fanny's husband had been a tailor and the fabrics used in the quilt were remnants left over from his shop. Made from multi-coloured silk, sateen, brocade and wool, the quilt was entirely sewn by hand. Most of the stitching is finely done, though some less skilful work may indicate that Fanny had help from a less experienced needlewoman. Some of the fabrics have deteriorated and the original templates can still be seen in place.

Olive met her future husband, Doug, in England during the years of the first World War. She brought the quilt to Australia in 1923 when she came here to be married. Doug and Olive lived on a farm at Lake Wyangan and their son Frank remembers the quilt being in constant use throughout his childhood.

ABOVE: *Gustav's Baby.* Made by Margaret Perry Carter, 1986. Collection Griffith Regional Art Gallery, Griffith, New South Wales.

The Griffith region has always had a diverse population and the Museum strives to reflect this multicultural heritage. A beautiful wholecloth quilt (2.5m x 2m) was donated by Maria Zilliotto and is believed to have been made in Italy by her grandmother. Maria's mother, Angela, brought the quilt to Australia when she came to join her husband in 1949. Sadly she died in 1958 when her daughters were still young children and so the exact history of the quilt is uncertain. Made from pale yellow sateen, it has a thick filling of woollen fleece and has been finely quilted in a diamond pattern with a Celtic design in the centre. Quilts such as this one were traditionally made in Italy to mark a special occasion, such as a daughter's wedding. Often specialists would be employed to do the quilting, though sometimes it would be done at home with several quilters working around a large frame.

A sampler quilt of pictorial blocks was made by the Creative Craft Association in 1988. The group had decided to design a badge for use by local quilters and the blocks made as proposals by each member were joined to make this quilt.

Griffith Regional Art Gallery

167 – 185 Banna Avenue
Griffith, NSW 2680.
Ph: (02) 6962 5991 Fax: (02) 6962 6119
10.30a.m. – 4.30p.m. Wednesday to Saturday. Closed Sunday to Tuesday, and the month of January.

The Griffith Regional Art Gallery provides visual exhibitions that change monthly. The permanent collection includes Australian designer jewellery with both historical and contemporary items to be enjoyed.

✷ The hanging is not on permanent display but may be viewed by appointment. Please contact the Gallery Director by telephone or fax.

✂ This hanging entitled *Gustav's Baby* was created by artist Margaret Perry Carter in 1986. The face and hand of the child are hand painted. He is depicted lying against a black background with a dramatic patchwork covering of bright fabrics, many of them having shine and glitter. The fabrics are recycled materials cut in shapes that create movement and give an effect of folds hidden beneath what is seen. The cover drapes to one side and falls as it would over the edge of a bed. Long fringing is sewn to the base.

Also in Griffith

A quilt was made for the Salvation Army Citadel, 103 Binya Street, by Jennifer Wheatley in 1995. The design was inspired by a Biblical text from Hebrews and depicts God as 'a consuming fire.' A white dove of peace represents the Holy Spirit and holds a twig of native wattle in its beak. The background was strip pieced, the motifs appliquéd by machine. The quilt may be seen between 9.00a.m. and 5.00p.m. Monday or Tuesday or at other times by appointment with Brian Savage. Telephone (02) 6964 3335.

Eight banners were appliquéd for St Alban's Cathedral in 1977 by members of the congregation. Each one depicts a different season of the church year. There is also a wonderful series of tapestry kneelers which were created between 1983 and '87. The Cathedral is located on the corner of Binya Street and Anzac Parade and is open everyday between 8.00a.m. and 5.30p.m. Visitors are welcome.

Several schools in Griffith also have quilts hanging on permanent display. Each one may be seen during school hours by contacting the Principal 24 hours in advance:

A quilt entitled *Grow to Know* was made in 1986 for Griffith North Public School, Boonah Street. Telephone number (02) 6962 1043.

A quilt of pictorial blocks was made by the school community in 1996 to celebrate the 75th Anniversary of St Patrick's Primary School. The school is located in Warrambool Street. Telephone number (02) 6964 2888.

The *Wade High 25th Anniversary Quilt* was made between 1996-'97 by past and present families of the school. The school is located in Poole Street. Telephone number (02) 6962 4022.

ABOVE: *The Maude Bicentennial Quilt.* Made by the Patchers and Quilters of the Hay Plains, 1988. 200cm x 200cm. Hay Shire Council, Hay, New South Wales.

Hay

The town of Hay is set on the banks of the Murrumbidgee River in the vast, flat region of western New South Wales known as the Hay Plains. An important rural centre half way between Sydney and Adelaide, Hay is well known for the excellence of its merino sheep studs. An interesting collection of photos and memorabilia from the early pioneering days is displayed at the Hay Gaol Museum in Church Street. Built in 1878, the Gaol was used as a Red Cross Maternity Home for some years so that many Hay residents claim to have been born in gaol! Displayed in a glass case in the cell block is a quilt made by teachers and children to commemorate the centenary of the little bush school in Maude, a tiny village just west of Hay. The Patchers and Quilters of the Hay Plains meet at the Gaol every Friday between 12 noon and 3.00p.m.

Hay Shire Council
Lachlan Street
Hay, NSW 2711.
Ph: (02) 6993 1003 Fax: (02) 6993 1288
9.00a.m. – 4.00p.m. Monday to Friday.

✷ The quilt is hung on permanent display in the foyer of the Hay Shire Council building and may be seen during office hours.

✂ The *Maude Bicentennial Quilt* (200cm x 200cm) was designed and made by the Patchers and Quilters of the Hay Plains. The project celebrated the Bicentenary in 1988 and many of those involved had to travel huge distances in order to participate. The quilt depicts a drover and his horse coming through the dust of the Hay Plains, bringing his sheep to drink at the Murrumbidgee. Majestic red river gums shade the river bank.

Initially, workshops were held with Mary Beeston and many new techniques were learnt. The scene was transferred onto a three inch grid and templates were cut for each piece before the hand stitching began. A sense of the immensity of those endless plains was captured with clever perspective and transition of colour. The stockman and his horse disappeared into the heat and dust of layers of tulle and silk organza. Traditional blocks were also incorporated into the quilt and there are Windmills, Flying Geese, and the Ohio Star pattern which is used as the emblem for the group.

Quilting took place around a large frame which was set up for the duration of the project at the Hay Gaol. The quilting design was drawn onto paper, traced onto tulle and then transferred to the quilt top. A mirage of quilted kangaroos, other native animals and birds, and a few 'secret things,' were added to contribute to the fascination of this unique quilt.

Goolgowi

The outback village of Goolgowi is to be found in 'Black Stump' Country, 50 kilometres north of Griffith. The area has a rich history dating back to the origins of European settlement in Australia. It is from the nearby town of Merriwagga that the name 'Black Stump' originated. During the year 1886, a bullocky and his wife were travelling together in this part of the country. While the bullocky sought feed for the animals his wife made a fire for the evening meal. The day was hot, windy and dusty, and when at last the bullocky returned, he found to his horror that his wife had been burnt to death. Known as man of few words, he was later to say the poor woman looked *'just like a black stump.'* Her remains are buried in the century old Gunbar Cemetery.

Goolgowi Community Hall
Farrer Street
Goolgowi, NSW 2652.
Ph: (02) 6965 1306 Fax: (02) 6965 1379
8.30a.m. – 5.00p.m. Monday to Friday.

✷ The wall hanging is mounted behind glass at the back of the stage. It can be viewed by contacting the Tourist Officer, Carrathool Shire Council.

✂ This delightful wall hanging (480cm x 150cm) was made by members of the Goolgowi community to celebrate the Bicentenary. The design commemorates the town's history in a progressive illustration that begins with the earliest settlement and traces development until 1989. It includes a kaleidoscope of images moving from old to new, illustrating for future generations the history and stories of the town. Some of these stories were collected from original pioneering families, some were pieced together from old photographs.

Many reminders of the harsh realities of farming life have been included – rabbit plaques devouring crops, mice infestations on wheat bags, a dust storm swirling around a haystack and a locust plague leaving nothing in its wake. The old town has been illustrated as it was in colonial times with general store, bakery, butchery and blacksmith. An amusing inclusion is the 'Beer Truck' which came to Goolgowi each Saturday and was a favourite spot for the locals to gather for a drink and a chat before the first pub was built!

The scene is unmistakably Australian. It includes many figures – some created from felt, some embroidered and appliquéd in different shapes and sizes. The eclectic combination imbues the work with a charming naive character. The old car has been fitted with windows of transparent plastic. Pigs and goats have been made from braid with vinyl tails, sheep from wool. Tulle has been painted silver to create the fence of a cow yard. Fur has been used for the rabbits and hand made yellow and white felt for the haystacks. The pride of a tiny rural community in their heritage and progress shines through this lovely quilt.

PHOTOGRAPHY GARRY BAZZACCO.

Deniliquin

The historic town of Deniliquin is set on the banks of the Edward River in South Western New South Wales. Its closest capital city is Melbourne, only a 3 hour drive away. The surrounding countryside is a rich and diversified farming area, long renowned for its merino sheep studs and more recently for its enormous rice production.

Deniliquin Council
End Street
Deniliquin, NSW 2710.
Ph: (03) 5881 2444 Fax: (03) 5881 4415
8.30a.m. – 5.00p.m. Monday to Friday.

OPPOSITE: Details from *Goolgowi Heritage Wall Hanging.* Made by the community, 1989. 480cm x 150cm. Goolgowi Community Hall, Goolgowi, N.S.W.

GOOLGOWI
NALL
JACKSON-CO

✷ The quilt is hung on permanent display in the Council Chambers and may be seen during office hours. It is advisable to ring before visiting to ensure the room is not in use.

✄ The *Deniliquin Heritage Quilt* (182cm x 200cm) was designed and made by members of Deniliquilters and Friends in 1995. The work commemorates 150 years of settlement from 1842 to 1992 and depicts the history of the town, its river setting, and many of the heritage buildings. Techniques included hand appliqué, embroidery, quilting, tapestry, fabric dyeing and printing.

Also in Deniliquin

At St Paul's Anglican Church, on the corner of Harrison and Wellington Streets, three ecclesiastical garments were embellished using Stained Glass appliqué by Mary-O Roberts. The inspiration for the design came from the stained glass windows behind the altar. The vestments are worn on Holy days at both Christmas and Easter as well as Saints' days. They may also be seen by appointment. Please contact the Minister's wife, Mrs Everett. Telephone number (03) 5881 2092.

Broken Hill

The outback city of Broken Hill is set in the Barrier Ranges amidst the vast red arid lands of far western New South Wales. The nearest capital city is Adelaide, approximately 500 kilometres away. Known as the 'Silver City,' Broken Hill has the richest deposits of silver, lead and zinc in the world. A few kilometres away, the Living Desert Reserve features a series of sculptures created by artists from huge sandstone rocks.

Broken Hill City Art Gallery
Cnr. Blende and Chloride Streets
Broken Hill, NSW 2880.
Ph: (08) 8088 5491 Fax: (08) 8087 1411
10.00a.m. – 5.00p.m. weekdays.
1.00p.m. – 5.00p.m. Saturday and Sunday.

The collection of the Gallery includes both traditional and contemporary Australian art with a special focus on local artists.

✷ The quilt is hung on permanent display and may be seen during the hours listed.

✄ This quilt provides a visual history of Broken Hill. It was designed and co-ordinated by Marcia Fillery and made in 1994 by Marcia and the Silver City Quilters. The central panel of black water-wave cotton represents the deep mine shafts and features early explorers and their maps. The Living Desert Sculptures are illustrated along the base with other important aspects of life and history down each side. Miners are shown in flannel clothes with leather suede hats, cap lamps and boots. Actual minerals are stuck to the fabric surface. The final border includes native flora found only in the Far West region. Techniques included hand and machine appliqué, strip piecing, collage and hand quilting.

Port Macquarie

The historic town of Port Macquarie is situated on the northern coast of New South Wales between Taree and Coffs Harbour. One of the oldest settlements in the state, it was established as a penal colony in 1821. Today it is a thriving regional centre, popular holiday resort and retirement location.

Port Macquarie Historical Museum
22 Clarence Street
Port Macquarie, NSW 2444.
Ph: (02) 6583 1108
9.30a.m. – 4.30p.m. Monday to Saturday.
1.00p.m. – 4.30p.m. Sunday.

The Port Macquarie Historical Museum is housed in a former dwelling and shop, originally built in the 1840s and classified by the National Trust. The collection includes relics dating from convict days and there is a wonderful display of costumes and uniforms. One treasured dress is dated c.1760 and was originally owned by the wife of an officer in the Port Macquarie penal settlement. There are trousseau items and heirloom underwear from the early 1800s and a collection of capes, most of them more than a century old.

✷ The items are permanently displayed within the Museum and may be seen during opening hours.

✄ A magnificent grand piano cover was made in Scotland during the mid 1880s by the Misses Noble. These two sisters were the maiden aunts of Ferguson Simpson who emigrated to Australia, bringing the cover with him. Upon Ferguson's death the cover passed to his daughter, Celta Mackie, and it was Celta's daughter, Mrs Ainslie Brown, who presented the family's treasured heirloom to the Museum.

The work has been made from exquisitely embroidered floral panels, each one worked on aubergine silk and bordered with burgundy velvet. Every panel features a delicate spray of flowers or a cluster of berries, all of them different and many done in raised stumpwork. There are daisies, pansies, roses, cherries, butterflies and moths, each motif created using silk threads and ribbons to achieve extraordinary realism. A visitor to the Museum actually reported her concern that bugs were attacking the work! Both the Misses Noble added their initials in gold and cream silk threads, encircling them with wreaths of twiggy foliage.

The cover has always been treasured and remains in remarkably good condition, evoking fragments of one family's history and encapsulating a lifestyle that now belongs to a distant past. Recently, a Scottish couple visited the Museum and added an intriguing detail to the story. They remarked on the amazing similarity of the cover to another that they had seen in the Palace of Holyroodhouse, Edinburgh. They wondered if the Misses Noble had also seen it and been inspired by it.

The Museum also has a pair of white Suffolk Puff pillow shams c.1900 of unknown maker. The puffs were cut from the 'blue bags' used for whitening linen in the days before bleaching powders existed.

PHOTOGRAPHY TED HUTCHISON.

Senior Citizens Centre
Munster Street
Port Macquarie, NSW 2444.
Ph: (02) 6583 7149 Senior Citizens Centre or
(02) 6583 4086 Betty McDonald.
(02) 6583 2705 Marge Elford.
12.30p.m. – 3.30p.m. Tuesday.
9.00a.m. – 3.30p.m. Wednesday.
9.00a.m. – 12 noon Thursday.
1.00p.m. – 3.00p.m. Friday.
22 wall hangings.

✷ The hangings may be seen in the main hall of the Senior Citizens Centre. Viewing times are listed above and no other functions are held in the hall during these times.

✄ This series of splendid wall hangings depicting the history of the Hastings region was created between 1985 and 1996 by the Port Macquarie Hastings Embroiderers' Group. The work was the inspiration of Glad Stanford who had spent her childhood in the area and was the descendant of a pioneering family. Motivated by the historical textiles she had seen while travelling in England, Glad determined to record the rich history of her own region in a series of pictorial hangings.

The first nine appliquéd and embroidered scenes were completed for the Bicentennial. They illustrate historical events from 1818 when the area was first explored by John Oxley. They include the Aboriginal inhabitants, the arrival of the Europeans and the early penal settlement, the harsh and lonely existence that was life for women on pioneer farms.

Sadly, Glad Stanford was never to see the hangings completed. She died in 1989. As a wonderful tribute to her inspiration, the work was continued by the dedicated group who had been involved from the beginning. Thirteen more panels were created during the next eight years, depicting the region's history from the 1880s to 1988. Involvement in both World Wars, historic landmarks and heritage buildings were all beautifully recorded

BELOW: Details of *Grand Piano Cover.* Made by the Misses Noble, c.1885. Port Macquarie Historical Museum, Port Macquarie, New South Wales.

in these murals. The final picture illustrated the fireworks on the Town Green, January 26, 1988.

The work was done by hand and machine using a multitude of different techniques and materials to achieve the desired effect. Padding was added to provide dimension. Some of the trees were crocheted, others machine embroidered. Ribbon, lace, beads and raffia were all included. The finished murals were mounted behind protective glass in beautiful timber frames.

In the Nearby Region

At Taree, 80 kilometres south of Port Macquarie, there is a beautiful embroidered wall hanging displayed in the Tourist Information Centre located on the Pacific Highway. For details see 'Newcastle – In the Nearby Region,' p. 48.

Armidale

The charming city of Armidale is situated high in the New England Ranges, midway between Sydney and Brisbane. Renowned for its stately Victorian buildings, many of them classified by the National Trust, it is the major city for the surrounding tablelands and a centre for learning. There are several galleries and museums and an abundance of coffee, antique and book shops.

'Booloominbah'
University of New England
Armidale, NSW 2351.
Ph: (02) 6773 3488 Fax: (02) 6773 5131
9.00a.m. – 5.00p.m. weekdays.
Weekends by appointment.

The stately country mansion of 'Booloominbah' was built between 1886 and '88 for pastoralist, Frederick White. It is set in picturesque gardens on a hill 5 kilometres outside Armidale and is now the administrative centre of the University of New England. The building is renowned for its remarkable stained glass windows and volunteers are available for guided tours if prior bookings are made.

ABOVE: Detail of *A Vision Splendid*. Made by Wendy Wright, 1987-'88. 302cm x 180cm. Booloominbah, Armidale, New South Wales. OPPOSITE: *The Hastings Heritage Wall Hangings*. Made by the Port Macquarie Hastings Embroiderers' Group, 1985-'96. Senior Citizens Centre, Port Macquarie, New South Wales.

✱ The quilt is hung on permanent display within a glass case and may be seen during office hours or at weekends by appointment.

✂ This quilted wall hanging (320cm x 180cm) entitled *A Vision Splendid* was designed by Jean Cooper and made by textile artist Wendy Wright between 1987 and '88. It was created to commemorate the fiftieth anniversary of the University of New England as an institute of higher learning. It also symbolised the 'vision splendid' of continued growth in teaching and research, and celebrated the 100th anniversary of the building of 'Booloominbah.' The quilt depicts the house alongside fabric panels made from the colours of the University faculties. The coat of arms was created from appliquéd leather and machine embroidery. Students, professors and the University Chancellor were made in stumpwork and applied to the strips. The roses and wisteria, so much a part of the New England environment, were hand sculptured and added to the borders. The virginia creeper which covers the walls of the building was machine embroidered using tapestry wool. Exactly 200 leaves were created to represent the Australian Bicentenary. Hand dyed silk, silk organza, velvet, wool, and cotton fabrics were used for the work and it was finished with hand quilting.

In the Nearby Region

At Inverell, a one and a half hour drive north west of Armidale, a pictorial heritage quilt was made to celebrate the Bicentennial and is hung on permanent display at the Inverell Art Gallery. Created by the Inverell Art Society Patchwork Group, the work depicts the region's past and present and was machine pieced, hand appliquéd, embroidered and quilted. The Gallery is located at 5 Evans Street and is open 10.00a.m. – 5.00p.m. Monday to Friday and 10.00a.m. – 1.00p.m. Saturday. Telephone (02) 6722 4983.

1818
1819
1820s
1830s

1830s
to
1880s

1880's

TO

Tamworth

The large rural city of Tamworth lies at the foot of the Moonbi Ranges in the picturesque Peel River Valley. First settled in 1827, the town prospered during the 1850s as a supply centre for diggers making their way to the nearby gold fields. Many buildings remain from this period and a heritage walk is available for visitors. Today the town is the commercial centre of a thriving sheep farming and grain growing region. Considered the 'country music capital of Australia,' there are several museums of country music history and even a guitar-shaped swimming pool.

Calala Cottage Museum
142 Denison Street
West Tamworth, NSW 2340.
Ph: (02) 6765 7492
2.00p.m. – 4.00p.m. Tuesday to Friday.
10.00a.m. – 4.00p.m. Saturday and Sunday.

Calala Cottage was built in 1875 as a town house for Philip Gidley King, the first mayor of Tamworth. Today it forms part of a village complex designed to depict the lives of settlers in the Peel Valley during the late 19th century. A large collection of embroidered linen, lace, and clothing is included in changing exhibitions.

✷ The skin rugs are permanently displayed within the cottage. The patchwork quilt is exhibited twice a year and may **only** be seen on these two occasions. It is shown on the weekend before Mothers' Day when the Tamworth Historical Society stages an exhibition entitled 'Living in the 1890s.' A second exhibition takes place during Spring, the exact weekend varying from year to year. Please check the date by ringing the cottage in advance.

✂ A beautiful patchwork coverlet of hexagons was made c.1850 by the late Mr. G. Copeland's grandmother. The work was created during a voyage from England to Australia. It was finely hand stitched in the Grandmother's Flower Garden design using printed cotton dress and shirting fabrics of the period. It was finished with a border of plain white cotton onto which little triangles of blue striped fabric were appliquéd. The work was not lined and because many fabrics are now very fragile it is kept in conservational storage except for brief periods of exhibition.

There are also two skin rugs. One was made from kangaroo pelts by the late Mr Ted Jeffries and was used by him during road building camps in the 1920s and '30s. The other was made from possum skins and formed part of the trousseau of the late Mrs E. Oliver.

Tamworth City Gallery
203 Marius Street
Tamworth, NSW 2340.
Ph: (02) 6755 4459 Fax: (02) 6755 4261
10.00a.m. – 5.00p.m. Monday to Friday.
9.00a.m. – 12.00noon Saturday.
1.00p.m. – 4.00p.m. Sunday.

The Tamworth City Gallery has had a long association with fibre and textile works. A biennial exhibition showing a diverse range of new work has been held since 1975. The emphasis has always been on selecting the most innovative examples from all over Australia with the aim of reflecting artistic developments and directions within the media. Several works are acquired from each exhibition. Many of Australia's best known contemporary quiltmakers have had work selected for exhibition. They include Wendy Lugg, Jan Irvine-Nealie, Lois Densham, Ruth Stoneley, Greg Somerville, Judy Hooworth and Sarah Crowest.

✷ The quilt collection is not on display but viewing of works can be arranged if requests are made at least one month in advance. Please contact the Gallery Director.

✂ The collection includes a quilt by Jane Whiteley entitled *From Within*. It was made in 1993 and purchased by the Gallery in the same year. In this work Jane wanted to emphasise the integrity existing between the stitch and the cloth. Using her own unique method of construction she created the quilt by hand, working 'from within outwards.' She stitched layers of fabric alternatively to the back and then the front, using red woollen thread and indigo dyed cotton gauze. Her quilting stitches became a component of the fabric, almost as the warp and weft threads do in the weaving process. There are small random stitches on the front of the work, while on the back, the large stitching in an obvious grid pattern echoes that of the woven cloth. Beneath the top layer of blue, there is a centre of red gauze which is only just apparent. Its addition provides a kind of energy in the quilt which *'rises to the surface from within.'*

Jan Irvine-Nealie's quilt *Collidascopic Rain* (210cm x 160cm) was made in 1986. It depicts the destructive beauty of a mushroom cloud, symbol of the pending threat to earth caused by man's self destructive technology. Shards of uncertainty descend to the ground inducing disturbance in our underworld, but from behind the cloud a rainbow emerges providing hope among the 'collidascopic rain.' The quilt was made from cotton fabric with a cotton filling and backing. It was airbrush dyed and hand quilted.

The collection also includes quilts by Lois Densham, Rose Marie Szulc and Ruth Stoneley.

ABOVE: Detail of *From Within*. Made by Jane Whiteley, 1993. RIGHT: *Collidascopic Rain*. Made by Jan Irvine-Nealie, 1986. Collection Tamworth City Gallery, Tamworth, New South Wales.

Calrossy Girls' School
140 Brisbane Street
Tamworth, NSW 2340.
Ph: (02) 6766 2965
8.30a.m. – 3.00p.m. Monday to Friday
during school terms.

✷ The quilt is hung on permanent display in the Multi-Purpose Centre of the School. It may be seen during school hours. The Centre is frequently occupied and therefore access may be restricted. Please make an appointment with the Bursar in advance.

✂ This quilt entitled *...And in the Beginning* was designed by textile artist Glenys Mann. It was made by Glenys and the Peel Cottage Quilters to celebrate the Bicentenary in 1988. The work depicts the Australian flag covering a rural scene of cultivated paddocks, much as Tamworth would have looked 'in the beginning.' The background was pieced by hand in 40cm blocks, the little settler's cottage, windmill and native gum leaves hand appliquéd in place afterwards. The work was quilted by hand and selected for inclusion in the Quilt Australia '88 exhibition.

Narrabri

Narrabri is found in the Namoi Valley, 160 kilometres north west of Tamworth. The Namoi River divides the town into three parts, hence the Aboriginal name of Narrabri, meaning Forked Waters. The huge Shire stretches from the Nandewar Ranges to the Pilliga scrub country and is a major cotton growing, sheep and wheat region. In addition to the hanging, there are always works from the Civic Art Collection on display in the Shire building.

ABOVE: *The Narrabri Heritage Wall Hanging.* Made by the Narrabri Arts and Crafts Society, 1994. 120cm x 190cm. Narrabri Shire Council Chambers, Narrabri, New South Wales. OPPOSITE, TOP: Detail of frill-neck lizard and red sorgham. OPPOSITE, BELOW: Detail of kookaburra and flowering eucalypt.

Narrabri Shire Council Chambers

46 – 48 Maitland Street
Narrabri, NSW 2390.
Ph: (02) 6792 1699 Fax: (02) 6799 6888
8.30a.m. – 5.00p.m. Monday to Friday.

✷ The wall hanging is permanently displayed in the Council Chambers and may be seen during office hours. It is advisable to ring in advance just to ensure the room is not in use.

✄ This magnificent three dimensional wall hanging (120cm x 190cm) was designed by local artist Robin Stieger and made by the Narrabri Arts and Crafts Society in 1994. Prue Anthony co-ordinated the project which skilfully combined both needlework and painting.

The work depicts a sweeping view of the Shire within three panels, the curved baseline representing the winding of the Namoi River. The Narrabri bridge creates a focal point leading into the town. The lovely old courthouse, church and grand-stand are depicted against a background dominated by the Nandewar Ranges, the wide plains on either side.

The mountains and sky were painted by Robin before the layers of stitched details were added. Hand dyed threads in French and colonial knots were used to form the red sorgham at the base. The bottlebrush was created with machine stitchery and appliquéd in place, the wattle hand embroidered. Flannel flowers were made from felt, their centres hand made pom poms and their petals given painted tips. The kookaburra and frill-neck lizard were painted and appliquéd, the folds in the lizard being manipulated by stiffening the fabric. The channels and banks carved through the ground to carry vital irrigation water were stitched through all layers of the hanging in deep lines of hand quilting.

At the completion of the project Robin Stieger was moved to comment:

'I am reminded of outback women through time who have always needed to make beautiful things, despite harsh and hard environments, whether in painting, needlecraft, or their gardens and homes. I am so glad that 'our place' has a record of the quality of that ability to create, alive and well in the 1990s.'

Lismore

Lismore is set in gently undulating countryside on the banks of the Wilson river. Its nearest capital city is Brisbane, 225 kilometres to the north, and it is only a half hour drive to Byron Bay. The region surrounding Lismore is dotted with picturesque villages and only a few kilometres away is Nimbin. This town with its colourful facades and psychedelic murals is the centre of an alternative lifestyle movement.

Richmond River Historical Museum
Lismore Municipal Building
165 Molesworth Street
Lismore, NSW 2480.
Ph: (02) 6621 9993
10.00a.m. – 4.00p.m. Monday to Friday
or by appointment.

The collection of the Museum includes a wealth of textiles. There are examples of embroidered linen, hardanger, gold thread work, tapestry, heirloom underwear and period clothing. A hand knitted blanket was made c.1905 by Mrs Angelo Roder using wool from her own sheep. A coverlet of heavy cream linen was created in Northern Ireland c.1900. It was beautifully hand stitched by Miss G. W. Irwin for her trousseau and features appliqué, embroidery and cut work. Another coverlet of finely embroidered net was made by Mrs W. Bryant and features the date '1899' stitched near the top.

✷ The patchwork and other textile items are displayed on a rotational basis. Visitors are welcome to see them when they are not on display by prior arrangement.

✄ A single bed Log Cabin quilt c.1890 is of unknown maker. It has been machine pieced in the design known as Straight Furrow – the diagonal lines formed by the placement of the light and dark strips resembling the furrows made in the soil during ploughing. Multi-coloured fabrics of silk, cotton and velvet have been used, most of them plain with a few printed designs. The quilt has a backing of red cotton and has been well used and mended.

A patchwork quilt of hexagon rosettes was made c.1960 by the late Miss L. Oakes who lived in Lismore for many years. The work was hand stitched from brightly printed dress cottons and edged with blue cotton. Ref 3884-H

A Signature quilt originated in the village of Dunoon, 18 kilometres north of Lismore and was presented to the Dunoon Parsonage in 1911. It bears the white hand embroidered names of parishioners and early ministers of the Methodist Church, each person having paid a small donation to have their autographs included. Ref. 2626

There is also a small patchwork cushion of Log Cabin design made during the 1970s by Jessie Cooke of Alstonville, near Lismore. Ref 4692-E

In the Nearby Region

In the town of Mullumbimby, a half hour drive north of Byron Bay, there is a fascinating nine metre square *Work in Silk* displayed in the Byron Shire Council Chambers. It was created in 1996 by Mirjam Koenig and depicts the beauties of the Shire using layered silks of many different textures. It can be viewed through the glass of the octagonal-shaped Council Chambers in Station Street, Mullumbimby. The Ranger at the main desk of the adjacent Council Administration building will also open the Chambers by request.

Wollongong

Long established as an important industrial centre, Wollongong is situated on the south coast 80 kilometres from Sydney. It is located at the base of the Illawarra escarpment and the countryside includes both spectacular coastline as well as huge tracts of natural bushland in the nearby national parks.

Illawarra Performing Arts Centre
32 Burelli Street
Wollongong, NSW 2500.
Ph: (02) 4226 3366
9.00a.m. – 5.00p.m. Monday to Friday.
9.00a.m. – 12.30p.m. Saturday.

✷ The panels are hung on permanent display in the foyer of the Arts Centre and may be seen during opening hours.

✄ This superb wall hanging (3m x 4m) entitled *Women of the Illawarra* was made between 1989 and '91 by the Embroiderers' Guild New South Wales, Wollongong Group. The work was co-ordinated by Judith Langdon and specially designed by local artist Trudi Last to suit its location in the new Performing Arts Centre. Trudi worked closely with the forty three women and one man involved with the project, providing help and support regarding the fabrics chosen and the techniques to be used. The quilt is predominantly appliquéd with details added in embroidery.

The three panels depict the Illawarra escarpment with local women of diverse backgrounds. An historical progression moves from pioneer days to the present. It begins with images of the Aborigines as the first settlers and concludes with a Wollongong TAFE Fashion Certificate graduate in 1988. The use of colour reinforces this progression, moving from black and white at the top to sepia tones and finally colour at the bottom. The work provides not only a visual history of the women of the Illawarra but a history of illustration, fashion and textiles as well.

Also in Wollongong

A large pictorial quilt celebrating the Year of the Family was made by the Wollongong Quilters in 1994. It is hung on permanent display in the Town Hall and Community Centre, Crown Street, and may be seen Monday to Friday during office hours. Telephone (02) 4225 2633.

Berry

The little township of Berry is about an hour's drive south of Wollongong. Its streets are shaded by old English oaks, elms and beech trees and many of the early buildings have been classified by the National Trust. There are numerous galleries and antique shops and the surrounding countryside is dotted with dairy farms and vineyards.

Berry Museum
135 Queen Street
Berry, NSW 2535.
Ph: (02) 4464 3097 Museum.
(02) 4464 1062 Historical Society.
11.00a.m. – 2.00p.m. Saturday.
11.00a.m. – 3.00p.m. Sunday.
Daily during school holidays.

ABOVE: *Women of the Illawarra.* Made by the Embroiderers' Guild New South Wales, Wollongong Group, 1989-'91. Illawarra Performing Arts Centre, Wollongong, New South Wales.

The Berry Museum is housed in a century old building of Gothic style. Its collection includes a delightful series of post cards written by Ida Lewers, the quiltmaker, to her nieces and nephews. They provide a glimpse of life in Berry during the early 1900s as well as an inkling into the character of this charming woman.

✷ The quilt is not permanently displayed in the Museum but visitors are welcome to see it by prior arrangement. Please contact the Historical Society at least a day in advance.

✄ A large Signature coverlet (228cm x 213cm) known as the *McIlvride-Lewers Quilt* was hand embroidered by Miss Ida Lewers in 1906. Ida was a maiden lady who kept house for her brother, the local Berry doctor. She was active in many good causes and made her quilt as a fund raiser, inviting visitors at the 1906 Berry Agricultural Show to autograph a plain white linen bedcover. Signatures were contributed by members of parliament, dignitaries, and many other people from the local community. Ida embroidered all the names in red, green and gold silk

ABOVE: The four panels of *God's Creation*. Made by St Martin's Parish Community, 1996. 295cm x 135cm each. St Martin's Anglican Church, Ulladulla.

thread, adding decorative badges, emblems and symbols to her work The quilt was then raffled the following year during the 1907 Agricultural Show. It was won by Master Gordon McIlvride and it remained in the McIlvride family for more than eighty years. It was given to the Berry Agricultural Association in time for their 100th Show in 1988 and was then placed in the Museum for safe keeping.

Ulladulla

Ulladulla is nestled on the shores of a small and picturesque natural harbour about a two hour drive south of Wollongong. It is the port for a large fishing fleet which provides much of the fresh fish for the Sydney market. A short drive north is the lovely village of Milton, depicted in the fourth wall hanging. Milton is classified by the National Trust as an historically important town and is renowned not only for its heritage buildings but for its giant fig tree, estimated to be 115 years old.

St. Martin's Anglican Church
Cnr. Green St. and Princes Highway
Ulladulla, NSW 2539.
Ph: (02) 4454 2030 Fax: (02) 4454 2031
The church is open between
10.00a.m. – 3.30p.m. Monday to Friday.
Services are held on Sunday at
8.15a.m., 10.00a.m. and 7.00p.m.
4 quilts.

✷ The quilts are hung on permanent display and visitors are welcome to see them. Please contact the Church by telephone to arrange a viewing time.

✂ The four St Martin's wall hangings (295cm x 135cm each) are entitled *God's Creation* and were made by the parish community in 1996. Their designs were based on water colour paintings by local artist Dianne Gee. Barbara Watson, who has made several inspiring ecclesiastical quilts, supervised and guided the work. The hangings represent several layers of meaning. God's Creation is symbolised by the light, water, sea creatures and birds of the first two panels, and then by the trees, animals, houses and roads in the

ABOVE RIGHT: Detail of *God's Creation* showing part of the rural scene illustrated in panel three.

second panels. Each one depicts a different view from the Church – north, south, east and west, to signify God's presence in all places around us. Each panel is shown at a different time of day and in a different season, signifying God being with us all day long and throughout the year.

The background of each hanging was strip pieced, the many details added in appliqué. Trees were padded to provide additional weight and texture. The tiny trunks were cut from leather and the cows in the fourth hanging were even given leather udders. The work took almost two years to create and was completed for the Easter Service of 1996.

Batemans Bay

The pretty coastal town of Batemans Bay is a half hour drive south of Ulladulla. It is a popular holiday destination, especially for residents of Canberra for whom it is the nearest seaside resort. Several charming country villages are nestled in the picturesque hills behind the Bay.

Batemans Bay Tourist Information Centre
Cnr. Princes Highway and Beach Road
Batemans Bay, NSW 2536.
Ph: (02) 4472 6900
9.00a.m. – 5.00p.m. everyday.

✷ The quilt is hung on permanent display in the Information Centre and may be seen during opening hours.

✂ A lovely quilt (200cm x 150cm) was made by the Batemans Bay Quilters to celebrate the Bicentenary in 1988. It was awarded a certificate from the local shire as well as a silver commemorative medal from the *Women's Weekly*. The central panel was designed by Jean Jackson using ideas collected from local school children. It depicts the early bullock teams loaded with timber logs, the fishing trawlers, tourist ferries and children playing on the beach. The work was appliquéd, embroidered and quilted by hand.

Detail of the *Changi Quilt* made for Australian Soldiers by internees of Changi Prison, 1942. Collection Australian War Memorial, Canberra.

QUILTS OF THE AUSTRALIAN CAPITAL TERRITORY

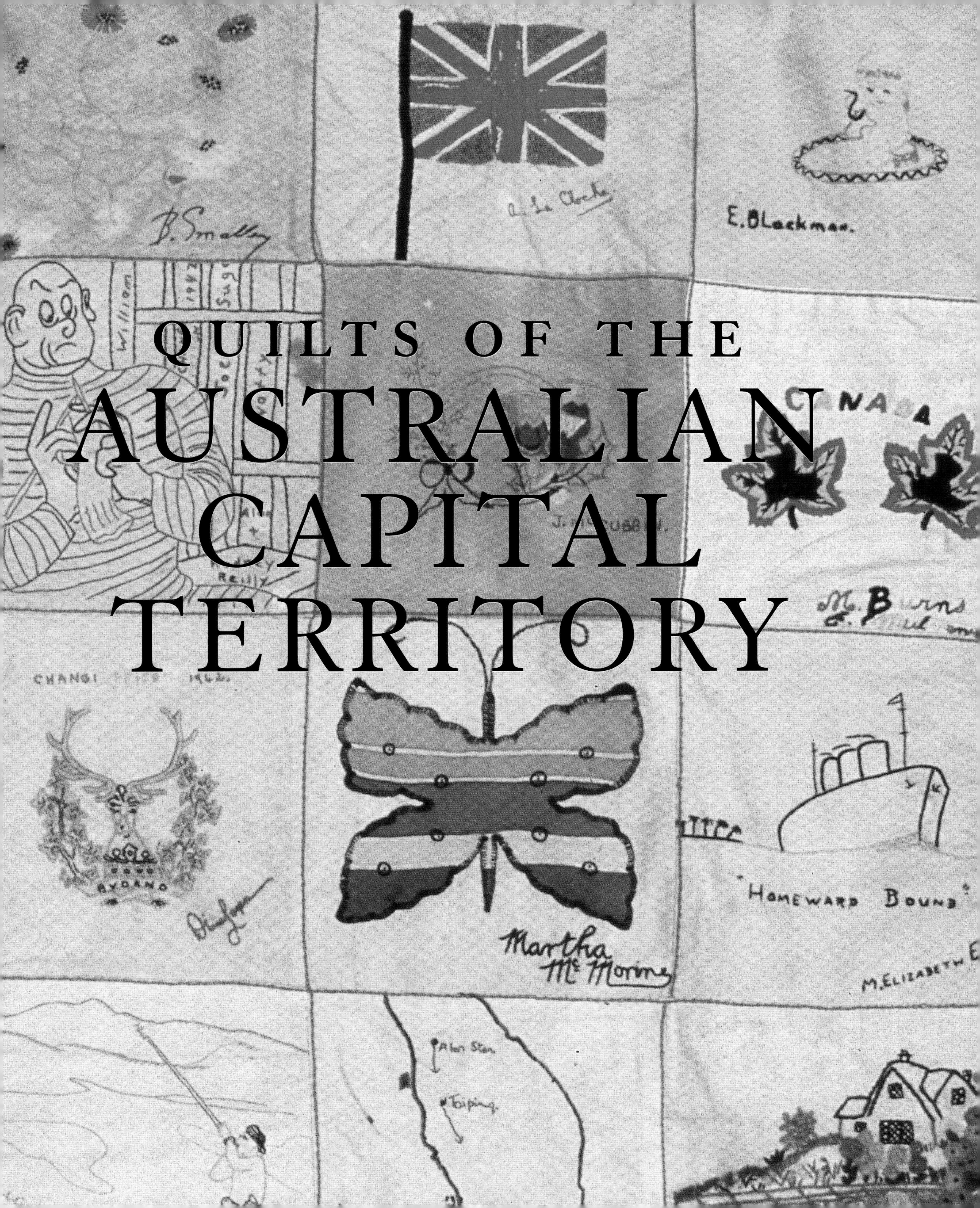

National Gallery of Australia
Parkes Place
Parkes, ACT 2600.
Ph: (02) 6240 6411 Fax: (02) 6240 6529
10.00a.m. – 5.00p.m. every day. (Open until 8.00p.m. on some Saturdays)
Approximately 30 quilts.

The National Gallery of Australia houses the national collection of art works from around the world with particular focus on Australian art. The collection contains paintings, sculptures, many works on paper, as well as textiles and decorative arts. The extensive collection of folk art quilts, the finest and largest of any art gallery in Australia, includes national treasures which were acquired primarily for their aesthetic qualities but which are also of great historical importance.

✷ A Collection Study Room has been established to allow visitors to see quilts or other works of art from the national collection that are not currently on display. Please note that 3 - 4 weeks notice in writing is required. Please contact Ms. Gyongyi Smee, Collection Study Room Officer, GPO Box 1150, Canberra 2601.

The Historical Quilt Collection

✂ Some of the country's most significant historical quilts are held in this collection. Included is the *Rajah Quilt,* (325cm x 337cm) a hand pieced and appliquéd coverlet made by unknown quiltmakers who travelled to Australia on the convict ship 'Rajah' in 1841. Until its purchase by the gallery, no examples of convict patchwork associated with Australia were known to have survived. The making of the quilt may have been supervised by Miss Kezia Hayter who travelled as a free passenger on the ship. A finely embroidered inscription in the outer border implies that the quilt was intended as a gift for the British Society of Ladies. This Quaker group worked with prison reformer Elizabeth Fry towards improving conditions for female convicts transported to Australia. Patchwork provided the women with an occupation during the long sea voyage and a means of earning money for the future. The *Rajah Quilt* was made in medallion style with a centre of Broderie Perse, the chintz birds and flowers beautifully appliquéd in herringbone stitch. Successive borders of squares, triangles, and appliquéd flowers provide remarkable examples of early nineteenth century fabrics.

The *Westbury Quilt* (200cm x 300cm) originated in the town of Westbury, Northern Tasmania, c.1900-1903 where it hung in the dining room of the Fitzpatrick Inn for many years. It is attributed to two sisters, the Misses Hampson, who were said to have owned a farm in the nearby countryside. It features embroidered scenes worked in white thread on Turkey-red Indian head cloth, many illustrating family life in Tasmania at the turn of the century. The central medallion depicts a regal Queen Victoria in Elizabethan costume. Surrounding blocks show village scenes, houses, farm animals, an emu and a kangaroo. The work is remarkable for its imagination and humour and includes many amusing Victorian sayings and tributes to the Empire. One valuable piece of advice is *'When a woman throws herself at a man's head she seldom hits the mark.'*

There are five delightful and inspiring folk art quilts created by Mary Jane Hannaford. They were made during the 1920s when Mary was in her eighties, though they were based on a work-book of drawings and poems completed in 1861 when she was only twenty one. The appliquéd hangings, thoughts and poems revealed much about Mary's life. However, although she had dated and initialled her work, it was only through a chance visit to the gallery by relatives that her identity and history were discovered. Mary had grown up in Australia, arriving with her parents at the age of two in 1842. She had one daughter, though she never married. She died in 1930 at the age of ninety.

Her quilts reveal her faith, love of animals and nature, and display a unique Australian character and humour. *Time* and *A Last Day* feature embroidered poems contemplating human mortality, each one a poignant reflection of her feelings about age and time passing:

'Tis easy to squander our years
in idleness folly and strife
But oh! no repentance or tears
can bring back one moment of life'

Adam and Eve depicts a whimsical Garden of Eden full of birds, animals, trees and flowers, and a child-like nativity scene. *Advance Australia Fair* features Aborigines and numerous Australian birds and animals. A classic Australian bridal party is illustrated in the *Wedding Quilt.* The voluminous bride is attended by a tiny girl and two bridesmaids, one with a baby in her arms. The upstanding groom sports a white beard and a gold watch-chain.

Kangaroos, emus and kookaburras appear frequently throughout Mary's quilts, along with numerous butterflies

OPPOSITE: *The Wedding Quilt.* Made by Mary Jane Hannaford, c.1922. 195cm x 169cm. Sequins, glass beads, mixed fabrics. Gift of Miss Swanson, 1997. Collection National Gallery of Australia, Canberra.

Will Swan
The White Hart

and simple flowers. All of them are stitched in a delightfully eclectic range of sizes. Each quilt is hand appliquéd and has irregular borders of pieced strips which waver and change direction unexpectedly. Cotton, linen, wool, rayon and silk fabrics have all been included, and sequins and glass beads have been added to some.

The Contemporary Quilt Collection

✂ *Macrocapa, the Rose of the West* (238cm x 173cm) was made in 1984 by Western Australian textile artist Marjorie Coleman. This work was the second in her Dullflower series and features hand appliquéd red flowers on a cream background. It is hand quilted, the quilting pattern taken from the leaves and nuts of the tree. The fabrics used are not 'quilter's fabrics,' but the dress and curtain materials preferred by the maker for their colour and personality. Marjorie was one of the first quiltmakers in the country to depict Australian flora and fauna in her work and has always urged quiltmakers to speak of their own time and place.

Still Life (153cm x 110cm) was made in 1990 by Victorian quiltmaker Deborah Brearley. It depicts her favourite flowers, the pansies, along with blue and yellow cups and saucers and a jug of bright yellow flowers. A zig zag border frames the work which was made using the techniques of painting, screen printing and cyanotype.

National Library of Australia

Parkes, ACT 2600.
Ph: (02) 6262 1370 Pictorial Library.
9.00a.m. – 5.00p.m. Monday to Friday.

✷ The quilt is held in the Pictorial Library and may be seen by appointment. Please contact the Pictorial Reference Librarian 2 days in advance.

✂ A small medallion quilt was made by Aboriginal children in Western Australia c.1840. It is believed that the work was supervised by Miss Elizabeth Irwin, niece of Colonel Irwin, the first Military Commander of the state. The quilt has a four pointed star in the centre surrounded by borders made from strips, pieced squares and rectangles.

Australian War Memorial

Main Building, Anzac Parade
Campbell, ACT 2601.
Ph: (02) 6243 4211 Fax: (02) 6243 4325
Main Building: 10.00a.m. – 5.00p.m. every day. (Opens 9.00a.m. during school holidays.)
Treloar Technology Centre: 10.00a.m. – 3.00p.m. Wednesdays and Sundays.
2 quilts.

The Australian War Memorial houses materials and records concerning Australia's participation in war. The main museum building is situated in Anzac Parade, 2 kilometres north east of City Hill. The Conservation Annex is located in the Treloar Technology Centre, Callan Street, Mitchell, and is just a short drive from the city centre.

✷ The Australian quilt is displayed in a specially lit showcase within the Main Building. The Japanese quilt is housed at the Conservation Annex of the Treloar Technology Centre.

✂ Three quilts were made by the female internees of Changi Prison during 1942. One was intended for the Australian soldiers, one for the British, and one for the Japanese. The Australian and Japanese quilts are now held by the War Memorial. The British quilt is at the Red Cross training headquarters at Barnett Hill in the United Kingdom.

The making of the quilts was the idea of Canadian internee, Mrs Ethel Mulvaney, who conceived the work as a way of boosting morale, alleviating boredom, and passing information concerning wives and children to the men who were held in separate camps. Mrs Mulvaney was a shrewd woman who obtained permission from the Japanese commandant to provide the quilts to the men, ostensibly as a gift to the wounded. She included the wounded Japanese in her request, though in fact the quilt made for their soldiers was also passed to the hospitals, and eventually to an Australian medical officer.

Each quilt was made from sixty six embroidered squares. Those on the Japanese quilt featured pretty floral motifs and scenes that the makers thought would please their captors. The Australian quilt was very different. On this work the women added many of their thoughts and feelings and it is this that makes it so intensely moving to see. Probably most poignant of all is the stick figure in the light beam of her cell with the words *'How long, O Lord, how long!'* Another image depicts a boat and the embroidered message *'Homeward Bound.'* It was made by Elizabeth Ennis who married her husband, Jack, just four days before Singapore fell to the Japanese. She chose the ship as her design because it had been her dream to sail home to Britain with Jack. Some years after the war, Elizabeth read about the quilt in an Australian newspaper. During a trip here she made an effort to see it but in those days it was not easy to find its whereabouts. The Red Cross was later to organise and send her some coloured photographs.

Very few of the contributors saw the completed quilts. The squares were assembled by only a few women and were quickly passed to the men's camps.

National Museum of Australia
Acton Peninsula
Canberra, ACT 2600.
Ph: (02) 6208 5250 Fax: (02) 6208 5299
Museum Registrar.
Opening hours to be advised on completion of the building.
26 quilts.

The National Museum of Australia, due to open in 2001, collects and presents the cultural, environmental and indigenous history of Australia. The collection of quilts is located in a separate building of the Museum at Mitchell, a short drive from the city centre. The Museum acquires quilts to illustrate the history of women's work and Australian craft traditions. They are considered to be important personal and household items which illuminate broader aspects of Australian social history.

✱ The quilts may be seen by appointment. Please contact the Registrar by fax or letter. Postal address: GPO Box 1901, Canberra, ACT, 2601.

✂ It is important to the Museum that each quilt acquired for its collection has with it a record of its social history. Such is the case for two of the most significant historical quilts.

The *Dunshea Quilt* (173cm x 125cm) was made c.1903 by Mary Jane Cochrane. Mary Jane had been born in County Tyrone and emigrated with her husband, William, to the Illawarra district of New South Wales in 1850. She was ninety four years old when she made the quilt for her great grand-daughter, Margaret. It was one of a pair made for Margaret and her twin sister, Esme. In 1926 Margaret had married Claude Dunshea, a war veteran who had received a major facial wound at the Battle of the Somme. Sensitive about his appearance, Claude worked as a labourer

ABOVE: *The Changi Quilt* made for Australian Soldiers by internees of Changi Prison, 1942. 130cm x 203cm. Collection Australian War Memorial, Canberra.

PHOTOGRAPHY LASZLO LAKK.

and spent much of his spare time prospecting in the bush near his Bowral home. The thrift Margaret had inherited from her great grandmother helped make ends meet, particularly during the Depression when the couple lost the house they had bought.

The quilt was used for many years in the Dunshea home. It was made from clothing scraps and features eight strips of mainly solid colours with square or rectangular patches between these bands. There are two layers only and the backing has been cut from furnishing fabric.

The *Little Red Riding Hood Quilt* was made in 1946 by a Ukrainian woman, Olga Basylevich, at a displaced persons camp in Neu-Ulm, Germany. An enchanting work, it features a three dimensional scene depicting Little Red Riding Hood and the wolf in a forest setting. It could be read as a response to war and displacement. Perhaps the story serves in this instance as an allegory for the rise of Nazism, or simply an object of beauty which transcended the grim circumstances of the camp.

The work has been appliquéd and embroidered using scraps of material. The backing is a grey blanket issued to each camp resident. The wolf has been made from fur and there are flowers of felt appliquéd to the forest floor. It is believed that Olga obtained thread by trading cigarettes with local residents. She eventually settled in America and gave the work to an Australian, Valerie Paling. Valerie later donated it to the Forest Hill Residential Kindergarten in Melbourne where it hung on the wall for many years.

The National Museum of Australia has made every effort to contact the copyright owner of the Little Red Riding Hood Quilt but has been unsuccessful. The Museum would be happy to hear from the copyright owner and would be prepared to pay a reasonable copyright fee.

The Museum is also home to the double-sided banners which were made for the Bicentennial travelling exhibition by many quilting groups from all over Australia. On one side of each banner a letter was appliquéd so that together they made up the words *'Australian Bicentennial Exhibition 88.'* Depicted on the reverse was a scene representing the area from which the banner originated.

Blundell's Cottage

Wendouree Drive (off Constitution Ave)
Parkes, ACT 2600.
Ph: (02) 6273 2667
10.00a.m. – 4.00p.m. Tuesday to Sunday.
2 quilts.

Blundell's Cottage houses the museum of the Canberra and District Historical Society. This little building was enclosed by the construction of the city of Canberra and Lake Burley Griffin, and today it is one of the only historic buildings in the Parliamentary Triangle. The collection includes rag rugs, hand stitched christening gowns, a cushion of Suffolk Puffs, and a cross stitch sampler made by Margaret Shumack c.1887.

✷ The quilts are permanently displayed and may be seen during opening hours.

✂ Blundell's Cottage was placed in the care of the Canberra and District Historical Society in 1964. At this time, a very frail old patchwork counterpane was found in the cottage and the Society approached the Embroiderers' Guild of

LEFT: *Little Red Riding Hood Quilt.* Made by Olga Basylevich at a displaced persons camp in Neu-Ulm, Germany, 1946. Collection National Museum of Australia, Canberra.

ABOVE: *Reflection.* Made by Christa Sanders, 1991. 200cm × 188cm.
Research School of Biological Sciences, Acton, ACT.

the A.C.T. to repair it. Sadly, the fabric fell to pieces when it was handled so the Guild undertook the making of a new quilt. The design was a copy of the original, a Nine Patch Rail Fence made from strips of multi-coloured cotton dress scraps. The strips were machine stitched together and the names of all the makers were hand embroidered onto the cotton backing.

There is also a quilt of suiting samples of unknown provenance c.1930.

Also in the City

The magnificent *Parliament House Commemorative Embroidery* was created by more than one hundred embroiderers from every state in Australia. The project was initiated by Dorothy Hyslop from the Embroiderers' Guild of the A.C.T. and designed by textile artist Kay Lawrence. It took eight years to complete and was finished for the opening of the building in 1988. It is now displayed in the gallery of the Great Hall of Parliament House and may be seen between 9.00a.m. and 5.00p.m. daily.

Research School of Biological Sciences
Australian National University
Biology Place
Acton, ACT 2601.
Ph: (02) 6249 2999 Fax: (02) 6279 8525
9.00a.m. – 5.00p.m. Monday to Friday.
2 quilts.

Acton is only a 5 minute drive north of the centre of Canberra. Turn from Biology Place into Sullivans Creek Road where a sign directs visitors to the Research School of Biological Sciences.

✷ The quilts are hung on permanent display in the lecture theatre of the Research School. It is advisable to ring reception before visiting to ensure the theatre is not in use.

✂ A quilt entitled *Reflection* was made by Canberra textile artist Christa Sanders in 1991. The work is autobiographical – the buildings, arches and floating cloud banks forming symbolic metaphors for past events, present times, lasting influences and dreams. In order to include all her thoughts and feelings, Christa makes a series of quilts revolving around a single theme. This was the fourth of eight quilts in a series entitled Dreams.

A quilt entitled *Falling Waters* was created by Christa in 1989. This work formed part of a series of Water Quilts celebrating her fascination with the beauty of a waterfall, one place she believes to be close to the essence of nature.

Both quilts were intricately pieced from a variety of fabrics including cotton, wool, polyester, silk, taffeta and satin. They were machine stitched, hand appliquéd and quilted. The sky and backgrounds were hand painted.

Erindale Library
McBryde Crescent
Wanniassa, ACT 2903.
Ph: (02) 6207 5678 Fax: (02) 6207 5718
9.30a.m. – 5.30p.m. Monday, Thursday and Friday.
9.30a.m.– 8.00p.m. Tuesday and Wednesday.
9.30a.m. – 5.00p.m. Saturday.
Approximately 12 quilts.

The suburb of Wanniassa is located in the Tuggeranong Valley about 20 minute's drive south of the city.

✷ A constantly changing exhibition of quilts may be seen during opening hours.

✂ This innovative programme of quilt exhibitions has been held at the Erindale Library for several years. The project was initiated by Trevor Reid, a Canberra quiltmaker and member of the Friends of the Library. The main objective was to change the traditional image of quilts by providing an opportunity to display them as works of art in a public space.

The library building, with its high vaulted ceiling and excellent lighting, provides a perfect exhibition space. The quilts are suspended on rods using a simple pulley system which enables them to be hung high above the shelves and to have both sides of the work on view.

The programme has been so successful that it has now grown to include twelve different exhibitions a year. Most of the quilts displayed are contemporary, though older quilts from private collections have been included, as well as the retrospective work of individual quilters. Information about each maker is available from the reference desk. In the future it is hoped that this vibrant library will be able to extend the programme to include talks which can be enjoyed by the local community as well as by visitors.

Kippax Uniting Church

Cnr. Luke St and Hardwick Crescent
Holt, ACT 2615.
Ph: (02) 6254 1733 Church office.
(02) 6254 6863 Marlene Greenwood.
The Church office is open between
9.30a.m. – 12.30p.m. Tuesday,
Thursday and Friday. Services are held
on Sunday at 10.15a.m. and 11.30a.m.

The suburb of Holt is approximately 14 kilometres north west of the city.

✷ Visitors are welcome during opening hours or by arrangement with the office. The designer is available to speak to groups by appointment.

✂ This spectacular wall hanging is entitled *Regeneration* (700cm x 300cm). It was designed by Marlene Greenwood and created by Marlene and members of the congregation between 1985-'87. The theme of the work was Christ as the Light of the World and from the beginning it was intended to be an integral part of the architecture of the new building. The hanging features light radiating in all directions from a huge silver cross. Pieced panels of golds and yellows increase in size as they extend further away from the cross. These warm tones touch and illuminate symbols of nature and humanity depicted in the concentric layers of the design.

The hanging was made from pieced sections overlaid with appliqué and surface design to resemble a contemporary stained glass window. It involved the techniques of printing, silk painting, quilting, trapunto, hand and machine embroidery, mola, smocking, cording, couching, beading, free machine needle-weaving, and pom poms.

The work features two pieces of encrusted appliqué created by Marlene. A seven layer reverse appliquéd pomegranate was made with needle-weaving and trapunto. Another piece extended the full width of the base and represented layers of earth with glowing sections of opals and seeds.

A complete photographic record with notes and samples was kept of the project and is available for perusal.

ABOVE: *Regeneration.* Made by Marlene Greenwood and the church community, 1985-'87. 700cm x 300cm. Kippax Uniting Church, Holt, ACT. BELOW: Detail showing reverse appliquéd pomegranate.

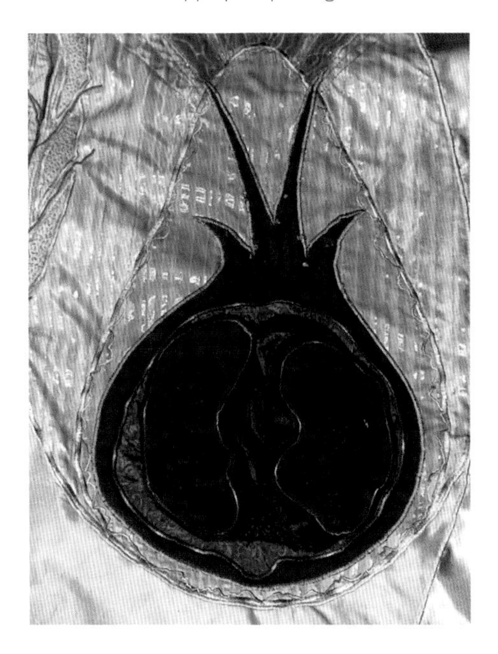

Coverlet of Silk Diamonds.
Unknown Maker, c.1880. Collection Schwerkolt Cottage, Mitcham, Victoria.

QUILTS OF
MELBOURNE
AND NEARBY
REGIONS

National Gallery of Victoria
180 St Kilda Road
Melbourne, Vic 3004.
Ph: (03) 9208 0222 Fax: (03) 9208 0245
10.00a.m. – 5.00p.m. daily except
Anzac Day morning, Good Friday and
Christmas Day.
12 quilts.

The National Gallery of Victoria has a very diverse collection of textiles. Included are Australian and European costumes, tapestries, embroideries and lace. There is also a small but beautiful collection of quilts and patchwork clothing. The Gallery is undergoing major refurbishment and this will result in the establishment of a permanent textile gallery specifically devoted to the exhibition of international works. There will also be another exhibition space devoted specifically to Australian material located in the new Museum of Australian Art, Federation Square, Melbourne, due to open in 2001. The Gallery's quilt collection will gradually be developed with the addition of the very best historical examples of work from Australia and overseas. Once this historical base has been firmly established contemporary works of the highest calibre will be acquired. It is hoped that a comprehensive collection of world class standard will be achieved and that it will span the decades, traditions, innovations and cultural variety of the art of quilting.

✷ A Textiles Study Room enables visitors to see particular works from the collection that are not currently on display. Study days can be arranged during the year for small groups from embroidery, lace and quilting guilds. Sometimes specialist talks can be given by the Curator concerning the items shown. Requests must be made in writing at least one month in advance to the Curator, Fashion and Textiles.

The Historical Quilt Collection

✂ A Log Cabin coverlet of Turkey-red and white cotton (200cm x 226cm) was created by an unknown maker between 1885 and '89. The work is reputed to have been made during a voyage to Australia and was intended as a gift for Miss Emmie Olley on the occasion of her marriage in 1889. The coverlet is edged with a wide cream fringe.

A wholecloth quilt of white cotton (263cm x 192cm) was created by Isabella Cooke during the 1930s. The work was quilted by hand and finished with a scalloped edging.

An exquisite patchwork doll's dress was made in Great Britain c.1865 by an unknown maker. The dress has a gathered skirt and fitted bodice and has been created from tiny silk diamonds finely stitched by hand over paper templates. Each diamond contains a hand embroidered flower. A bow is tied at the back of the dress and when this is gently lifted it can be seen that the colour and sheen of the fabrics have changed little over the years.

A dressing gown of Crazy Patchwork was made by Mrs Annie Ellis of Geelong. It was given to her niece, Mrs Annie Champion in 1935 for her trousseau. The random shaped pieces have been cut from brightly coloured satins, silks, cottons, wools and brocades, most of them heavily embellished with machine embroidered motifs. The gown is lined with royal blue satin, edged with matching blue braid, and is in perfect condition.

A Diamond-in-a-square quilt (177cm x 177cm) was made in America by an unknown quiltmaker c.1925. This lovely work was machine pieced and hand quilted from wool and cotton in colours of purple, blue and deep red. Its purchase followed the enormous success of the Gallery's 1997 exhibition of Amish quilts entitled *Lit from Within*. This exhibition focused on quilts made in Pennsylvania between 1875 and 1950 and was a landmark in Australia. It was the first time that a major overseas collection of quilts had been displayed in a prestigious state gallery.

The Contemporary Quilt Collection

✂ *Welcome to the Doll House* (182cm x 154cm) was created by South Australian textile artist Sarah Crowest in 1997. It features photographic transfer images of some of the dolls Sarah has accumulated over the years. Her collection began to grow in earnest when she found 'The Hulk,' her daughter's lost childhood toy. His grimacing green face appears on the quilt and has became a symbol of valued things, lost and found again. The work was machine pieced and then hand quilted. It was made from dyed, screen printed, and painted cotton fabrics and embellished with embroidery.

Museum of Victoria
222 Exhibition Street
Melbourne, Vic 3000.
Ph: (03) 9651 6777 Fax: (03) 9291 2150
9.00a.m. – 5.00p.m. Monday to Friday.
2 quilts.

The Museum of Victoria collects and presents artefacts relating to social history, indigenous studies and natural science. The old premises in Swanston Street have been vacated and a new exhibition centre is being built which is due to open in the year 2000. The textile collection includes over five hundred garments

Doll's Dress. Unknown Maker, c1865. Silk, lace. Gift of Lady Nicholson and her daughter, 1951. Collection National Gallery of Victoria, Melbourne.

and accessories by Australian designer, Prue Acton. The quilts form part of the collection of Social History. They are currently held in a separate building located at Moreland, 6 kilometres north of the city. The Museum is keen to expand its collection of quilts. It wishes to acquire quilts having a provenance which is in some way connected to Victoria.

✷ The quilts may be seen by appointment. Requests must be made in writing 4 weeks in advance to the Senior Curator, Australian Society Programme.

✂ The *Rilli Quilt* (232cm x 149cm) was created during the 1950s by an unknown maker in Sind, Pakistan It was presented to the Museum of Victoria in 1992 by Dr and Mrs Kazi on behalf of the Muslim community and was the first acquisition to the museum's collection of Muslim artefacts. In Pakistan Rilli quilts are traditionally created using a folded paper-cutting technique. Squares of cotton fabric are folded and cut so that when opened out they make circular patterns. These are then appliquéd to a plain background and quilted. This beautiful quilt has been made from fifteen squares, each one hand appliquéd with paper-cut flowers. The centre has been surrounded by borders of plain cotton in colours of red, navy, yellow, rust, black and cream. The work has been hand quilted and finished with a red backing, a border of small prairie points, and three tassels in each corner.

The *Elizabeth Hawkey Quilt* (216cm x 216cm) was donated to the museum in 1992 by the Goulburn Valley Quilters of Shepparton. It had been made in Victoria during the late 19th century by Elizabeth Hawkey who had emigrated to Australia from England in 1866. The quilt had remained in the Hawkey family for several generations. It was given to the Goulburn Valley Quilters by Elizabeth's great granddaughter, Mrs Nancy Vibert, who had slept under it as a child. It is a rare example of a double-sided quilt, both the front and back having been pieced by hand in similar geometric combinations of squares, triangles and rectangles. The fabrics include printed cottons of pink, brown and pale blue. The work has been quilted by hand and a woollen blanket has been used as a warm filling.

Department of Immigration and Multicultural Affairs

2 Casselden Place
Melbourne, Vic 3000.
Ph: (03) 9235 3290 Fax: (03) 9235 3266
9.00a.m. – 4.00p.m. Monday to Friday.

✷ The quilt is hung on display in the reception area of the 25th floor. It may be seen during working hours.

✂ This quilt (2m x 5m) was created in 1995 to celebrate fifty years of migration to Australia. It was designed and made by Jeanette Goedemoed and Marie Gross with contributions from many migrant families. The project stirred the memories and emotions of all those involved. Each pictorial panel expresses the feelings experienced by the migrants as well as their first impressions of Australia. The loneliness felt for relatives and friends, the problems encountered in not speaking English, and the sense of being torn between two countries were among the experiences shared by many. The work was framed with borders depicting native plants and animals of Victoria which were made using a variety of media by artist Cheryl Fox.

Telstra Corporation Limited

242 Exhibition Street
Melbourne, Vic 3000.
Ph: (03) 9634 1111
8.00a.m. – 7.00p.m. Monday to Friday.

✷ The quilt is hung on display in the atrium of the building and may be seen during the hours listed above.

✂ This contemporary triptych is entitled *Salient Steel* (200cm x 200cm) and was designed and made in 1997 by mixed media artist, Sharyn Hall. It was the winning entrant in the inaugural AQIPP (Australian Quilts in Public Places) Exhibition, organised by the Australian Quilters' Association. The aim of the exhibition had been to encourage the purchase and display of Australian quilts as works of art for prominent locations throughout Melbourne. *Salient Steel* was designed especially for the Telstra location. The colour of the large granite wall on which the quilt would hang, existing art works, as well as the surrounding building space were all taken into consideration. Sharyn began with photographs which she cropped and collaged into kaleidoscope designs before heat transferring them onto silk organza. These images formed the centres for the reversible Log Cabin piecing which frames them. The Japanese technique of Sashiko quilting was used to complete the work.

Metro Craft Centre

42 Courtney Street
North Melbourne, Vic 3051.
Ph: (03) 9329 9966 Fax: (03) 9329 2272
10.00a.m. – 5.00p.m. everyday.
4 quilts.

The Metro Craft Centre is located in a building classified by the National Trust and

OPPOSITE: *The Rilli Quilt.* Unknown Maker of Sind, Pakistan, c.1950. 232cm x 149cm. Collection Museum of Victoria, Melbourne.

ABOVE: Detail of *Salient Steel*. Made by Sharyn Hall, 1997. 200cm x 200cm. Telstra Corporation Limited, Melbourne.

originally used as Melbourne's Metropolitan Meat Market. There are three separate galleries, the main hall, conference centres and a coffee shop. Studios have been established where resident craftspeople can be seen working in a wide variety of media. Included is the Quilt Gallery, a co-operative run by a group of Melbourne quiltmakers, through which quilts, smaller items of patchwork, and hand dyed fabrics are sold.

✷ The quilts are kept in storage but are exhibited regularly. They may also be seen by appointment. Please contact the Friends of the Metro 3 weeks in advance.

✂ The collection includes Lois Densham's *Life's Full Circle* (200cm x 200cm). Made in 1983, this collage work was created from recycled wool, cotton, velvet, synthetics and linen. It represents a man's life-time from childhood through to old age and was designed with the purpose of creating contact with each viewer. Pieces of crochet, embroidery, knitting, gloves, ties, cords and medals were sewn to the clothing. The work was machine pieced and hand quilted.

Barbara Macey's *Night* (183cm x 183cm) is a dramatic black quilt made in 1978 from cotton, lawn, rayon, taffeta and synthetic satin. Barbara discovered that every black fabric she bought was unique and different from all the others. She became fascinated with the varying light effects she could achieve by placement of the fabrics using different grain directions. *Night* is based on the traditional Log Cabin pattern but is uncompromisingly contemporary in its design.

There is also a strip pieced quilt entitled *Japanese Ragtime* created by Jean Mansfield in 1977, and John Corbett's *Mercado,* a free-form Log Cabin quilt purchased in 1989.

St Mary's Anglican Church
163 Howard Street
North Melbourne, Vic 3051.
Ph/Fax: (03) 9329 5193
The Church is open every day between 8.00a.m. and 5.30p.m. Services are held on Sunday at 8.00a.m. and 10.00a.m.

This lovely old stone Church is situated very near the Metro Craft Centre.

✷ The frontal is displayed in the small side chapel and visitors are welcome to see it. Please contact Father Jim Brady.

✂ An altar frontal entitled *All Things Bright and Beautiful* was made in 1991 by Lois Densham. It was created as a memorial and tribute to Linda Guy, a parishioner of St Mary's who died tragically in India. Linda had worked as a highly respected psychiatric nurse in Melbourne for many years. The demands of her profession and the desire to find answers to problems in her own life were foremost in her mind when she left for India. The design of the altar frontal was inspired by Lois's hope that Linda might yet find her answers in the beauty of the world. Many friends and relatives gave fabric to be included in the work which was machine appliquéd, hand embroidered and quilted.

Australian Red Cross (Victoria)
171 City Road
South Melbourne, Vic 3205.
Ph: (03) 9685 981 Fax: (03) 9685 9997
Archives Office.
10.00a.m. – 4.00p.m. Monday to Friday.
29 quilts.

The beautiful collection of Signature quilts held by the Red Cross provides a valuable and poignant record of Australian history from both World Wars.

ABOVE: *All Things Bright and Beautiful.* Made by Lois Densham, 1991. St Mary's Anglican Church, North Melbourne.

✷ The quilts may be seen by appointment. They may also be made available for loan for purposes of display or research. Requests must be made in writing to the Archives Supervisor.

✂ Most of the war-time quilts in the collection are Signature quilts made from white cotton squares on which names have been embroidered in red thread. These quilts were made for two purposes – fund raising and to commemorate the lives of individual soldiers. People paid a small donation to have their signatures included. Sometimes other motifs were added, generally patriotic in nature. One example is the *Longwarry State School Quilt,* (214cm x 130cm) made between 1916 and 1918 and including the names of all the children at the school. The Archives has a photograph of these children, each one recently traced and named by Mr Fred Bruton of Melbourne whose Longwarry relatives contributed to the making of the quilt.

The *Rockingham Quilt* was made by members of the Rockingham Ex-Patients Association during World War II. Rockingham was a convalescent home located in Kew and owned by the Red Cross from 1940 to 1977. It offered service and ex-servicemen the opportunity to learn new skills by providing classes ranging from basket weaving to carpentry. The quilt was made as part of this programme and many of the signatures have been worked around the names of businesses or government services that supported it.

The tradition of raising money from Signature quilts was revived again in 1991. Helen Gritscher, Ann Lhuede and quiltmakers from the Australian Quilters' Association designed and prepared Signature quilt kits which were sent out to Red Cross branches throughout the state. The embroidered blocks were returned and sewn together into two quilts which toured Victoria and raised $14,000 for the organisation.

Parish of Christ Church
8 Glenlyon Road
Brunswick, Vic 3056.
Ph: (03) 9380 1064 Fax: (03) 9388 0623
There is no permanent secretary in the parish office. Please leave a message and your call will be returned.

The suburb of Brunswick is located approximately 6 kilometres north of the city centre.

This lovely Italianate church was built in 1857. The Parish Hall in which the quilt is displayed is situated adjacent to the church.

✷ The quilt is hung on display as the focal point of the refurbished Parish Hall. Visitors are welcome to see it by appointment. Please ring the parish office 24 hours in advance.

✄ This beautiful wool quilt (199cm x 150cm) was created in 1997 by Margaret Rolfe, one of Australia's most respected and influential quiltmakers. It was made from squares of woollen fabrics which Margaret had collected over many years. The wool for the binding and the flannelette backing were the only new materials purchased. The design of interlocking crosses was created using the rich dark colours of purple, navy, brown, and olive-green, combined with a brilliant orange, pink and apricot. The quilt was machine pieced and tied with navy blue wool. It was purchased for the Church as a memorial to a much loved parishioner.

Domestic Violence and Incest Resource Centre
139 Sydney Road
Brunswick, Vic 3056.
Ph: (03) 9380 4343 Fax: (03) 9380 4373
Administration office.
9.00a.m. – 5.00p.m. Monday to Friday.

The Domestic Violence and Incest Resource Centre is dedicated to helping the victims of domestic violence.

✷ The Women's Coalition Against Family Violence are happy for visitors to see the banner and will loan it for appropriate occasions. Please contact the office by telephone or fax.

✄ *'No more domestic violence. This week at least four women and children will die at the hands of men they trust.'* This is the text on the banner designed by Lois Densham and made by Lois and members of the Women's Coalition Against Family Violence in 1989. This diverse group included lawyers, police women, social workers, women and young children from refuges. The text was appliquéd by machine onto a background created from kitchen tea towels and damask tablecloths.

University of Melbourne
Office of the Alumni Association,
216 Leicester Street
Carlton, Vic 3053.
Ph: (03) 9344 7469
9.00a.m. – 5.00p.m. Monday to Friday.

The suburb of Carlton is located just a short walk north of the city centre.

✷ The quilt is hung on permanent display in the foyer of the building and may be seen during office hours.

✄ This quilt of University life and history was designed by Ruth Walker, a graduate of Melbourne University. Ruth was also the founder of the Hamilton Quilters who created the work during 1988. The residential colleges which are so important to country students are symbolised by their crests. Each faculty is represented by the triangular colours in the border, the triangles being made from the same fabrics as the academic hoods. The University buildings, both old and new, are shown by the battlements and cloisters. The ivy, eucalypt leaves and green areas of lawn depict the beautiful grounds. The oval in the centre represents recreation and extra-curricular activities, the open book a symbol of learning. The work was made from fabrics of cotton, silk, linen, wool, velvet and leather. The techniques of hand appliqué, piecing, embroidery and quilting were used in its creation.

St James Anglican Church
68 Penders Street
Thornbury, Vic 3071.
Ph: (03) 9484 1762 parish office.
(03) 9489 3631 Patricia McArthur.
The church is open between
9.00a.m. – 5.00p.m. daily.
Services are held on Sundays at
8.00a.m. and 9.30a.m.
and during the week at varying times.

The suburb of Thornbury is located approximately 8 kilometres north of the city centre.

St James Anglican Church was built in 1968 and has six beautiful stained glass windows. In addition to the quilt, there are also beaded, appliquéd and embroidered vestments, frontals, and banners made by Glenda Owen and Morna Sturrock.

RIGHT: *Wool Quilt.* Made by Margaret Rolfe, 1997. 199cm x 150cm. Parish of Christ Church, Brunswick, Victoria.

✷ The quilt is hung on display except for the period of Lent prior to Easter. Visitors are welcome to see it. Contact the parish office 24 hours in advance.

✂ This inspiring work (152cm x 204cm) was created in 1994 by Patricia McArthur. Entitled the *Easter Quilt*, it celebrates this joyous time in the life of the church and was made using an original design by American quiltmaker, Mickey Lawler. The colours and shapes represent a symbolic expression of the Resurrection of Christ. The sombre colours at the base are transformed through the rose coloured cross of the risen Christ in the centre. The intensity of bright and dramatic colour increases towards the top as an expression of the majesty of Almighty God on High. The work was pieced and quilted entirely by hand using plain cotton fabrics. It took six months to complete and its making provided comfort, solace, and hope for the maker during a time of great anxiety.

ABOVE: *Fancy Dress Costume of Crazy Patchwork.* Unknown Maker, c.1900. Collection Heidelberg Historical Society Museum, Heidelberg, Victoria. BELOW: *Quilt of Hexagon Rosettes.* Unknown Maker, c.1900. Collection Schramms Cottage, Doncaster, Victoria. OPPOSITE: *Easter Quilt.* Made by Patricia McArthur, 1994. 152cm x 204cm, St James Anglican Church, Thornbury, Victoria.

PHOTOGRAPH PADDY CHILDS GREEN.

Schramms Cottage
Victoria Street
Doncaster, Vic 3108.
Ph: (03) 9844 2392 or (03)9850 4568
Doncaster-Templestowe Historical Society.
2.00p.m. – 5.00p.m. Sunday
or by arrangement.
2 quilts.

The suburb of Doncaster is located approximately 15 kilometres north east of the city.

This historic stone cottage was built in 1874 by Paster Max Schramm, a German scholar who was one of the first to settle in the heavily timbered high land of Doncaster. Classified by the National Trust, the cottage consists of four rooms as well as a large school room at the rear. The cottage has been beautifully furnished with antiques by the Doncaster-Templestowe Historical Society who have also restored the garden to its old world charm.

✷ Both quilts are displayed on beds within the cottage and may be seen during opening hours.

✂ A quilt of random hexagon rosettes (190cm x 242cm) was created during the early 20th century by an unknown maker. It was brought to Australia from England in 1924. The work was made in the English method over paper templates using fabrics of silk, satin, and brocade. It has a wide navy moire border and a backing of cream cotton twill.

A single bed coverlet of Suffolk Puffs was purchased from an opportunity shop and is believed to date from the 1960s. It has been made from small circles of multi-coloured cotton prints.

Heidelberg Historical Society Museum
Old Court House
Jika Street
Heidelberg, Vic 3084.
Ph: (03) 9853 0823 President or
(03) 9457 2113 Archivist,
Heidelberg Historical Society.
2.00p.m. – 5.00p.m. Sundays.
Groups by appointment.

The suburb of Heidelberg is located approximately 12 kilometres north east of the city.

The Museum is housed in the Old Court House built in 1899. Its collection includes silver, china, photographs, and memorabilia from the early 19th century, a time when Heidelberg was an area of gentlemen's large estates and farm properties. There are also heirloom night gowns, hand stitched underwear, baby

PHOTOGRAPHY ROBINA AND TONY SUMMERS.

clothes, and a pair of men's braces worked in cross stitch with maroon silk lining. Two fob-watch pockets and a matching pin cushion have been made from maroon satin and decorated with a grey and white beaded leaf motif.

✷ The patchwork costume is not on permanent display but visitors are welcome to see it provided prior notice is given. Please contact the museum one week in advance.

✂ This skirt, jacket and matching cap of Crazy work date from the turn of the century and are of unknown maker. It is believed they were created in Melbourne for Miss Emily Dodds and were intended to be worn as a fancy dress costume. The fabrics include multi-coloured scraps of plain and printed silk, satin, velvet and brocade, and each patch has been outlined in gold feather stitch. The work has been edged with black lace and embellished with gold braided anchors and stars. The cap has been finished at the crown with multi-coloured ribbons.

Australian Turkish Cultural Association

85 Church Street
Richmond, Vic 3121.
Ph: (03) 9428 8250 Fax: (03) 9428 9899
9.00a.m. – 5.00p.m. Monday to Friday.
15 quilts.

The suburb of Richmond is only a few kilometres east of the city centre.

This Association was established to provide assistance to the Turkish community in Victoria with a wide range of services. It gives support to newly arrived migrants and organises many cultural, recreational and arts activities.

✷ The quilts are exhibited at special events. Visitors are very welcome to call at the Association to see them. Please contact Halil Demirbas.

✂ This series of quilts was created during 1987 as part of a project entitled *Evimiz,* or *Our House*. Lois Densham and Hatice Kahvecioglu worked with a group of women from the Turkish community to design and make the quilts within the theme of 'Peace for Our Children.' The women had come to Australia from a country racked by poverty and in which those who disagreed openly with government policy were persecuted. The welfare and future of their children were the focus of their lives and these feelings were reflected in the quilts. Several depict the figures of the women with their children and have been appliquéd to backgrounds created from silk screened designs. The figures have been padded for realism and dimension, their faces embroidered. Many of the clothing pieces were knitted by hand and then appliquéd in place. Turkish knotted lace was also made and many details were hand embroidered. The quilt entitled *Anatolian Women and Children* was hung on display at the Melbourne Concert Hall for some months, providing both a tribute and an evocative insight into the lives of the Turkish women who made it.

Como Historic House

Cnr. Williams Road and Lechlade Avenue
South Yarra, Vic 3141.
Ph: (03) 9827 2500 Fax: (03) 9827 6910
10.00a.m. – 5.00p.m. daily.
Closed Good Friday and Christmas Day.

The suburb of South Yarra is located approximately 5 kilometres south east of the city centre.

The gracious colonial mansion of Como was built in 1847. It was the home of the Armytage family for almost a century and many of the furnishings and antiques displayed within were originally owned by them. In addition to the patchwork quilt, there are several hand knitted coverlets dating from the turn of the century.

✷ The quilt is permanently displayed in 'Freddy's Room' and may be seen during a guided tour of the house. Tours are available every half hour starting at 10.15a.m.

✂ This Signature coverlet is referred to as the *Friendship Quilt* and is believed to have been made for Como by members of the Camberwell Voluntary Group during the 1960s. It consists of four panels of embroidered white squares separated by borders of crocheted lace. Each square features an embroidered star in the centre and the initials of Armytage family members in each corner. The embroidery has been worked in stem stitch using thick red cotton thread. A wide border of trailing flowers frames the panels and has been finished with an edging of crocheted lace.

City of Glen Eira

Cnr. Hawthorn and Glen Eira Roads
Caulfield, Vic 3162.
Ph: (03) 9524 3333 Fax: (03) 9524 3399
9.00a.m. – 5.00p.m. Monday to Friday.
2 quilts.

The suburb of Caulfield is located approximately 12 kilometres south east of the city centre.

The City's Permanent Art Collection has been established over many years to adorn the various offices and halls of the council building. The majority of the collection

ABOVE: *Anatolian Women and Children.* Made by women of the Turkish community, 1986. Australian Turkish Cultural Association, Richmond, Victoria.
RIGHT: *Wave 3.* Made by Barbara Macey, 1980. Collection City of Glen Eira, Caulfield, Victoria.

comprises works on paper. In addition to the quilts, there are also ceramic pieces, weaving, and a rag rug.

✷ The *Caulfield Quilt* is permanently displayed in the foyer of the council building. Barbara Macey's quilt is not always displayed but may be seen by arrangement. Please contact the Visual Arts Co-ordinator two days in advance.

✄ *Wave 3* was made by Melbourne textile artist Barbara Macey in 1980. It was the third in an extensive series of quilts designed to illustrate the myriad possibilities of contemporary wave forms which could be achieved using the Log Cabin pattern. The work was created entirely from brown fabrics and includes cotton, taffeta and synthetics. Each block is a quarter circle within a square, manipulated to make the waves. The effects of light and shadow come from the great variety of fabrics used and from the different grain directions in which they were placed.

The *Caulfield Quilt* was made in 1985 by fifteen local quiltmakers under the guidance of Ruth Caple. It was created as part of the 1984-'85 City of Caulfield Community Arts Fibrecraft Project. This project involved the community in a great variety of fibre arts and resulted in the making of banners, maps, tapestries, puppets and a Chinese Dragon fibre sculpture. The quilt features pictorial blocks which depict cultural and architectural aspects of the City. Each block was appliquéd, embroidered and quilted by hand.

The Embroiderers' Guild, Victoria

170 Wattletree Road
Malvern, Victoria 3144.
Ph: (03) 9509 2222 Fax: (03) 9509 2109
Guild Rooms: 10.00 a.m. – 3.00p.m.
Monday to Sunday.
Guild Office: 10.00a.m. – 3.00p.m.
Monday to Friday.
Closed public holidays.
Approximately 20 quilts.

The suburb of Malvern is located approximately 10 kilometres south east of the city centre.

The Guild was established in 1960 to provide a centre for the promotion and teaching of needlework, especially embroidery. It is located in a delightful house in Malvern and

PHOTOGRAPHY TONY AND ROBINA SUMMERS.

ABOVE: *Unfinished Patchwork Quilt of Pieced Stars.* OPPOSITE: Detail of *Tumbling Blocks Quilt.* Unknown Maker, c.1890. 142cm x 121cm. Donated by Mrs R. Barlow. Collection Embroiderers' Guild, Malvern, Victoria.

it is here that they conduct classes, lectures and seminars, as well as holding exhibitions of work. Special interest groups, including a patchwork group, meet each month.

The Guild has established a collection of embroidery and embroidery tools, hand made lace, and quilts. There are examples of many different styles of patchwork, each one representing the popular designs of the period in which it was made. The collection policy for the future is to acquire old quilts that fill gaps in the existing collection and new quilts by quiltmakers who are considered to add new dimensions to the craft.

✷ The quilts are included in regular exhibitions and may also be seen by request. Please apply in writing 3 to 4 weeks in advance to the Secretary.

The Historical Quilt Collection

✂ An unfinished quilt of silk Tumbling Blocks (142cm x 121cm) was made c.1890. It was donated to the Guild by Mrs R. Barlow, a member of both the British and Australian Embroiderers' Guilds. The quilt has no backing and the paper templates are still clearly visible behind each patch. It is believed that some of the work was done in England

ABOVE: *Crazy Patchwork Tea Cosy*. Unknown Maker, c.1890. Collection Embroiderers' Guild, Malvern, Victoria. OPPOSITE: *Quilt of Random Hexagons*. Made by Miss Birch and Mrs Brien, c.1870. 200cm x 246cm. Collection Schwerkolt Cottage, Mitcham, Victoria.

and some in Australia as papers from both countries have been used for templates. Several feature printed illustrations of koalas. The fabrics include silks, satins, velvets and brocades of varying ages with some pieces believed to date from the 1860s. Several of the diamonds have been cut from men's ties.

An unfinished mosaic quilt (80cm x 70cm) dates from the 1850s and is of unknown maker. It features a central medallion of tiny stars, each one created from diamonds and surrounded by hexagons. Small hearts, flowers and stars have been appliquéd to the background.

A quilt of Crazy Patchwork blocks (190cm x 180cm) was made in Australia c.1890 by Edith Maud Strachan. The blocks have been created from silk and velvet fabrics and finished with a border of deep red silk.

A tea cosy of Crazy Patchwork dates from the 1890s and is of unknown maker.

The Contemporary Quilt Collection

✂ A triptych (270cm x 370cm) was created by Susan Denton and purchased by the Guild in 1989. Susan's innovative quilts were often inspired by the bush and the Great Barrier Reef. This work formed part of her 'Reef' series. It was made with precise geometric piecing of rectangles to achieve movement and curves through sweeps of colour lines.

Barbara Macey's *Circle 3* is a framed patchwork panel (145cm x 55cm) of black and white strips. It was made in 1973, the same year in which Barbara began conducting classes in Log Cabin patchwork at the Guild.

The *Georges Panel* (154cm x 250cm) is a three dimensional work designed by Hester Hopkins and made by members of the Guild in 1980. It depicts Georges famous Collins Street store with its many patrons parading by in embroidered and patchworked clothing.

Schwerkolt Cottage
Deep Creek Road
Mitcham, Vic 3132.
Ph: (03) 9873 4946 or (03) 9874 6592
Nunawading & District Historical Society.
2.00p.m. – 5.00p.m. Saturdays,
Sundays and public holidays.
4 quilts.

The suburb of Mitcham is located approximately 20 kilometres east of the city.

Schwerkolt Cottage was built in 1884 by August Schwerkolt who arrived in Australia from Prussia in 1849. The property was run as a mixed farm with fruit trees, dairying, poultry, beehives, winemaking and a stone quarry. Mrs Schwerkolt travelled regularly to Kew to sell the farm produce. Exhibits in the nearby Historical Museum trace the development of the region from farmland to residential suburb. There is also a wonderful textile collection that includes needlework, costumes, and lace and provides insights into changing fashions and use of leisure time.

✷ The quilts are permanently displayed in the cottage. They may be seen during opening hours or at other times by appointment with the Nunawading & District Historical Society. Please contact the Society 48 hours in advance.

✂ A quilt of random hexagons (200cm x 246cm) was made in 1870 by Miss Birch and her sister, Mrs Brien. Both women worked as dressmakers and had access to the many scraps of fabric left over from the making of their client's garments. The quilt has been hand stitched in the English method over paper templates using fabrics of plain and printed cottons. Two rows of darkly coloured hexagons have been worked around the outside to create a border.

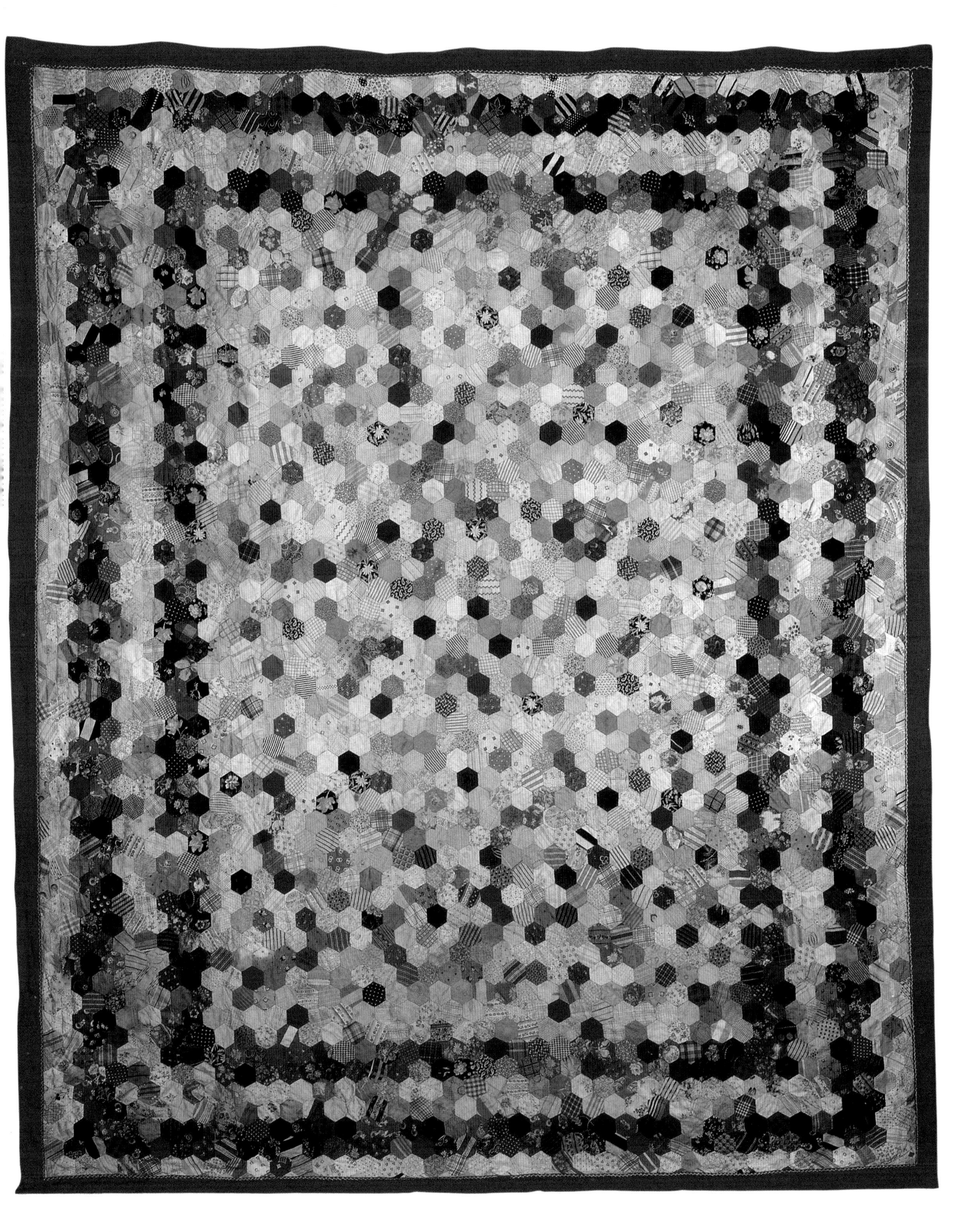

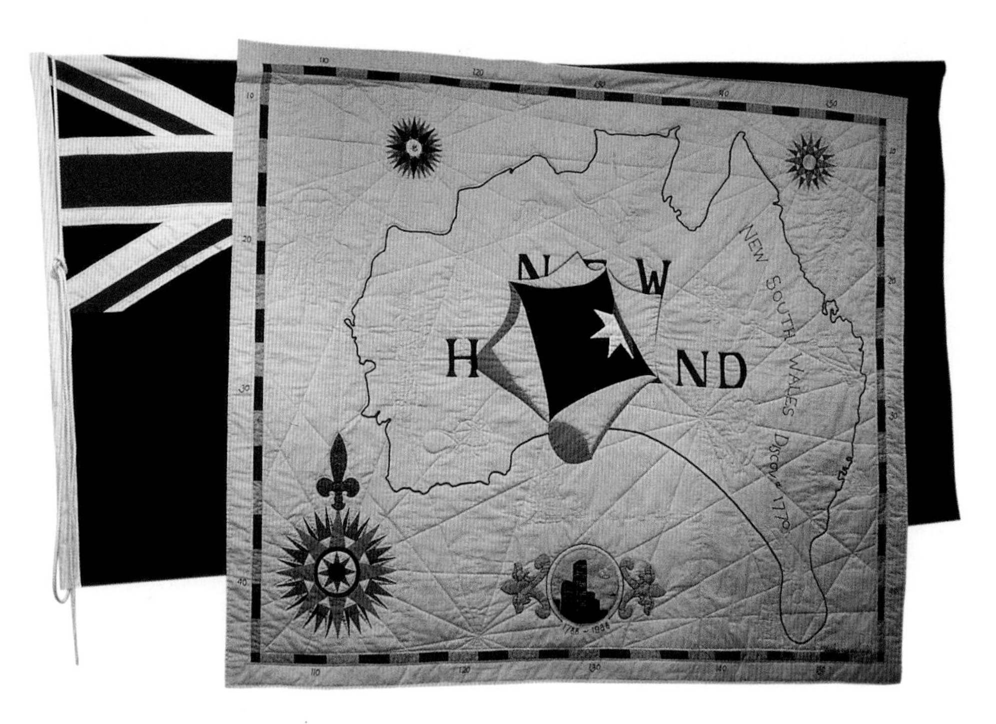

ABOVE: *Past, Present and Future.* Made by Waverley Patchworkers, 1988. 160cm x 234cm. Waverley City Gallery, Wheelers Hill, Victoria. OPPOSITE, TOP: *Unfinished Coverlet of Silk Diamonds.* Unknown Maker, c.1880. 134cm x 148cm. BELOW: Detail of *Quilt of Random Hexagons.* Made by Miss Birch and Mrs Brien, c.1870. 200cm x 246cm. Collection Schwerkolt Cottage, Mitcham, Victoria.

The work has been finished with an edging of red cotton twill embroidered with feather stitching.

A little cot quilt (55cm x 95cm) of white gathered hexagons dates from the turn of the century and is of unknown maker. The work has been finished with a scalloped edge and a corded fringe.

An unfinished coverlet (134cm x 148cm) of silk diamonds dates from the 1880s and is of unknown maker. The diamonds form a design of six pointed stars and have been pieced by hand over cardboard templates. Some of the templates still remain in place behind the outer patches. The fabrics are plain and printed velvets, brocades and silks and in common with many unfinished pieces, the work remains in excellent condition.

A patchwork counterpane was hand stitched by Maria Ann Knight. Maria was born in England in 1829 and emigrated to Australia at the age of twenty six in 1855. The work was hand stitched from cotton dress prints in a simple design of squares and rectangles. Maria died in 1908 and was buried in Castlemaine. The quilt was donated to the Society by her great great granddaughter, Mrs Hampton. Mrs Hampton had found the cover after the death of her parents. It was stored in a trunk along with a beautiful christening robe and several etchings that had also been made by Maria.

Williamstown Historical Society Museum

5 Electra Street
Williamstown, Vic 3016.
Ph: (03) 9397 1534 Museum.
(03) 9397 5423 Mrs J. Ridley,
Williamstown Historical Society.
2.00p.m. – 5.00p.m. Sundays
or by arrangement.

The historic bay-side suburb of Williamstown overlooks Hobson's Bay and is a 15 minute drive south of the city. Established as a maritime village in 1835, it was named after King William IV and is Melbourne's oldest suburb. Many of the original buildings are still nestled around the beach front with its jetty, pier and old shops.

The Historical Museum is housed in the lovely old Mechanics Institute building c.1860. The collection includes many costumes. There are hand stitched trousseau items, a fine lawn christening gown, and a cream silk wedding dress dating from the mid 19th century. There is also a wealth of embroidered linen, hand knitted and crocheted coverlets, a beautiful beaded tea cosy and a tiny patchwork doll's quilt of pieced squares.

✷ The quilt is hung on permanent display and may be seen during opening hours or by arrangement.

✂ This Signature quilt (167cm x 225cm) was begun during the first World War and completed some years afterwards. Many of the signatures were collected by Captain Stewart Hansen and sent home to his mother who lived in Williamstown. Mrs Hansen and her friends embroidered the names, bordered each square with red cotton and stitched them onto a backing sheet. One of the squares contains the signature of Captain Albert Jacka, the first Australian to receive the Victoria Cross for bravery. Sadly, Captain Hansen was never to see the completed quilt. Having survived the Gallipoli campaign, he was fatally wounded on the battlefields of France.

PHOTOGRAPHY TONY AND ROBINA SUMMERS.

ABOVE: *Crazy Patchwork Quilt featuring Australian Coat of Arms.* Made by Septima and Mabel Jones, c.1900. Collection Kyneton Museum, Kyneton, Victoria.

PHOTOGRAPHY STEPHEN WEST.

Waverley City Gallery
170 Jells Road
Wheelers Hill, Vic 3150.
Ph: (03) 9562 1569 Fax: (03) 9562 2433
10.00a.m. – 5.00p.m. Tuesday to Friday.
12 noon – 5.00p.m. Saturday and Sunday.

The suburb of Wheelers Hill is located approximately 20 kilometres south east of the city.

✷ The quilt is displayed intermittently throughout the year but may also be viewed at other times by appointment. Please contact the Gallery.

✂ *Past, Present and Future* (160cm x 234cm) was designed and made by Waverley Patchworkers for the Quilt Australia '88 Exhibition. An authentic Kincaid sea chart c.1790 was the initial inspiration. It was used to represent 'the past' by depicting the country as it was known at the time of settlement. It was intended that the quilt would have the appearance of a desk top draped with the Australian flag, the old sea chart resting on top of it. Cotton fabric was tea dyed to reproduce the semblance of age and three Mariners' Compasses were hand pieced and sewn to the map.

A three dimensional effect was achieved by depicting the chart with a torn section curling back so that one of the stars of the flag could be seen beneath it. The Australian flag was chosen to represent 'the present' with the face of Queen Elizabeth quilted below the Union Jack. It is fascinating that quilts are able to capture in fabric the historical perspective of the period in which they are created, and since the making of this work both the design of our flag and the role of the Queen in Australia have been debated.

Optimism in our country's 'future' was embroidered in rosy colours in the legend of the chart. The work involved the techniques of hand and machine piecing, appliqué, and embroidery. Lines of latitude, longitude, and paths of navigation were hand quilted into the design, along with historical figures, native animals and the First Fleet. The work took fifteen months to complete and was chosen as one of the twenty best quilts in the Quilt Australia '88 exhibition.

Kyneton

The picturesque town of Kyneton is set in the undulating hills of the Macedon Ranges about an hour's drive from Melbourne. The gold rushes of the 1850s were to lead to rapid development of the region as local farms and stores supplied food and provisions to diggers. Much of the 19th century character of the town remains and there are beautifully restored colonial buildings. Kyneton is also renowned for its lovely Botanic Gardens, first planted in 1866. Throughout the region there are galleries, restaurants, antique shops, and mountain wineries.

Kyneton Museum
67 Piper Street
Kyneton, Vic 3444.
Ph: (03) 5422 1228
11.00a.m. – 4.00p.m. Friday, Saturday, Sunday, all school and public holidays.
Open by arrangement any day for large groups and tours.
Several quilts and other small items of patchwork.

Kyneton Museum is housed in a colonial Georgian building c.1855. Its treasure trove of textiles includes many examples of handmade lace, beading, white eyelet work, tatting, crochet, and embroidery.

Several tapestries and cross stitch samplers date from the early 19th century. The large collection of costumes includes Victorian dresses, christening gowns, hand made trousseau underwear, beautiful wedding and evening gowns, and flapper dresses from the 1920s. In addition to the patchwork quilts, there is also a beautiful hand knitted bedspread.

✷ Some quilts are on permanent display and those in storage may be seen by arrangement. Please contact the Museum 24 hours in advance.

✂ The collection includes a quilt of Crazy Patchwork (84cm x 116cm) made by Septima Jones and her daughter, Mabel c.1900. Septima had married David Jones in 1883 and the family lived in Kyneton where David worked as a contractor. It was customary during this era for needlework skills to be passed down from mother to daughter and in addition to the many items created by Septima, the Museum also has several made by Mabel. The two women made this quilt around the time of Federation, expressing their patriotism for the country by embroidering the Australian Coat of Arms and the words *'Advance Australia'* into the centre. The fabrics include silk, satin, velvet, wool, and cottons, and each patch has been decorated with feather stitch.

A doll's quilt of Crazy Patchwork (58cm x 76cm) was made by Mrs McDonald of Kyneton c.1910. It was created from a colourful variety of dressmaking scraps including cotton, silk, satin, velvet and grosgrain ribbon. Each patch was embellished with embroidery and a crocheted motif was sewn to the centre. The work was probably made by mother and child and has a border of floral cretonne and a backing of red paisley cotton.

ABOVE: *Doll's Quilt of Crazy Patchwork.* Made by Mrs McDonald, c.1910. Collection Kyneton Museum, Kyneton, Victoria.

Lancefield and Romsey

The historic little town of Lancefield and neighbouring village of Romsey are just a short drive from Kyneton. Both have a rich heritage of Victorian architecture dating from the 1850s, much of it built from wealth acquired during the gold rush. The original general store, post office, and court house have all been retained in Lancefield's main street, and many of the buildings are shaded by wide 19th century verandahs.

Lancefield Court House Museum

55 Main Road
Lancefield, Vic 3435.
PO Box 11, Romsey, 3434.
Ph: 03) 5429 1833
1.30p.m. – 4.00p.m. Sundays
or by appointment.

The Museum is housed in the old Court House c1888. Its collection of historical memorabilia includes several gowns dating from the 1870s, some featuring appliquéd decoration. There is also a christening dress, hand crocheted cot cover, and a beautiful cross stitch sampler made in 1845 by Marianne Lawrence, aged 12 years.

✷ The Signature quilts made in 1896 and 1996 hang back-to-back in a specially designed glass case. They may be seen during opening hours or by arrangement with the Romsey and Lancefield Districts Historical Society.

✂ A beautiful Signature quilt (188cm x 134cm) was made in 1896 by Mrs Condon of Rochford. Miss Anderson, also of Rochford, painted the rose, thistle and shamrock in the central panel. The quilt formed part of the *'Lancefield Presbyterian Sale of Gifts'* held in the Mechanics' Institute Hall in February, 1896, and the following account was reported in the '*Lancefield Mercury:*' '*The first thing that strikes the eye, and which is the centre of attraction, is the magnificent quilt, hung against the wall at the back of the stage. The quilt contains 465 autographs beautifully worked with various coloured crewel silks on a background of royal blue satin, and is lined with old gold sateen.*'

Each signature was embroidered on a separate blue satin square, the edge of which was outlined in feather stitch. A fee was charged to have each name included and the sum of twenty three pounds was made. The quilt was then raffled to earn the very substantial profit of thirty two pounds and fifteen shillings.

A second quilt was made in 1996 to commemorate the centenary of the 1896 work and to capture the names of current residents of the towns. The embroidered signatures were machine stitched by Elaine Lobb with contributors paying a $2.00 fee in order to be included.

McCrae

McCrae is one of many beautiful villages on the western coast of the Mornington Peninsula, the boot shaped promontory between the bays of Port Phillip and Western Port. The town was named after the first permanent settlers, the pioneering McCrae family who built their home on the slopes of Arthurs Seat in 1844. Several of the little coastal villages nearby became fashionable seaside resorts during the 1870s and many of the beautiful homes, gardens, and shops still remain. Inland from the coast, the rolling hills are dotted with berry farms, orchards, and wineries, and there are numerous antique shops, studios and galleries.

McCrae Homestead and Museum
11 Beverley Road
McCrae, Vic 3938.
Ph: (03) 5986 5688 or (03) 5981 2866
(03) 5986 6244 after hours.
12.00 noon – 4.30p.m. daily.
Groups by appointment.
2 quilts.

The McCrae Homestead was built in 1844 for Andrew McCrae, his wife Georgiana and their eight children. One of the earliest colonial homes on the peninsula, it was built of drop log construction using timbers taken from the surrounding hillside and bricks transported from Melbourne by sea. Georgiana had drawn the plans herself and her sketches survived to provide the National Trust with a meticulous record for the authentic restoration of the property. Many original furnishings remain, along with memorabilia and personal effects belonging to the family. Georgiana was a renowned artist, musician, diarist and linguist and her work is housed in the museum adjacent to the house.

✷ The quilts are permanently displayed on antique beds within the homestead and may be seen during opening hours or by appointment.

✂ An extremely rare and lovely patchwork quilt (260cm x 240cm) was made in England in 1798 by Mrs Elizabeth Leadbeater. The maker's initials and date have been embroidered in cross stitch into the centre of the work using grey thread.

The top has been made from hexagons and finely hand stitched in the traditional English method over paper templates. A simple Four Patch border of squares surrounds the hexagons. Some of the fabrics are wonderful examples of block printed cottons in colours of soft brown, purple, red, pink, cream and grey-blue. The prints include striped rows of foliage and floral trails. Many years later, a printed cotton strip border has been machine stitched around the outside edge. The work has been finely quilted by hand, the many thousands of tiny stitches apparent on the plain cream cotton backing. It was donated to the National Trust by Mrs C.C. Edmondson during the early 1970s. Certainly one of the very oldest quilts in Australia, Elizabeth Leadbeater's work is the earliest signed and dated example in *Australia's Quilts: a Directory of Patchwork Treasures.*

A silk mosaic quilt (200cm x 220cm) of unknown maker c.1880 has been created from triangles stitched together into groups of six to form hexagons. A wide border has been made from rows of squares, each square pieced from four triangles. The work has been hand stitched over papers which still remain behind each triangle and can be seen through the cotton backing. The fabrics are frail but beautiful examples of plain and printed silks and satins and provide a fascinating glimpse of the fashions of the era. This was a time when glorious colours were available in silks but black was still used extensively, especially for the long periods of mourning following the death of a loved one.

Geelong

The largest provincial city in Victoria, Geelong overlooks Corio Bay and is approximately an hour's drive south west of Melbourne. The earliest settlers to the region established sheep grazing properties during the 1830s and Geelong became a major centre for the storage and sale of wool. The discovery of gold in 1851 was to lead to a huge increase in the population and many of the town's heritage buildings date from this period.

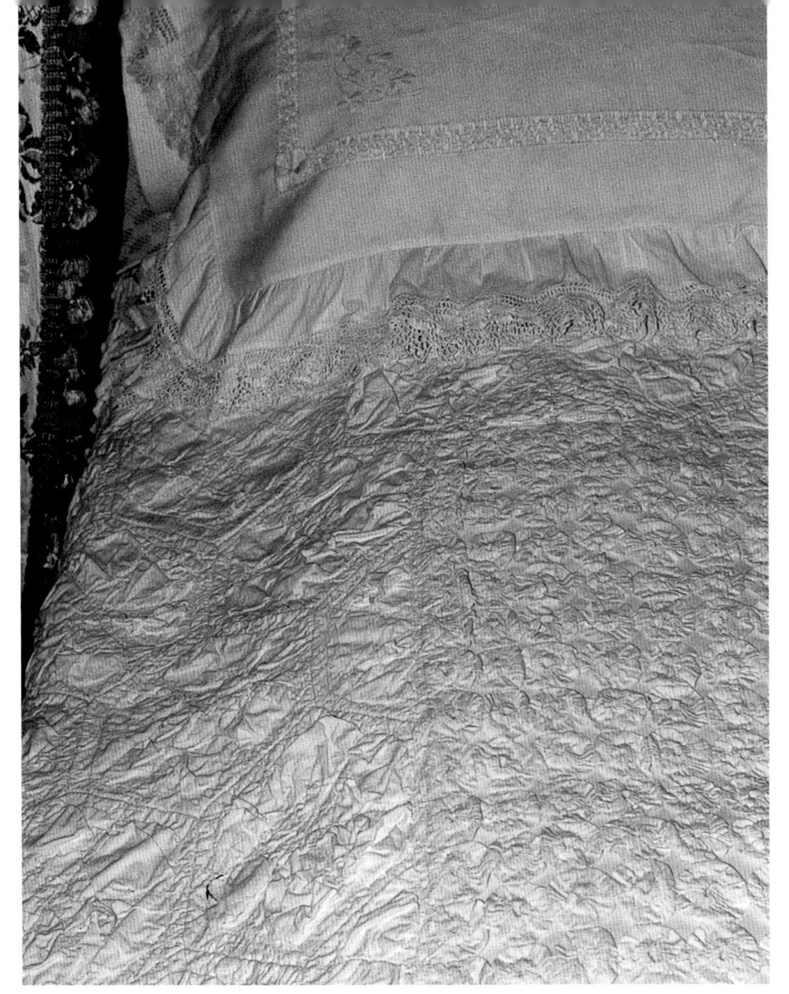

ABOVE: *Patchwork Quilt of Gathered Hexagons and Suffolk Puffs.* Unknown Maker, c.1900. RIGHT: *Doll's Quilt of Tumbling Blocks.* Unknown Maker, c.1890. Reproduced courtesy National Trust of Australia. (Victoria) – Barwon Grange, Geelong.

More than one hundred have been classified by the National Trust. The foreshore is dotted with historic characters created from bollards by local artist, Jan Mitchell. There are many interesting villages in the countryside nearby and the spectacular Great Ocean Road is only a short distance away.

Barwon Grange

Fernleigh Street, Newtown
Geelong, Vic 3220.
Ph: (03) 5221 3906 Fax: (03) 5224 2253
11.00a.m. – 4.30p.m. Wednesday, Saturday, Sunday and public holidays between September and April.
Appointments can be made for viewings, functions, or bus tours at all other times.
Closed Good Friday, Christmas Day, and May to August.
2 quilts.

Newtown is a suburb of Geelong just a few minutes drive south of the city centre.

The delightful property of Barwon Grange was built in 1855 for Geelong merchant, Jonathon O'Brien. Overlooking the Barwon River, the house provides a rare example of a riverside home that reflects both the tastes and aspirations of successful middle class people during the gold rush era. An auction-listing providing concise details of the house contents appeared in the 'Geelong Advertiser' in 1856 and has been used by the Trust as a guide in the acquisition of furniture and artefacts for the property. The collection includes costumes dating from the 1850s, a pair of Victorian fans embroidered with tiny cross stitch bouquets, a petit-point foot stool, framed tapestry and cross stitch samplers, and several examples of Berlin wool work.

✷ The quilts are displayed in the main bedroom and nursery and may be seen during opening hours or by appointment.

✂ A beautiful white counterpane c.1900 features a combination of gathered patches and was created by a skilled but unknown needlewoman. The work has a central square of Suffolk Puffs, each puff less than four centimetres in diameter. Surrounding the centre are rows of large gathered hexagons, each one formed by gathering the excess fullness of a larger hexagon over the top of a smaller one to achieve a ruched appearance. Stab stitches have been made through the centre of each hexagon and the work has been finished with a crocheted edging. It is displayed on a mahogany half-tester bed of Biedermeier style.

A tiny pieced quilt of Tumbling Block design was made c.1890. It was found in

PHOTOGRAPHY IAN ROBERTS.

ABOVE: Detail of *Patchwork Quilt of Hexagons.* Made by Elizabeth Leadbeater, 1798. Reproduced courtesy National Trust of Australia (Victoria) – McCrae Homestead and Museum, McCrae, Victoria. BELOW: Detail showing Elizabeth Leadbeater's initials and the date, 1798.

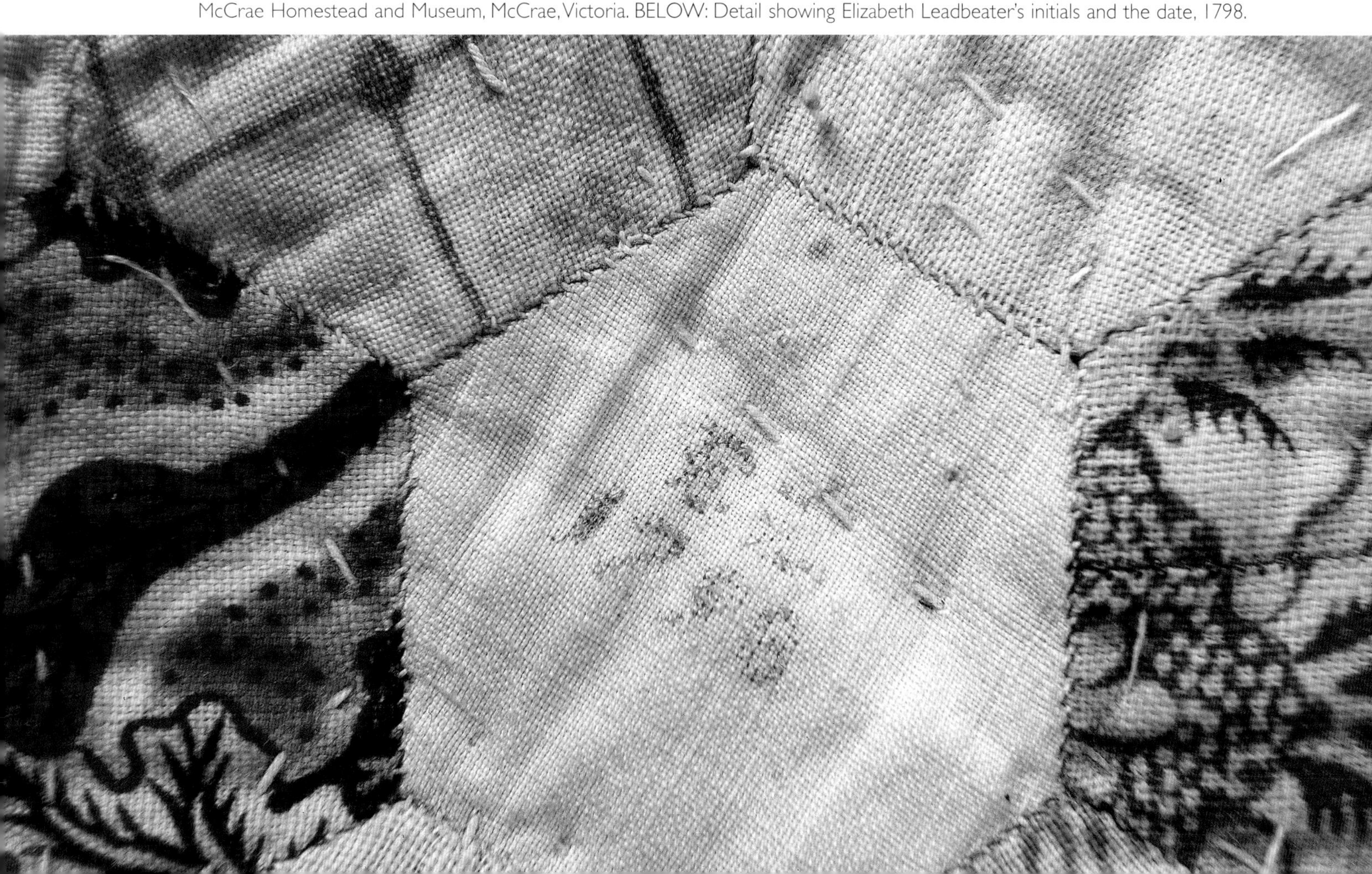

ABOVE: *Silk Mosaic Quilt.* Unknown Maker, c.1880. Reproduced courtesy National Trust of Australia (Victoria) – McCrae Homestead and Museum, McCrae, Victoria. BELOW: Detail of *Silk Mosaic Quilt.*

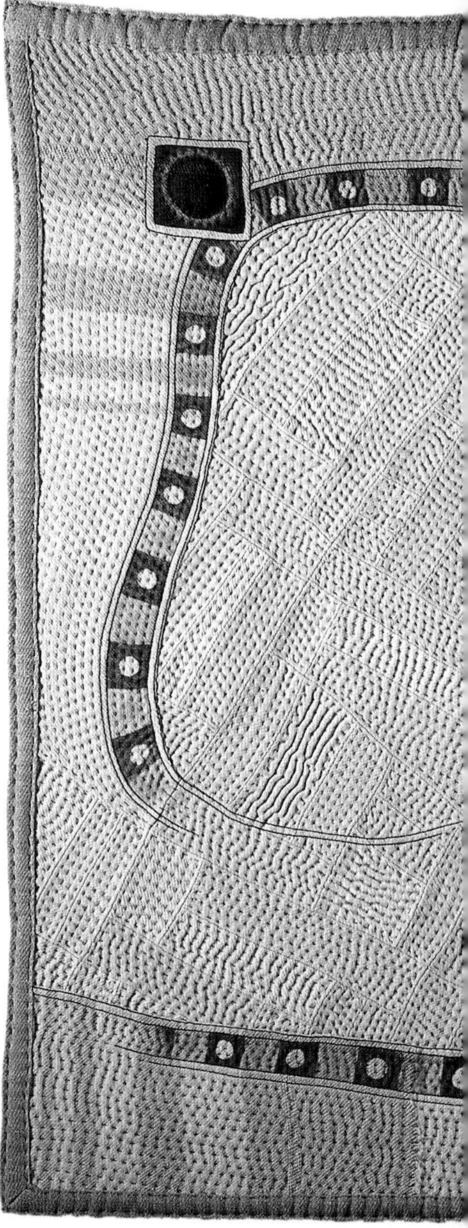

Portobello Road, London, and purchased for Barwon Grange. The work has been stitched by hand using the traditional English method over paper templates. The templates have been cut from letters on which the faded ink of the copperplate hand writing is still clearly visible. Fabrics include silk, satin and brocade, some plain, others printed, striped and water-marked. The quilt is displayed on a half-testa mahogany doll's bed which still has the original canopy of purple silk.

The National Wool Museum

Cnr. Moorabool and Brougham Streets
Geelong, Vic 3220.
Ph: (03) 5227 0701 Fax: (03) 5222 1118
10.00a.m. – 5.00p.m. daily.
Approximately 20 quilts.

The Museum is housed in an historic bluestone wool store located just one block from the waterfront. Its collection brings to life Australia's wool heritage from its earliest beginnings to the present day.

✷ The quilts are displayed intermittently throughout the year but may also be seen by appointment. Please contact the Curator 2 weeks in advance.

✄ The 'Running Stitch Collection' is held by the Museum. 'Running Stitch' was formed in 1983 by Lois Densham, Barbara Macey, Jan Ross-Manley and Susan Denton. The aim of the group was to raise the profile of contemporary quilts in Australia and to increase

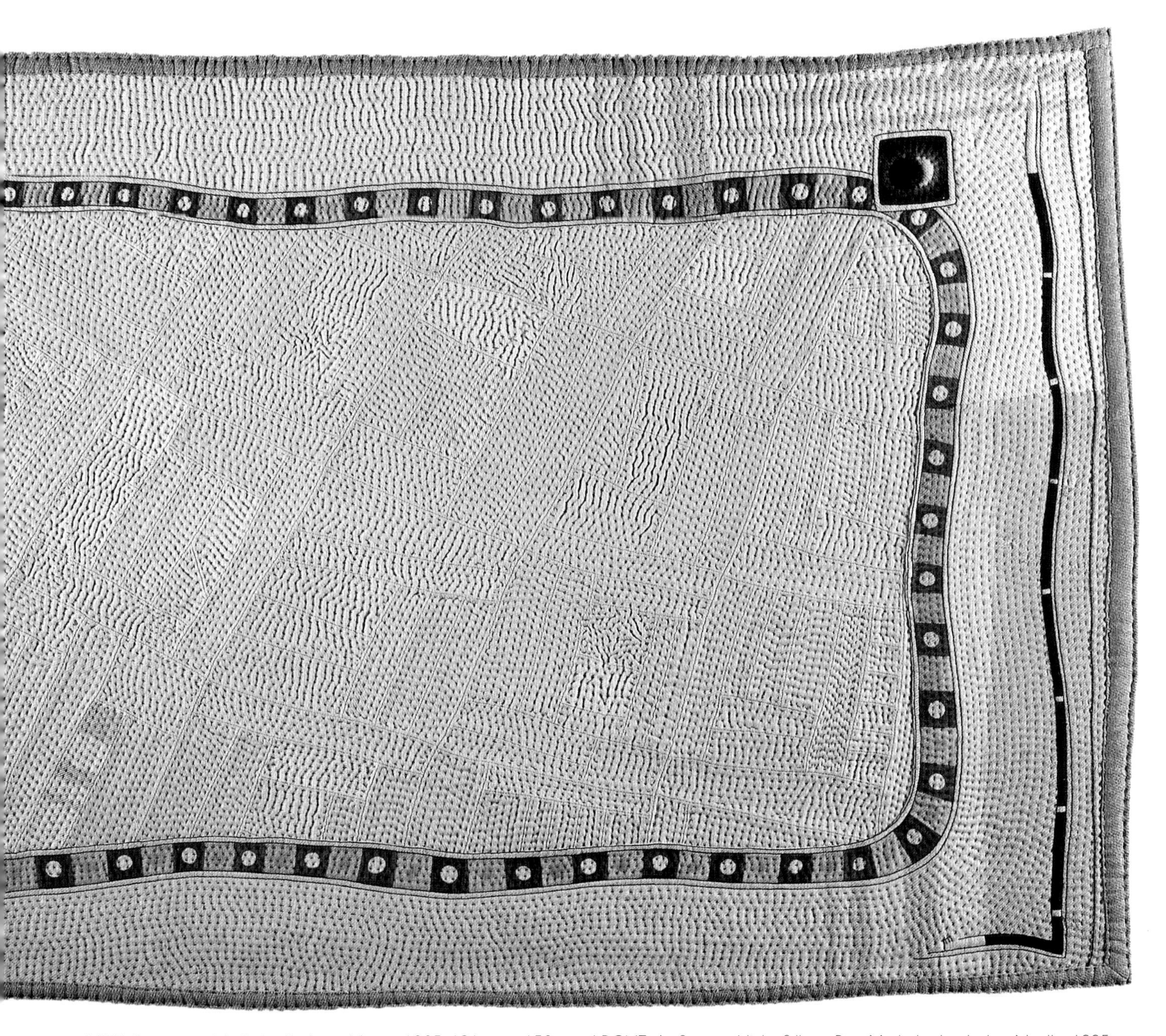

LEFT: *Diversions.* Made by Barbara Macey, 1985. 131cm x 158cm. ABOVE: *As Sure as Night follows Day.* Made by Jan Irvine-Nealie, 1995. 110cm x 190cm. Collection National Wool Museum, Geelong, Victoria.

awareness of our quilting heritage. They documented reminiscences, anecdotes and general information about patchwork and the tradition of the wagga, and created a 'living museum' with the aim of making it available for educational, historical and cultural viewing.

Included is *Anzac Anniversary* (150cm x 150cm) made by Lois Densham in 1985. This work of recycled tartans and plaids commemorated the 70th anniversary of the First World War and was appliquéd by hand and machine, and quilted by hand.

Diversions (131cm x 158cm) was made by Barbara Macey in 1985. Barbara was inspired to create this contemporary interpretation of a traditional form by her discovery of a Scottish Herringbone quilt.

A beautiful contemporary wool quilt was added to the permanent collection following an exhibition organised by 'Running Stitch' in 1995. *As Sure as Night follows Day* (110cm x 190cm) was made by Jan Irvine-Nealie from recycled worn woollen blankets with a woollen batting. The fabrics were crazy pieced, airbrush dyed and hand quilted.

Queenscliff

One of Victoria's oldest settlements, Queenscliff is set on the Bellarine Peninsula overlooking the entrance to Port Phillip Bay. It is only 30 kilometres east of Geelong and may be reached by road or water. An historic town dating back to the 1850s, it began as a fishing village and sea pilot's station, the pilots employed to guide ships safely through the treacherous waters of Port Phillip Heads. From the 1880s it developed as a favourite holiday destination and many stately guest houses and hotels were built. The town has retained much of the charm and character of the early years and many of the historic buildings have been restored to their former glory.

Queenscliffe Historical Museum
Hesse Street
Queenscliff, Vic 3225.
Ph: (03) 5258 2511
2.00p.m. – 4.00 p.m. every day
except Christmas Day and Good Friday.
Closed occasional Mondays and Tuesdays
during winter.
2 quilts.

The Museum collection includes a lovely whitework bedcover incorporating a wide range of cutwork, pulled thread techniques and embroidery over the entire area of the quilt. There are many items of costume that illustrate both the quality and everyday use of lace in late 19th and early 20th century Queenscliff. A recently completed extension to the Museum enables the display of many items previously held in storage.

✱ Mrs Keen's quilt has been mounted in a specially designed case and is permanently displayed. Mrs Wilkinson's quilt is not always displayed but may be seen by request. Please notify the Museum in advance if groups will be visiting.

✄ The Museum has two Australian quilts, one dating from the 19th century, the other from the Depression years of the 1930s. It is remarkable that both quilts are signed and dated and have been kept in the area in which they originated.

Mrs Elizabeth Keen lived in the tiny village of Fyansford, just west of Geelong, where she was the proprietor of the Junction Hotel. She had worked as a dressmaker and was a renowned needlewoman. Her quilt (233cm x 266cm) is signed and dated in cross stitch *'Mrs E. Keen, Junction Hotel, Fyansford, 1879.'* The work is a rare example of an early Australian quilt made of repeating blocks. Each block has been sewn over paper templates and created from cottons, silks, velvets and wools. The central nine blocks form a diamond pattern and have been made from hundreds of very tiny squares. The outer blocks have been sewn in a Variable Star design with a cat appliquéd to the centre of each star. There are borders of cats and horses and each horse has been embellished with silk covered buttons and tassels.

A quilt (214cm x 138cm) of hexagons was made in 1938 by Mrs M. Wilkinson. Mrs Wilkinson lived in Queenscliff where her husband was a Colonel in the Australian Defence Force Establishment at nearby Swan Island. Her quilt has been made from small hexagons sewn over paper templates. A central rosette contains the date and the initials *'M.W.'* Plain and printed cotton fabrics have been used for the work, the border and rosettes in 1930s blue and the background in taupe.

RIGHT: *Patchwork Quilt.* Made by Elizabeth Keen, 1879. 233cm x 266cm.
Collection Queenscliffe Historical Museum, Queenscliff, Victoria.

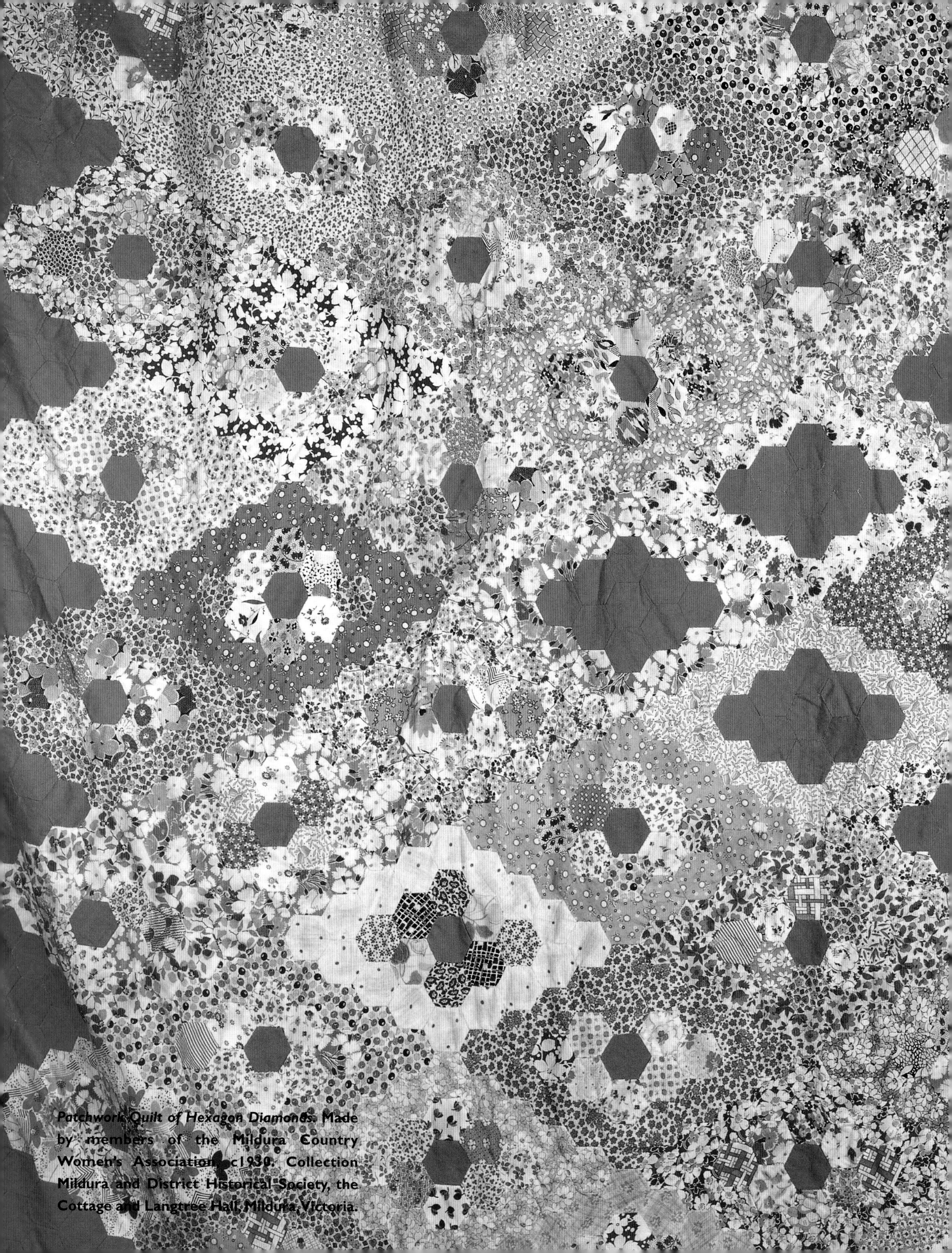

Patchwork Quilt of Hexagon Diamonds. Made by members of the Mildura Country Women's Association, c1930. Collection Mildura and District Historical Society, the Cottage and Langtree Hall, Mildura, Victoria.

QUILTS OF VICTORIA

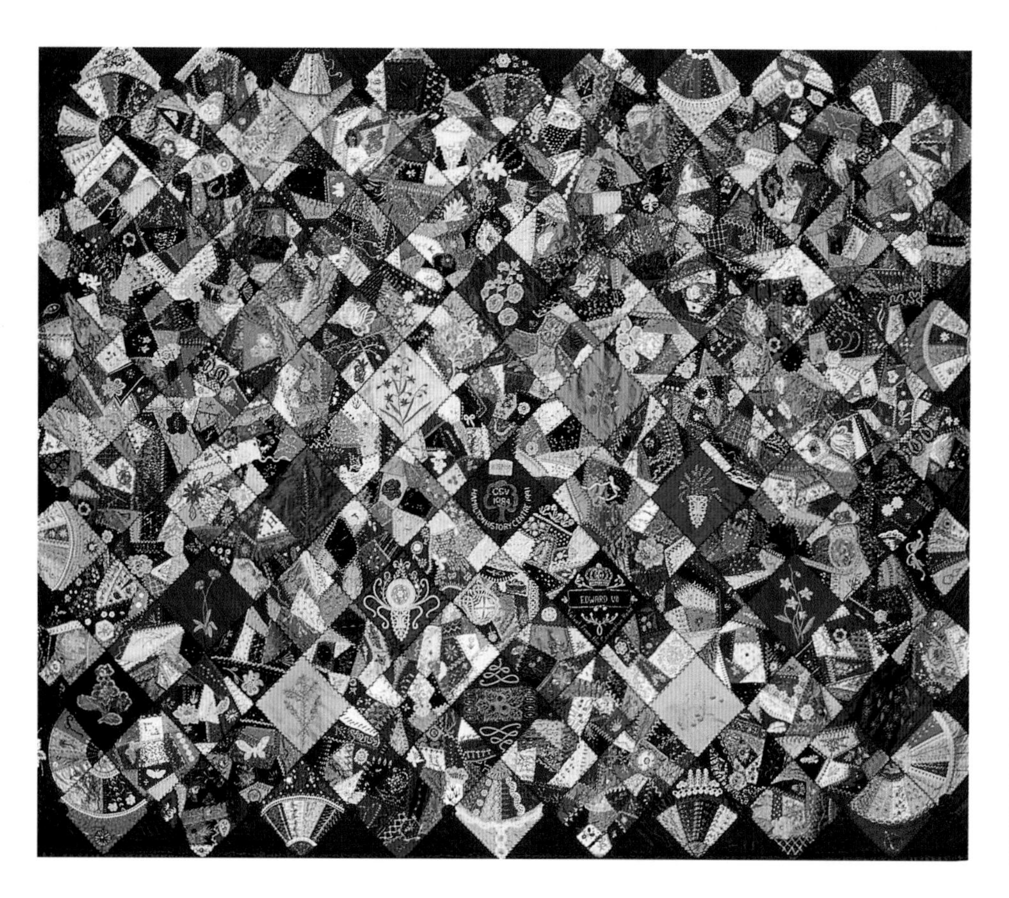

Hamilton

Hamilton is only an hour's drive from the Grampians and a similar distance from the historic seaside towns of Portland, Port Fairy and Warrnambool. The centre of one of the finest wool producing areas in the world, it is also the starting point for the Mary MacKillop Pilgrim's Drive which culminates in Penola, South Australia. Since the early 1980s the Hamilton Quilters have been creating magnificent quilts for the enjoyment of the community. They are now displayed in several buildings throughout the town.

Hamilton History Centre
Mechanics Institute
43 Gray Street
Hamilton, VIC 3300.
Ph/Fax: (03) 5572 4933
2.00p.m. – 5.00p.m. Sunday to Friday.
Closed Saturday.

The Hamilton History Centre specialises in genealogical and local history research and has a small museum which includes an extensive collection of lace.

✷ The quilt is permanently displayed and may be seen during opening hours.

✄ A beautiful Crazy Patchwork quilt entitled *It's Magic* was designed by Beryl Andersen and made by the Hamilton Quilters in 1996. More than 2,500 hours were spent creating this masterpiece which was appliquéd, pieced and embroidered by hand. Among the Crazy patches there are eight embroidered squares depicting wildflowers native to Western Victoria. The fabrics include silk, satin, velvet, laces and treasured remnants. One piece of velvet came from the robe worn by Edward VII at his coronation ceremony in 1901. It had been sent to the quiltmaker in Australia by an English relative in 1924. The quilt features exquisite embroidery and unusual threads which were collected from local bazaars and sales. One maker chose to embroider tiny red roses in memory of her late husband. Lace from a baby's christening frock and fifty year old pearl beads from a family wedding dress were also stitched to the work.

Hamilton Art Gallery
Brown Street
Hamilton, VIC 3300.
Ph: (03) 5573 0460
Fax: (03) 5572 2910
10.00a.m. – 5.00p.m. Monday to Friday.
10.00a.m. – 12 noon and
2.00 – 5.00p.m. Saturday.
2.00p.m. – 5.00p.m. Sunday.

The Gallery houses a diverse collection of fine and decorative arts comprising silver, glass, porcelain, prints, tapestries and

PHOTOGRAPHY JOHN KIELY.

ABOVE: *It's Magic.* Made by the Hamilton Quilters, 1996. Hamilton History Centre, Hamilton, Victoria.

furniture. Paintings include colonial art of Western Victoria, 18th century landscapes by Paul Sandby, and contemporary works.

✷ The quilt is not displayed but may be seen by prior arrangement with the Gallery. Please contact the Director by telephone or fax one week in advance.

✄ A heritage quilt (201cm x 150cm) was designed by Diane Pettigrew and made by members of the Hamilton Quilters in 1984. It depicts historic buildings within the town as well as many of the old homesteads and settlers' cottages to be found in the surrounding countryside. The contemporary design features the buildings clustered within several large three dimensional blocks. Photographs were taken of every site and fabrics were selected carefully to match each one. The work was hand appliquéd and quilted and many details were added in hand embroidery.

The Performing Arts Centre
113 Brown Street
Hamilton, VIC 3300.
Ph: (03) 5573 0429 Fax: (03) 5572 2910
9.00a.m. – 5.00p.m. Monday to Friday.
Evenings during performances.

✷ The quilt is hung on permanent display in the foyer of the theatre. It may be seen daily during box office opening hours or evenings when performances are presented.

✄ This lovely quilt entitled *Prologue* (300cm x 170cm) was designed by Pat Wilmot and made by the Hamilton Quilters in 1994.

The theatre features a wide variety of performances so Pat included figures representing music, drama and dance. Prologue stands in the foreground. He introduces the performance and holds the traditional masks of comedy and tragedy. Each performer is illuminated by a beam of white organza light. They are dressed with incredible attention to detail and the hair and shoes on each one is perfect. There is a tiny bracelet and earrings on the female dancer, diamond checked pants on the male. The singer wears a frilled collar, opal waistcoat and blue velvet coat. The stage is framed by swagged curtains, their gold tie-backs, trims and folds adding dimension to the scene. The design of the stage setting is so realistic that it achieves a trompe l'oeil effect and the viewer feels part of the audience.

ABOVE: *Prologue.* Made by the Hamilton Quilters, 1994. The Performing Arts Centre, Hamilton, Victoria. OPPOSITE: Details showing Prologue with his masks of comedy and tragedy, and the two dancers and singer illuminated by beams of white organza light.

The size of the quilt was planned so that it would not appear dwarfed by the large space in which it would hang or by the strong art work already in place. Colours were chosen to complement the interior of the theatre. Fabrics usually associated with theatrical costumes were used in the work. They included silk, satin, chintz and taffeta. Braid, gold threads, beading and embroidery were added. The stage setting was hand pieced, appliquéd, embroidered and quilted, and the braided border was machine pieced and quilted.

Hamilton College
1 Chaucer Street
Hamilton, VIC 3300.
Ph: (03) 5572 1355 Fax: (03)5572 4998
8.30a.m. – 5.00p.m. Monday to Friday, including school holidays.

✷ The quilt is hung on permanent display in the foyer of the main building and visitors are welcome to see it by arrangement. Please telephone the Principal's Secretary.

✂ Hamilton College was founded in 1871. This quilt (145cm x 185cm) was designed by Nanette Templeton and Marie Pye and made by the Hamilton Quilters in 1996 to commemorate its 125th Anniversary. The bluestone clock tower, chosen as the focal point, was created using the water colour technique. An ingenious combination of light and dark squares were machine stitched together to form the picture. The tower was framed by trees and foliage and set against a perfect blue sky. The two clock faces were hand embroidered and then reverse appliquéd into position. The

PHOTOGRAPHY JOHN KIELY.

ABOVE: *Hamilton College 125th Anniversary Quilt.* Made by the Hamilton Quilters, 1996. 145cm x 185cm. Hamilton College, Hamilton, Victoria. *Blue Wren Splendour.* Made by the Hamilton Quilters, 1992. Hamilton Base Hospital, Hamilton, Victoria.

flag was also appliquéd to the background. The work was finely quilted by hand, an ivy leaf design included around the outside to reflect the ivy clad walls of the building.

Hamilton Base Hospital

Forster Street
Hamilton, VIC 3300.
Ph: (03) 5571 0222 Fax: (03)5571 0300
8.00a.m. – 8.30p.m. daily.

✷ The quilt is hung on permanent display in the stairwell of the hospital and may be seen during the hours listed.

✂ This beautiful quilt entitled *Blue Wren Splendour* was designed by Sherri Robertson and made by the Hamilton Quilters in 1992. The design was specially planned to impart tranquillity and provide visual stimulation for patients, visitors and staff. The central medallion features the hospital's logo with its floral motif of the Grampians tea-tree. The floral blocks depict trees, shrubs, native wildflowers and garden flowers, many of them drawn from actual specimens. Exquisite life-size blue wrens feature throughout the foliage and were created with fabric paints and crayons before being stitched into place. Fabrics were chosen carefully to match each shade of foliage and flower and a variety of threads were used to embroider stamens, leaf veins and other details. The work was appliquéd, embroidered and quilted by hand.

Hamilton Institute of Rural Learning (HIRL)

North Boundary Road
Hamilton, VIC 3300.
Ph: (03) 5572 3699 HIRL
10.00a.m. – 2.00p.m. Monday and Tuesday.
9.30a.m. – 3.30p.m. Wednesday and Friday.
Other times by arrangement.
2 quilts.

Hamilton is the last remaining place on the Australian mainland where the Eastern Barred Bandicoot is still to be found. HIRL records the story of this endangered species and undertakes research programmes to ensure its long term conservation.

✷ The quilts are hung on permanent display in the Bandicoot Information Centre. They may be seen during the opening hours listed or at other times by arrangement. The HIRL office is run by volunteers. If closed please contact the Visitor Information Centre. Telephone (03) 5572 3746 or Fax (03) 5571 2229

✂ The *Bandicoot Quilt* was designed by Carole McEwan and made by the Hamilton Quilters in 1986. It illustrates the life and death relationship that exists between the bandicoots and the city of Hamilton. The central square depicts a nocturnal scene encompassing the habitats of both the bandicoots and

PHOTOGRAPHY JOHN KIELY.

ABOVE: The *Bandicoot Quilt.* Made by the Hamilton Quilters, 1986. Hamilton Institute of Rural Learning, Hamilton, Victoria. Detail shows the bandicoot with the bugs that make up his summer diet. The phases of the moon indicate the nocturnal behaviour of the animal.

the community. Squares on either side contain two adult bandicoots. Created from velvet with meticulous attention to detail, the animals' colour and size mirror nature exactly. The top half of the quilt relates to the life of the bandicoot. The phases of the moon were made from white moire taffeta and indicate the bandicoot's nocturnal behaviour. The grasses, garden mulch and bugs make up the summer diet of the animals. The lower half of the quilt presents a plea for more care for the endangered bandicoot and its habitat. It includes four different species of native flora, once common but no longer so. Below them, the chief predator and villain, the cat. The foreground depicts the habitat as it could be, with flora, cats and bandicoots in proper proportion. Black Sawtoothed borders convey a sense of unease concerning the unresolved relationship between the two halves of the quilt. The work was made from velvet, silk, and taffeta. It was hand appliquéd, pieced, embroidered and quilted.

A large wall hanging entitled *Fabric of our Community* (225cm x 225cm) was created in 1987 by a small and diverse group of textile workers. It was made under the guidance of Anne Marie Power and depicts a sweeping view of the Hamilton district. Weaving, felting, dyeing, printing, hand and machine embroidery, beading, knitting, canvas work and quilting were all combined to create the work.

Also in Hamilton

A wall hanging was created by a small group of local quiltmakers for the restored Gardener's Cottage in the Hamilton Botanic Gardens. The work features a central medallion depicting the historic cottage which was built in 1882. Abutilons (Chinese Lanterns) were chosen to illustrate the blocks surrounding the centre. The work was appliquéd, embroidered and quilted by hand. The Gardens were founded in 1870 and contain huge old trees, several classified by the National Trust. They are located on the corner of Thompson and French Streets. The hanging may be seen by contacting the Secretary, Friends of the Gardens. Telephone (03) 5572 1839 or PO Box 230, Hamilton.

Coleraine

Coleraine lies in the spectacular Wannon Valley, 35 kilometres north west of Hamilton. Surrounded by high tablelands, this historic village is renowned for its Points Arboretum which features one of the largest collections of eucalypt species in Australia. Historic gardens abound throughout the region and more than 20 properties are regularly open to the public. 'Nareen,' owned by former Prime Minister, Malcolm Fraser, is one such garden.

Coleraine Tourist and Exhibition Centre
Old Railway Station
Coleraine, VIC 3315.
Ph: (03) 5575 2733 Fax: (03) 5575 2005
10.30a.m. – 4.30p.m. everyday.

✷ The quilt is hung on display and may be seen during opening hours.

✂ This quilt (200cm x 100cm) was created by a group of local quiltmakers to celebrate the Bicentennial in 1988. It depicts many of the wildflowers found in the countryside surrounding Coleraine and incorporates all four seasons. Enlarged representations show the tiny flowers that grow along the road sides, often unnoticed by people passing by. The background of hand painted kangaroo grass was quilted with a design of butterflies, moths, leaves and insects. The flowers were appliquéd and embroidered by hand using a variety of textured materials. Beads, cord and ribbon were added to create stems, stamens and seed pods.

In the Nearby Region

Only 30 kilometres from Coleraine, the town of Casterton is set in the rolling hills of the Glenelg Valley. The Casterton Historical Museum has a remarkable embroidered coverlet made by the late Jean Hutcheson Murray, granddaughter of one of the earliest pioneers of the district. The extraordinary story of the work was published in the *Casterton News*, January 1968. Jean had never seen tape-work until she was taught the art by her friend, Caroline Hayman, before the turn of the century. She purchased some tape from Buckley and Nunn but not having sufficient to finish, she left the cover to lie on a shelf for sixty nine years. In 1967 Jean bought more tape in Casterton and completed the work she had begun in 1898. It can be seen displayed at the museum in Jackson Street on Sunday afternoons between 2.00p.m. and 4.00p.m. or by appointment. Telephone (03) 5581 2106 or (03) 5575 3294.

Port Fairy

The charming fishing village of Port Fairy is nestled on the banks of the Moyne River overlooking Portland Bay. It is approximately 30 kilometres west of Warrnambool on the rugged 'Shipwreck Coast,' an area so treacherous that in the past more than 80 vessels have come to grief. Port Fairy is one of Victoria's oldest settlements, its maritime traditions dating back to the early 1800s when the region was frequented by whalers and sealers. Today, many visitors are attracted by the charm of the historic buildings, the galleries, craft and antique shops, as well as the wharf area and beaches.

Moyne Shire Council
Princes Street
Port Fairy, VIC 3284.
Ph: (03) 5568 2600 Fax: (03) 5568 2515
9.00a.m. – 4.30p.m. Monday to Friday.

✷ The quilt is hung on permanent display at the top of the stairs and may be seen during the office hours listed.

✂ A *Port Fairy Heritage Quilt* (157cm x 190cm) was created by local quiltmakers to celebrate the Bicentennial in 1988. It features twelve appliquéd and embroidered blocks framed within black and white borders. The blocks depict many of the town's most notable historic buildings and was hand appliquéd, embroidered and quilted.

Port Fairy History Centre
Old Courthouse
Gipps Street
Port Fairy, VIC 3284.
Ph: (03) 5568 2263
2.00p.m. – 5.00p.m. Wednesday, Saturday, Sunday and everyday during school holidays.
Other times by prior arrangement.

The History Centre is located in the historic bluestone courthouse c.1859. It houses the Historical Society museum and archives. The collection includes costumes dating from the late 1800s to contemporary items.

✷ The quilt is not permanently displayed but may be seen by prior arrangement. Please ring 24 hours in advance.

✂ A Grandmother's Flower Garden Quilt (240cm x 240cm) was made by Mrs J. Grimshaw of Port Fairy c.1950-'60. The rosettes were cut from printed dress cottons and surrounded by a border of plain white hexagons. The work has no filling and has been finished with a wide dusky pink border of cotton sateen.

Mott's Cottage
5 Sackville Street
Port Fairy, VIC 3284.
Ph: (03) 5568 2682 Fax: (03) 5568 2833
Visitor Centre & National Trust contact.
1.00p.m. – 4.00p.m. Wednesdays, Saturdays and Sundays, or by appointment.

Mott's Cottage is one of Port Fairy's earliest houses. It is believed that the first stage of the building was constructed in 1845 for two whalers, Mott and Stevenson. Sarah Mott lived in the house between 1918 and 1944 and through long association with the family it has come to be known as Mott's Cottage. Today it houses a collection of

National Trust memorabilia as well as the offices of the Port Fairy Genealogical Society. In addition to the quilt, there is a hand made rag rug, a cross stitch sampler, and two wool embroidered pictures of 19th century sailing vessels.

✷ The quilt is displayed on a 19th century bentwood bed and may be seen during the opening hours listed or by appointment.

✄ This pieced scrap quilt c.1890 is of unknown maker. It is believed to be of English origin and has been made in medallion style. A central Square-within-a-square is surrounded by ten successive borders of pieced strips and triangles. The fabrics include a variety of printed shirting and dress cottons in colours of brown, pink, red, and blue. The work is entirely hand stitched, has no filling, and has been finely quilted by hand.

Portland

The oldest town in the state, Portland is only an hour's drive from Hamilton and about the same distance from the South Australian border. Settled by the Henty family in 1834, it has more than 200 historic buildings dating from the 1840s and '50s. The fascinating wharf area handles vessels from small coastal fishing boats to bulk carriers. The town's architectural heritage, protected beaches and fine fishing, as well as the abundance of galleries and museums, make it a popular holiday destination. The historical museum, History House, is located in the Old Town Hall, Charles Street, and has a wonderful collection of memorabilia including an old appliquéd wall hanging.

Portland and District Hospital
Bentinck Street
Portland, VIC 3305.
Ph: (03) 5521 0333
8.00a.m. – 8.00p.m. daily.
2 quilts.

✷ Both quilts are hung on permanent display in the hospital, *Serendipity* in the foyer and *Lodestar* in the chapel. They may be seen during the hours listed.

✄ *Serendipity* (200cm x 150cm) was designed by Pat Wilmot and made by Pat with a group of friends in 1993. It depicts a tranquil ocean scene with seagulls fossicking on the sand. The background was strip pieced and machine sewn using hand dyed fabrics. The seagulls were appliquéd and embroidered by hand.

Lodestar (150cm x 90cm) was designed and made by Pat to mark the completion of the hospital's major re development in 1993. A variety of silks and polished cottons were included in the work, which was hand and machine pieced and embellished with metallic threads and sequins.

The Steam Packet Inn
33 Bentinck Street
Portland, VIC 3305.
Ph: (03) 5523 2671 Fax (03)5521 7287
Visitor Information Centre.
2.00p.m. – 4.00p.m. Thursday to Sunday.
Other times by arrangement.
2 quilts.

The Steam Packet Inn is one of Victoria's oldest buildings. It was built in 1841 for former convict, Samuel Hutchinson, and constructed of Tasmanian hardwood which Hutchinson shipped from Launceston to Portland. The Inn has enjoyed a colourful and sometimes notorious history, serving over the years as a hotel, a police barracks, a residence and a guest house. One licensee was in trouble with the law for allowing

LEFT: *Patchwork Quilt.* Unknown maker, c.1890. Reproduced courtesy National Trust of Australia (Victoria) – Mott's Cottage, Port Fairy, Victoria.
RIGHT: *Quilt of Wildflowers.* Made by Coleraine Quilters, 1988. Coleraine Tourist and Exhibition Centre, Coleraine, Victoria.

prostitution. Today it is leased to the National Trust who have furnished it in the style of a 19th century residence and opened it as a house museum.

✷ The patchwork cover is permanently displayed on an old iron bed and may be seen during opening hours. The appliquéd coverlet is not always displayed but may be seen by request. Please ring the Portland Visitor Information Centre.

✂ A patchwork counterpane (218cm x 230cm) of simply pieced squares and rectangles is on long term loan to the National Trust from Olive Williamson of Heathmere, near Portland. The work was made c.1880-'90 by her grandmother, Sarah Barr, in Bradford, England. It was brought to Australia in 1923 by Olive's mother, Susan Heliger. Mrs Heliger used the quilt on her own bed for many years. Olive treasured it as a family heirloom though she used it infrequently because of its considerable weight. The work is a reversible counterpane, both sides made by hand from cotton shirtings and dress prints which are now faded with age. It has been finely hand quilted with a four-petalled daisy motif.

An appliquéd coverlet c.1850 (220cm x 237cm) was donated to the Trust by Miss Vera Stewart. It is believed that it was made by her grandmother during the long sea voyage to Australia from Scotland. Cotton dress fabrics in brown and white prints were used for the appliqué with a background of heavy white cotton twill. A large four-petalled daisy motif was stitched by hand to the centre and surrounded by smaller daisies, their shapes probably created using the paper-cut-out method popular with children. The coverlet was finished on all sides with a wide scalloped border.

PHOTOGRAPHY IAN MCKENZIE.

Mildura

Mildura is set in picturesque countryside on the banks of the Murray River. It is approximately 200 kilometres from Swan Hill and one and a half hour's drive from the Riverland region of South Australia. The town was established during the 1880s by the Chaffey Brothers whose development of an irrigation settlement was to lead to the growth of vineyards and a thriving citrus industry. The original Chaffey homestead, 'Rio Vista,' is open to the public as a house museum and arts centre.

The Cottage and Langtree Hall

79 Walnut Avenue
Mildura, VIC 3500.
Ph: (03) 5021 3090 Thea or Barbara Cornell.
10.00a.m. – 4.00p.m. Tuesday to Sunday.

Langtree Hall c.1889 houses a folk museum with a collection of historical memorabilia from the early days of Mildura. The Cottage was originally part of a country hotel in Dunnolly, Victoria, and has been relocated to Walnut Avenue in front of Langtree Hall. It is owned by the Cornell family who are restoring it to original condition and using it to display

ABOVE: *Patchwork Quilt of Hexagon Diamonds.* Made by members of the Mildura Country Women's Association, c1930. Collection Mildura and District Historical Society, the Cottage and Langtree Hall, Mildura, Victoria. LEFT: Detail showing edging of coloured bias binding.

a wealth of memorabilia. There are beautiful christening gowns, clothing, lace, antique toys and items on loan from the Mildura and District Historical Society. In addition to the patchwork quilt, there is an antique Marcella quilt, a coverlet of embroidered tulle and several traditional satin padded eiderdowns. The Cottage is surrounded by a garden of old lime, olive, walnut and pine trees.

✷ The quilt is displayed on an old iron bed in the cottage and may be seen during the hours listed. Please telephone a day in advance if you would like to view more of the collection of old textiles.

✂ This quilt of hexagon diamonds (180cm x 240cm) is owned by the Mildura and District Historical Society and is on permanent loan to the Cottage. It was made during the 1930s by members of the Mildura Country Women's Association and the President, Mrs Edie Lawn, was responsible for assembling most of the work. It was displayed on special occasions and always covered the President's table during the monthly meetings. The hexagons had been stitched by hand over paper templates using plain and printed cottons in the pastel colours of the period. The quilt was edged with several rows of coloured bias binding and it is recorded in the CWA minutes as having *'90 yards of window cording within the bias edging and 2,025 hexagons'.*

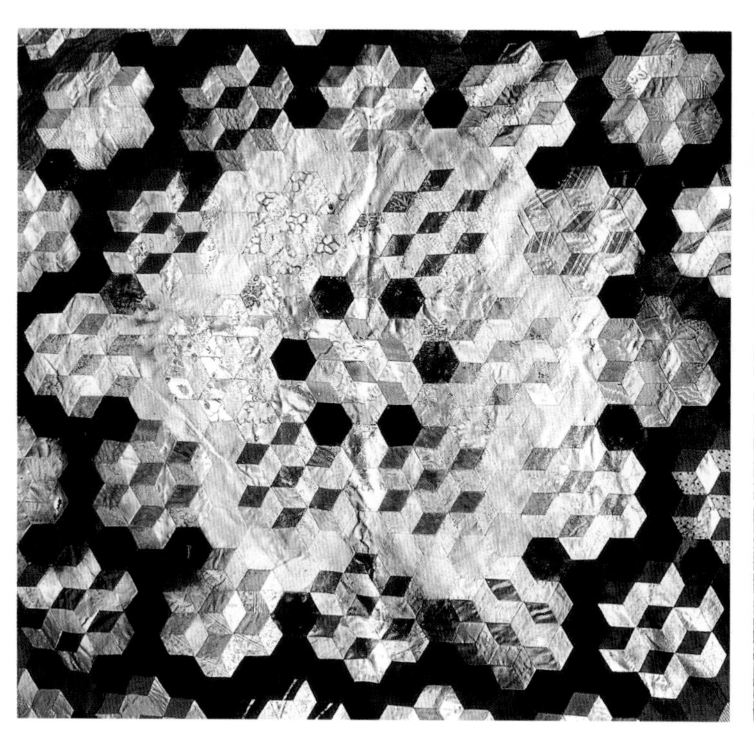

PHOTOGRAPHY GREG CRUIKSHANK.

ABOVE: *Silk Quilt of Tumbling Block Rosettes.* Created by an unknown maker, c.1890. Collection Swan Hill Pioneer Settlement, Swan Hill, Victoria.

Swan Hill

The vibrant and prosperous town of Swan Hill is found on the Murray River approximately 200 kilometres south east of Mildura. The original settlement developed around the punt which provided the only opportunity of crossing the river within 100 kilometres. A huge Moreton Bay Fig tree in Curlewis Street, one of the largest in Australia, was planted over a century ago and commemorates the visit to Swan Hill of the famous explorers Burke and Wills. The historic homesteads of 'Murray Downs' and 'Tyntyndyer' are open to the public as a house museums, providing a fascinating insight into life during the early years.

Swan Hill Pioneer Settlement
Horseshoe Bend
Swan Hill, VIC 3585.
Ph: (03) 5032 1093 Fax: (03) 5032 1096
8.30a.m. – 5.00p.m. everyday.
2 quilts.

Swan Hill Pioneer Settlement is a working 19th century river port village. It has been re-created on the banks of the Murray River to bring to life the history of the Mallee and Swan River region between the 1860s and '90s. An old homestead, stables, shops and business houses have been filled with an extensive collection of historical items. Many of the buildings date from the early pioneering days and have been relocated to the site.

✷ The quilts are located in Towaninie Homestead and may be seen during opening hours.

✂ A lovely silk quilt (152cm x 156cm) dating from the Victorian era is of unknown maker and history. It features an intricate design of hexagon rosettes created from the Tumbling Block pattern. Light coloured silks have been used through the centre of the quilt, dark brown and black hexagons highlighting the outer rosettes. Border rows have been made from silk triangles and each corner features a large star surrounded by pink silk diamonds. The work is finished with gold braided tassels and has a backing of glazed linen.

A cot quilt (126cm x 72cm) of yellow and white hexagons is also of unknown maker. It was created c.1960 from printed cottons in a radiating diamond design.

Dowling House
429 Campbell Street
Swan Hill, VIC 3585.
Ph: (03) 5032 3719 Fax: (03) 5033 1580
9.00a.m. – 4.00p.m. Monday to Friday,
except December 20th – January 13th.

Dowling House was moved to Swan Hill from the central Victorian goldfields by bullock dray in 1912. Today it is used as a Community Education Centre.

✷ The mural is permanently displayed in Room 3 and may be seen during the hours listed. Usually notice is not

ABOVE: *Swan Hill Bicentennial Mural.* Made by members of Crafts Swan Hill with Lois Densham, 1988. 250cm x 150cm. Dowling House, Swan Hill, Victoria.

required before visiting but it may be advisable to telephone in advance during the months of June and November when examinations are held.

✂ This lovely heritage mural (250cm x 150cm) was designed and made as a Bicentennial project in 1988. It illustrates the environment and history of the town from pioneer days to the present and was created by members of Crafts Swan Hill with the assistance of textile artist Lois Densham.

The work consists of three large panels, each one having a wide border featuring colourful depictions of native plants, animals and birds. The variety of fruits and grains grown in the region – the peaches, grapes, rice and wheat are also included. The Murray River winds its way through all three panels providing a link. The diverse techniques used in creating the mural included appliqué, lace-making, embroidery, stencilling, cross stitch, machine and hand knitting.

Kerang

The small rural town of Kerang is to be found on the Loddon River approximately 60 kilometres south east of Swan Hill. It is the centre of a thriving and diverse agricultural region of cereal crops, citrus orchards, rice, dairying, sheep and horses. The marshlands and lakes in the countryside surrounding Kerang provide a home to thousands of pelicans, ibis and other bird life.

St Johns Anglican Church
Cnr Victoria and Wyndham Streets
Kerang, VIC 3579.
Ph/Fax: (03) 5450 3770 Church office
or Jill Swifte
(03) 5452 2061 or (03) 5452 2877
The church is open between
8.00a.m. and 5.00p.m. every day.
Sunday services: 8.00a.m. and 9.30a.m.

✱ The quilt is hung on permanent display within the church and visitors are welcome to see it during the hours listed. Jill Swifte, the designer, may be available to speak to groups by appointment.

✂ This inspiring quilted wall hanging (475cm x 210cm) was designed and made by Jill Swifte between 1994 and '96. It was commissioned by the family of Murray Denyer to be a memorial to their father. Mounted on the wall above the altar, the hanging provides a focal point within the church and promotes an atmosphere of peace and contemplation.

The work was made in two separate parts, the lower quilt hung slightly behind the top quilt providing a three dimensional effect. The design features the ancient concept of the Tree of Life. A wooden cross, the symbol of Christian faith, emerges from the trunk. The dove of peace hovers protectively above it supporting the vine, symbol of the church family. The branches of the vine spread to the top of the quilt and then trail down both sides, curving at the lower

THIS PAGE: *The Karkarooc-Mallee Quilt.* Made by Carol Heath and the women and children of Hopetoun, 1990. 212cm x 170cm. Yarriambiak Shire Council, Hopetoun, Victoria.

PHOTOGRAPHY SHARLENE FERGUSON.

edge to visually combine the large uneven scallops of the border into the foliage of the tree. The background of the quilt was made from hundreds of tiny squares pieced together by machine and is remarkable for its effects of light and shadow. The appliqué, embroidery and quilting were all done by machine and many of the fabrics were hand dyed.

Hopetoun

Named after Australia's first Governor General, Lord Hopetoun, this small and picturesque town is situated in the southern Mallee region. It is approximately 60 kilometres north of Warracknabeal and a half hour drive from Patchewollock. The Hopetoun Arts and Crafts Group have been responsible for several diverse projects in which they have recorded their proud pioneer heritage. They have faithfully restored the National Trust classified 'Lake Corrong Station Homestead,' now open to the public as a house museum. They have also created a huge heritage wall mural depicting historic buildings, early pioneers, wildflowers, and over 200 species of birds. The stunning contemporary leadlight mural displayed at the Shire office near the quilt was also the work of this talented group.

Yarriambiak Shire Council
Hopetoun Municipal Office
75 Lascelles Street
Hopetoun, VIC 3396.
Ph: (03) 5083 3001 Fax: (03) 5083 3309
9.00a.m. – 5.00p.m. Monday to Friday.

✷ The quilt is displayed in the main entrance to the Council Chambers and may be seen any week day during opening hours.

✂ The *Karkarooc-Mallee Quilt* (212cm x 170cm) was created to commemorate the tenth anniversary of the Hopetoun Arts and Craft Group in 1990. It was designed and made by Carol Heath and the women and children of the Hopetoun region.

The large central block illustrates an early settler's cottage. It is similar to the one built in 1851 for Peter McGinnis and his family, the first European settlers in the area. In the foreground, a pioneering woman copes with her washing, her clothes-line strung between poles and busy black chickens scavenging nearby. Heritage buildings and the major rural industries of wheat and wool surround the centre. Native birds and wildflowers feature in the corners and border. An antique button from the blouse of an early pioneer was used as the cottage door knob. The work was machine pieced, hand appliquéd, quilted and embroidered.

Warracknabeal

Warracknabeal is set on the banks of the Yarriambiack Creek half way between Horsham and Hopetoun. The centre of a rich grain growing region, many of the town's fine historic buildings have been classified by the National Trust. A walking tour has been prepared as a guide for visitors. The Historical Centre, located in Scott Street, provides a fascinating glimpse into the past. There is a large collection of clocks as well as period clothing, embroidery, and a hand knitted coverlet c.1900.

Yarriambiack Shire Council
Warracknabeal Municipal Office
34 Lyle Street
Warracknabeal, VIC 3393.
Ph: (03) 5398 0100 Fax: (03) 5398 2502
9.00a.m. – 5.00p.m. Monday to Friday.

✷ The murals are displayed in the Function Room of the council building and may be seen during office hours.

✂ The Warracknabeal murals were designed and made as a community project to celebrate the Bicentennial in 1988. Initiated by the Arts Council, the aim was to encourage and extend the skills of local craftspeople while creating a work that would illustrate the richness and diversity of the region.

Each panel was divided into three sections. The narrow band across the top provides a view of the countryside from ground level. It sweeps out over cultivated fields towards the horizon. The central band shows an aerial view depicting the township as the focal point, rural farmlands sewn in abstract form around it. The lower border features separate pictorial blocks and includes illustrations of native trees, a Chinese garden on the banks of the creek and an original flour bag from the local mill. The Yarriambiack Creek winds through all three panels providing continuity. A diverse range of fabrics, many of them recycled, provides texture and interest. Colours suggest the changing seasons and agricultural variations. Techniques included piecing, appliqué, quilting, embroidery by both hand and machine, screen printing, hand dyeing and knitting.

Detail of *Warracknabeal Bicentennial Mural.* Made by Warracknabeal Arts Council, 1988. Yarriambiack Shire Council, Warracknabeal, Victoria.

Patchewollock

The small town of Patchewollock is midway between Hopetoun and Ouyen. Since the beginning of settlement local farmers have had to contend with the uncertain rainfall, rabbits and soil erosion of this semi-arid region. Despite the harsh realities of rural life however, the grassy plains and rolling hills surrounding the town have been developed into an important grain growing and wool area. During Spring the entire region is transformed by masses of wildflowers and special tours are arranged for visitors.

Patchewollock Memorial Community Centre
Federation Street (Main Street)
Patchewollock, VIC 3491.
Ph: (03) 5084 1242 Fax: 03) 5084 1292
Patchewollock Newsagent.
7.00a.m. – 10.00pm Monday to Friday.
8.00a.m. – 9.00p.m. Sundays.

The Patchewollock community is one of great spirit. The Community Centre in which the quilt is displayed was completed in 1980 and today it is the focus of many local activities. It was built entirely by local townspeople and they began by learning brick-laying in order to undertake the job.

Those who proved to be the most talented builders had their wheat crops harvested by others so that work on the hall could proceed. Little wonder that with such tremendous rural spirit and determination the community was then able to create this heritage wall hanging.

✷ The hanging is permanently displayed in the Centre. It may be seen by contacting the Patchewollock Newsagent where a key to the hall is held.

✄ This wall hanging (5m x 2.5m) was designed and made in 1988 by one hundred men, women and children from Patchewollock and the surrounding region. It was a Bicentennial project of the local Arts and Craft Group who were assisted and guided by Lois Densham.

The town of Patchewollock was featured as the focal point, surrounded by images of the rural landscape in which it is set. The role and influence of women, both past and present, was also a major theme. Other images relate to water, education, religion, recreation and sport and all were featured against the background of the environment – the heat, fire and dust which are part of the life of this rural community.

The hanging was made from fabrics of many different colours and textures. Old lace, beads, sequins, buttons, badges, and raw wool were added. Metal was used for the windmill, wood for the cross and clothesline. Techniques included hand and machine appliqué and embroidery, stencilling, knitting, crochet, photo-etching and rug hooking.

In the Nearby Region

The little town of Walpeup is about a half hour drive north of Patchewollock. A wonderful tapestry mural entitled *Walpeup 1989* was created by this small Mallee community in 1991. It depicts the many facets of life in the town and is hung on permanent display in the Walpeup Memorial Hall. It may be seen by inquiring at the Walpeup Milk Bar or by contacting Jean Corbett. Telephone (03) 5094 1370.

Wycheproof

The little Mallee town of Wycheproof is located on the Calder Highway, half way between Melbourne and Mildura. It is one of the few outback Australian towns to have a railway through its main street. Willandra Farm Museum is to be found in an early homestead at the southern end of town. Its collection includes period nightwear, dresses, hats and flags. The museum is open weekends by arrangement and if prior notice is given an exhibit of old tablecloths, crocheted rugs, and beaded women's wear can be arranged. Telephone (03) 5493 7227.

Buloke Shire Council
367 Broadway
Wycheproof, VIC 3527.
Ph: (03) 5493 7400 Fax: (03) 5493 7395
9.00a.m. – 5.00p.m. Monday to Friday.

✷ The quilt is hung in the foyer of the Shire building and may be seen during opening hours or by arrangement.

✄ This history quilt of Wycheproof (200cm x 140cm) was made between 1992 and '94 by seventy one members of the local community. Designed and co-ordinated by Carol Heath, the project celebrated the centenary of the region. The shape of the quilt represented the boundary of the Shire. A variety of pieced, appliquéd and photographed blocks illustrating the history and development of the area were stitched to the background. The images included the wheat, wool and salt industries and the rural nightmares of dust storms and drought. The embroidered words *'They came in countless millions'* recalled the horrors of the mice plagues.

Strip piecing in the colours of the Mallee symbolised the environment and the Aboriginal inhabitants who lived in the region before white settlement. Hand spun and dyed wool from the area was couched to the fabric before it was cut and pieced. French knots were used to tie the three layers together as well as for textural effect. Medals, ribbons, insignia, and embroidered medallions representing every township in the Shire were added. The multitude of techniques included embroidery, tatting, crochet, leather work, fabric painting, dyeing, piecing and appliqué.

Ballarat

One of the most famous gold mining towns in Victoria, Ballarat is situated in the central highlands about 100 kilometres north west of Melbourne. It is a beautiful city of wide tree-lined streets, stately homes and a fine heritage of architecture built with the wealth acquired from the diggings. Australia's only civic rebellion took place in Ballarat in 1854. The miners, led by Peter Lalor, erected the Eureka stockade in defiance of the harsh licence fees imposed by the government. Twenty five miners and four troopers died when the stockade was stormed by soldiers. The reconstructed town of Sovereign Hill, just outside Ballarat, was established to bring these events to life and to depict the day to day existence of the miners and their families.

Ballarat and District Aboriginal Co-operative

5 Market Street
Ballarat, VIC 3350.
Ph: (03) 5331 5344 Fax: (03)5333 1637
or contact the
Project Co-ordinator, Marjorie Pickford
Ph: (03) 5332 1643
9.00a.m. – 5.00p.m. Monday to Friday.

✷ The quilt is not permanently displayed but visitors are welcome to see it by arrangement. Please contact by telephone 24 hours in advance.

✂ A unique quilt (173cm X 213cm) depicting the Aboriginal heritage of Ballarat was made in 1995 by members of the Ballarat and District Aboriginal Co-operative. These women formed the Tooreebulluk Patchwork Group, believed to be the first Koori patchwork group in the state. Funded by the Melbourne Institute of Textiles, the project was co-ordinated by Marjorie Pickford and Carol Heath.

The design was created from a series of wide strips, some appliquéd, others pieced. It reflects the Victorian heritage of its makers by including their own traditional imagery rather than that of the indigenous people of Central and Northern Australia. It depicts Koori women dancing under a brightly pieced sun, native plants and animals. 'Bunjil,' the spirit eagle, peers down upon his prey of lizards from the top of the quilt. Hands were included in black and white fabric, their fingers touching to symbolise the close association between black and white communities.

The work was made from cotton fabrics in the traditional Aboriginal colours of red, black and yellow. Techniques included hand and machine appliqué, strip piecing, and embroidery.

PHOTOGRAPHY CAROL HEATH.

ABOVE: *Wycheproof Centenary Quilt.* Made by the community of Wycheproof with Carol Heath, 1992-'94. 200cm x 140m. Buloke Shire Council, Wycheproof, Victoria.

Montrose Cottage and Eureka Museum

111 Eureka Street
Ballarat, VIC 3350.
Ph/Fax: (03) 5332 2554
9.30a.m. – 5.00p.m. daily.
3 quilts, a skin rug, and other items.

This charming and historic bluestone cottage is located just 900 metres from the site of the Eureka Stockade. It was built in 1856 by John Alexander, a stone mason from Montrose in Scotland, and it was the first miner's cottage to be constructed on the Ballarat goldfields. Faithfully restored with original furnishings, the property contains many treasures. They include antique wedding dresses, lace, rag rugs in glorious colours, some looped, others punched, and several cross stitch samplers dating from 1821 to 1843. Many of these things are believed to have been made by the Alexander family. The cottage garden features an enormous old apple tree surrounded by roses, herbs, and fuchsias.

✷ The quilts and other textiles are on permanent display within the cottage and may be seen during opening hours. It is requested that large groups telephone a few days in advance.

✂ A Log Cabin cot quilt is believed to have been made by a member of the Alexander family during the late 19th century. The cotton fabrics are both printed and plain and each block features the traditional red 'chimney square' in the centre.

A red and white patchwork quilt of Pinwheel design is also believed to have been made by the Alexander family c.1890. The pieced blocks have been surrounded by border strips of the same red and white fabrics. The work has been backed with cream cotton and quilted by hand in a diamond pattern.

A platypus rug has been made from twenty five pelts stitched together and backed with a lining of blue woollen baize. The rug was used by Colonel Greenfield of the Ballarat Rangers during field exercises in the 1880s and was given to the owners of Montrose Cottage by the late Brigadier Hurley. It has a decorative border of scalloped leather.

A beautiful patchwork cushion of Log Cabin design c.1890 has been made in the intricate Pineapple pattern. It includes a great variety of wool, cotton and silk fabric strips and each seam has been covered with herringbone stitch.

ABOVE: *Patchwork Cushion.* Believed to have been made by a member of the Alexander Family, c.1890. Collection Montrose Cottage and Eureka Museum, Ballarat, Victoria.

Ballarat Fine Art Gallery
40 Lydiard Street North
Ballarat, VIC 3350.
Ph: (03) 5331 5622 Fax: (03) 5331 6361
10.30a.m. – 5.00p.m. daily.

The Ballarat Fine Art Gallery is Australia's oldest and largest regional gallery. Located in historic Lydiard Street and housed in a handsome 19th century building, it has an important collection of early Australian art and work from the artists of the gold fields. There is a small but valuable collection of oriental rugs and carpets and a number of heritage costumes. Of particular interest is the original Eureka flag raised at the stockade of 1854.

✷ The quilt is not permanently displayed but may be seen by appointment. Please contact the Registration Assistant by telephone a few days in advance.

✂ A huge quilt entitled *Celebration of Women of Ballarat – Past and Present* (490cm x 184cm) was made in 1988 to mark International Women's Day. Created by a group of local quiltmakers, the work includes portraits of more than 200 Ballarat women from the past and present who have contributed to the town through their social, cultural or community work. The portraits were applied to silk fabric using the photo transfer method and machine stitched together into three panels. The quilt was embellished with embroidery, appliquéd ribbons and laces, and finished with machine quilting.

Ararat

The rural City of Ararat is nestled on the eastern slopes of the Grampian Mountains, a two hour drive north west of Melbourne. It is the centre of a prosperous farming region producing fine merino wool and is also one of Australia's most acclaimed wine growing areas. The pioneering Seppelt's Great Western Vineyard was established here in 1865. Its underground cellars, which are open to the public, were built by gold miners and are now classified by the National Trust.

Ararat Gallery
Town Hall
Vincent Street
Ararat, VIC 3377.
Ph: (03) 5352 2836 Fax: (03) 5352 4961
11.00a.m – 4.00p.m. Monday to Friday.
12noon – 4.00p.m. Sundays,
public holidays and
Saturdays during Victorian school holidays.
Approximately 12 quilts.

The Gallery is housed in the city's impressive late Victorian Town Hall. The strength of the permanent collection is contemporary fibre and textile art. Diversity of art forms and concepts are explored through a changing programme which includes touring exhibitions alongside those from the permanent collection. There is a strong component of quilts and works based on quilting traditions. There are also woven tapestries and art forms incorporating embroidery. Important sub-collections include Textile Miniatures, the Art of the Japanese Package, the Lady Barbara Grimwade Costume Collection, and a collection of screen printed fabric lengths and samples from Australian designer, Frances Burke.

✷ The Gallery rotates displays of its permanent collection every three to four months and quilts are included in these exhibitions. Viewing of works in storage is possible for special interest groups and students by prior appointment. Please contact the Gallery Director.

✂ The collection includes two quilts by Lois Densham. *Pink and Black Landscape* (173cm x 100cm) was made in 1976 and is a padded and stitched work created from recycled fabrics and stretched on a frame. Ropes were used to achieve the three dimensional effect of the tree trunks with the canopy of pink leaves being appliquéd and machine embroidered. *Wheatfields* (62cm x 160cm) was made in 1987 and is an interpretation of an eclectic farmyard landscape. It features appliqué, hand and machine embroidery, and stencilling and was created from recycled fabrics including cotton, lurex, tulle, and satin.

Barbara Macey's quilt *Wave 2 – Jordanville Cutting* was made in 1980 and features two panels (163cm x 128cm).

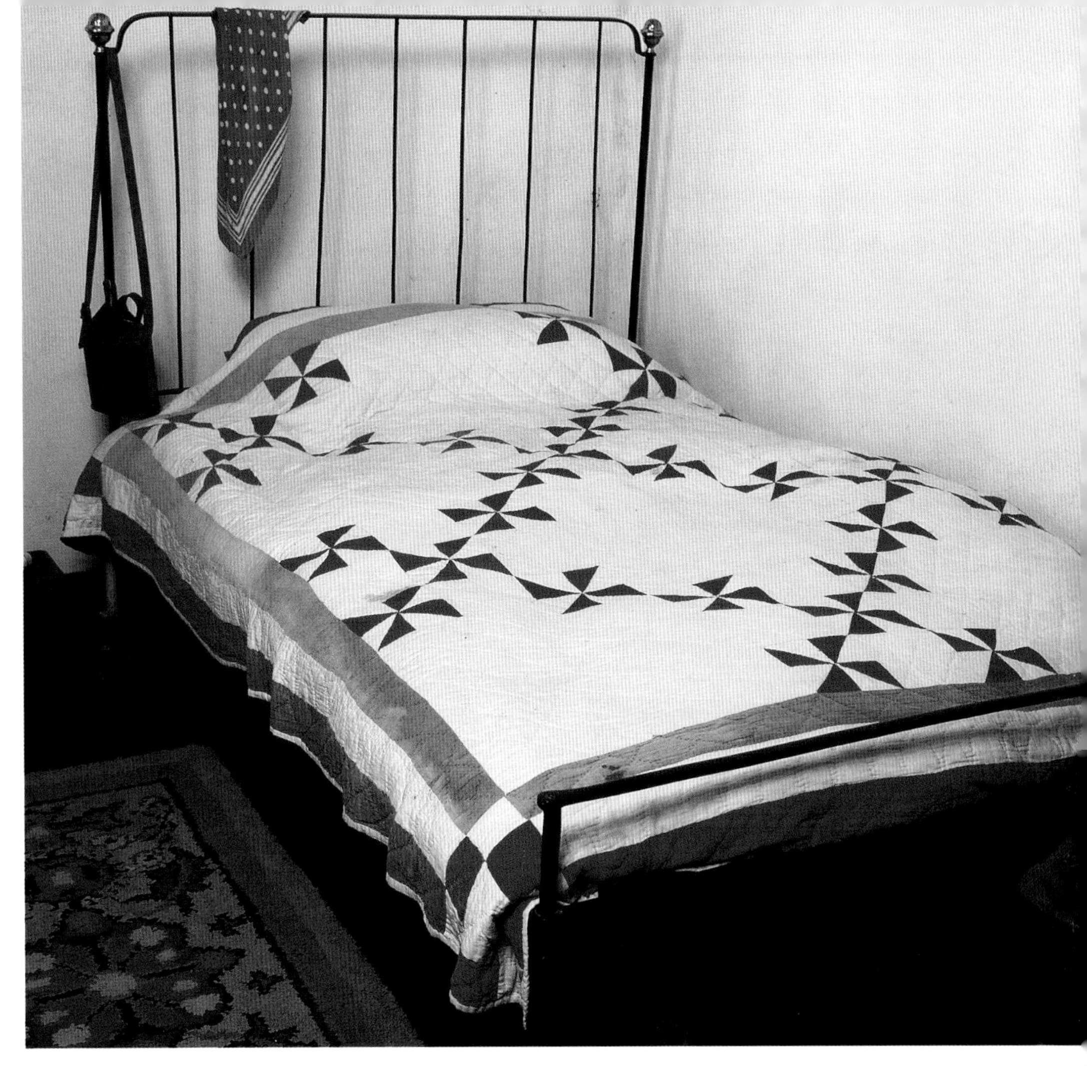

PHOTOGRAPHY ANDREW WILSON.

TOP: *Pinwheel Quilt.* BELOW: *Log Cabin Cot Quilt.* Both believed to have been made by members of the Alexander Family, c.1890. Collection Montrose Cottage and Eureka Museum, Ballarat, Victoria.

It was inspired by the beauty of the rock lining the railway cutting at Jordanville which had broad diagonal streaks glowing with rich and subtle pinks and apricots. The abstract design of the quilt employs a non-traditional Log Cabin block in a very contemporary form.

Jan Irvine-Nealie's *Juxtaposed* (100cm x 120cm) was made in 1990. One of a series of quilts based on the theme of energy, it depicts an energised motif and a static motif, the 'active' juxtaposed with the 'inactive.' Made of silk, the work was airbrushed dyed and hand quilted. It has a filling of wool and a cotton backing.

Sarah Crowest's *Red Counter Pain* (231cm x 173cm) was made in 1994. This quilt is a sequel to *Motherhood*, held by the Powerhouse Museum, Sydney, and is concerned with the mixed emotions and torn feelings involved in being both an artist and a mother. There are never enough hours in the day to nurture one's child and also be creative. *Red Counter Pain* is more acquiescent and hopeful in its outlook and depicts Sarah's daughter, Bini, in a circlet of gum leaves. It expresses an acceptance of life's cycles, as well as pleasure in the richness and diversity provided by the duplicity of roles. The quilt was machine pieced using dyed, screen printed and painted cottons and has a cotton backing and border.

Rose Marie Szulc's quilt *Lucky Dip of Life – What Prize Do You Win?* (182cm x 130cm) was made in 1989. Through the contemporary use of quilting and appliqué techniques the artist questions the impact of unseen elements (such as luck and chance) on our lives, ourselves and our work.

LEFT and OPPOSITE: *Red Counter Pain*. Made by Sarah Crowest, 1994. 231cm x 173cm. Collection Ararat Gallery, Ararat, Victoria.

Langi Morgala Museum
48 Queen Street
Ararat, VIC 3377.
Ph: (03) 5352 3117 or (03)5352 2541
1.00p.m. – 4.00p.m. Saturday and Sunday.
Schools and groups at
other times by appointment.
2 quilts plus other small items.

The Museum is housed in a beautiful brick and bluestone building c.1874. Its name is derived from two Aboriginal words and means 'Home of Yesterday'. The interior walls have been hand painted by local artist, Stan Kelly, and depict the early mining and pioneering days of the town. The collection includes lovely costumes, examples of crochet, tatting, needlepoint, and lace.

✷ The quilts are permanently displayed and may be seen during the hours listed.

✂ A pieced and appliquéd medallion quilt (200cm x 215cm) of unknown maker was brought to Australia from Ireland in 1854. The central square features hearts and leaves made using the folded paper-cutting technique which had been very popular in Ireland during the 19th century. The motifs have been stitched by hand onto a background of cream cotton and surrounded by successive borders of Flying Geese and zig zag pattern. The fabrics include printed dress cottons in colours of cream, brown, Prussian blue and cochineal pink. The work has a lining of damask and has been pieced, appliquéd and finely quilted by hand.

A quilt of Suffolk Puffs (200cm x 224cm) is also of unknown maker and dates from the early 20th century. It features a large central diamond of yellow puffs, a backing of green sateen and a wide edging of scalloped crochet.

ABOVE: *Bendigo Heritage Quilt.* Made by Bendigo YMCA 'Y's Workbox' Craft Group, 1988. 140cm x 250cm. North Central Goldfields Library, Bendigo, Victoria.

Bendigo

One of the most beautiful towns in Victoria, Bendigo sits at the junction of five highways, approximately an hour and a half drive north of Melbourne. Settled during the 1840s, it was the discovery of gold that was to lead to a huge increase in the population and development of the town. Among the immigrants were thousands of Chinese and their lasting influence on the culture of the region can be experienced by visiting the Golden Dragon Museum, the Joss House, or one of the excellent Chinese restaurants. Numerous outstanding examples of Victorian architecture date from the 1850s and '60s and were built from wealth acquired during the gold rush. There are many other historic towns in the surrounding countryside and the vineyards of the Pyrenees and Grampians are only a short distance away.

North Central Goldfields Library
251 – 259 Hargreaves Street
Bendigo, VIC 3550.
Ph: (03) 5443 5100 Fax: (03) 5441 2247
10.00a.m. – 7.00p.m. weekdays.
10.00a.m. – 5.00p.m. Saturday.

✷ The quilt is hung near the stairway leading to the mezzanine level of the Library and may be seen during the opening hours listed.

✂ This lovely pictorial quilt (140cm x 250cm) was made as a Bicentennial project during 1987 and '88 by the Bendigo YMCA 'Y's Workbox' Craft Group. Designed by Carolyn Marrone and co-ordinated by Pam Crammond, the quilt took more than 3000 hours to create. The central oval features the Alexandra Fountain, its granite column made from textured materials including velvet, crepe and moire taffeta. A border of hand embroidered wildflowers encircles the fountain, the cluster of grapes at the top a symbol of the local wine industry.

Eight pictorial segments surround the oval, each one depicting a different aspect of the town's heritage. There is the gold mining scene representing the founding of Bendigo, the bottle kiln from the historic Bendigo Pottery, and the beautiful Gothic building of Sacred Heart Cathedral – hand pieced and embroidered with a double layer of brown tulle to provide the shadowing. Hargreaves Mall is illuminated by lamp light made from layers of shaded tulle threaded with lurex to achieve the subtle glow. The head of the 'Sun Loong,' or world's longest Chinese imperial dragon, was created with intricate embroidery, beading and tatting, its scales made individually from silver lurex.

Other fabrics used included cotton,

taffeta, velvet, raw silk, and satin. Braid, ribbons, fringing, pure wool and beads were added. The multitude of techniques included hand appliqué, quilting, embroidery, crochet, tatting, beading, tapestry, tucking and pleating.

Bendigo Osteopathic Clinic
361 Napier Street
Bendigo, VIC 3550.
Ph: (03) 5442 4710 Fax: (03) 5441 7767
8.30a.m. – 6.00p.m. Monday to Saturday.

Napier Street is part of the Midland Highway which continues north to Echuca.

✷ The quilt is hung in the waiting room of the clinic and may be seen during the opening hours listed.

✂ This quilt entitled *Thompson's Foundry at the Maine* (150cm x 150cm) was made by Lois Densham in 1988. It commemorates the centenary of the establishment of Thompson's Foundry in the town of Castlemaine, a short drive south of Bendigo. It also records the part played by Lois's ancestors in the history of the foundry. A family tree in the bottom right corner includes the names of Lois's great grandfathers, one of whom worked at the foundry during its earliest years. His father had been responsible for the design on the Australian gold sovereign coin which features St George and the Dragon. Lois made a rubbing of St George using an embossed cake tin and this can be seen near the family tree. The central picture on the quilt was inspired by a photograph from the Foundry Archives. It depicts a huge boiler in the process of being transported from Castlemaine to Sydney by twenty eight horses. The quilt was appliquéd by hand and machine and finished with hand quilting.

ABOVE: *Thompson's Foundry at the Maine*. Made by Lois Densham, 1988. 150cm x 150cm. Bendigo Osteopathic Clinic, Bendigo, Victoria.

Benalla

The small rural city of Benalla is located approximately 200 kilometres north east of Melbourne. Established around the banks of Lake Benalla, the town has a number of original buildings remaining from the 1860s and '70s when it developed as the centre of a rich grain growing district. The beautiful Holy Trinity Anglican Church was built in 1865 and has a wonderful collection of tapestry cushions and altar kneelers made for the seats of every pew. Designed in the 1980s by a former Rector, Reverend Ray McInnes, they were embroidered by members of the parish community. Altar frontals have also been created for each season of the church year.

Benalla Costume and Pioneer Museum
14 Mair Street
Benalla, VIC 3672.
Ph/Fax: (03) 5762 1749
9.00a.m. – 5.00p.m. daily.
2 quilts, quilted clothing, and other small items of patchwork.

The Museum is housed in the original Mechanics Institute Hall. The collection includes items relating to the distinguished life of Australian war hero, Sir Edward 'Weary' Dunlop, who was born in Benalla. Changing exhibitions of period clothing dating from 1770 to the present day are exhibited in three large costume galleries. Each one follows a theme and the costumes are enhanced with appropriate accessories, furniture and other items.

ABOVE: *Crazy Patchwork Cushion.* Made by Mrs T. Waugh, Senior, c.1900. BELOW: *Quilted Petticoat.* Made at 'Booth & Fox's,' Dublin, 1865. OPPOSITE: Detail of *Hexagon Medallion Quilt.* Made by Mary Jane Block, 1871. 250cm x 178cm. Collection Benalla Costume and Pioneer Museum, Benalla, Victoria.

✷ The quilts and other items are not permanently displayed but visitors are welcome to see them provided prior notice is given. Please contact the museum one week in advance.

✂ The collection includes a hexagon medallion quilt (250cm x 178cm) made by Mary Jane Block in 1871. Mary Jane married John Kelly in 1872 and lived in Violet Town, 20 kilometres south of Benalla. The central medallion of her quilt features thousands of tiny hexagons, each one with sides only one centimetre in length. They have been hand pieced from cotton fabrics over paper templates and form distinct borders of stripes and rosettes. A hand appliquéd border of hearts, stars and other motifs surrounds the medallion. At some later stage the patchwork has been machine stitched to a damask backing. Three motifs have been hand appliquéd across the width of the damask at the top and bottom and three border strips of red cotton have been machine stitched around the edges. The work was donated to the museum by the maker's granddaughter. Ref 626

A Crazy Patchwork medallion quilt is of unknown maker, c.1920. Its central square of Crazy patches surround a circular motif of triangular wedges. The work has been made from multi-coloured silk and velvet in both plain and printed designs, each patch outlined with contrasting herringbone stitch. It has a heavy filling and a backing of floral cotton. Ref 212

There are several cushions in the collection. One of Crazy Patchwork was made c.1900 by Mrs T. Waugh, Senior, of Benalla. The fabrics are multi-coloured silks and velvets and each shape has been outlined with feather stitch. The words *'Faith,' 'Charity,' 'God is Love,'* and *'Watch and Pray'* have been hand embroidered in gold thread. Ref 72

There are several items of quilted clothing. Included is a red printed cotton half-petticoat with plain red lining and cotton draw-string waist. It has been filled with down and tamboured around its width in wavy lines. Purchased in Benalla by the museum, the label on the petticoat identifies it as having come from Booth & Fox's, Dublin, 1865. Ref 1356

PHOTOGRAPHY DENNIS HAYES.

Chiltern

The little town of Chiltern, originally known as Black Dog Creek, is situated midway between Wangaratta and Wodonga. It has retained much of its 19th century character and many of the original buildings remain just as they were during the gold rush of the 1850s. Several other charming historic towns, including Beechworth and Yackandandah, are located in the picturesque countryside nearby. There is a magnificent historical tapestry hung on permanent display at the Beechworth Visitor Information Centre.

Lake View Homestead
Victoria Street
Chiltern, VIC 3683.
Ph: (03) 5726 1317 Homestead.
(03) 5726 1459 After hours.
10.00a.m. – 4.00p.m. Saturday, Sunday, public and school holidays.
2 quilts.

Lake View Homestead was the childhood home of distinguished Australian author, Henry Handel Richardson, (the pseudonym used by Ethel Richardson). Ethel wrote eight novels during the late 19th century, the most famous of which was 'The Getting of Wisdom.' Following her father's death, Ethel's mother was forced to sell the family home and possessions, and because Lake View had always been renowned for its elegance and beauty the townspeople flocked to the auction. Ninety years later when the National Trust purchased the property, many of those who owned items from the Richardson auction, donated them to the Trust to furnish the house authentically. There are two large embroidered pictures, several rag rugs, and four cross stitch samplers, the earliest dated 1805 and made by a ten year old child. There are also two old and beautiful hand knitted bedspreads.

✷ The quilts are permanently displayed within the house and may be seen during the opening hours listed.

✂ The two patchwork quilts at Lake View Homestead were donated to the National Trust and the makers are unknown. The single bed quilt now displayed on the old iron cot is believed to be of English origin and dates from the 1830s. It has been made by hand from printed cotton dress fabrics in a Tumbling Block design and is framed by borders of strips and Squares-on-point. It has a backing of cream cotton and has been finely hand quilted in an all-over chevron design, each row of tiny zig-zag stitches only 7.5 cm apart.

The second quilt of double bed size has been made from hexagon rosettes and is believed to date from the mid 20th century. It was recently discovered underneath a mattress where it had obviously remained hidden for many years. It has been stitched by hand over paper templates and the fabrics are silks, satins, cottons and cotton sateens. It has been edged with burgundy satin and the original backing of brown silk has been covered by an old pink bedspread, probably to provide additional warmth.

Euroa

Euroa is set in the lovely Goulburn Valley, a half hour drive from Benalla. Settled by pastoralists during the 1830s, the town prospered during the gold rush as a supply centre for prospectors making their way to the diggings. In 1878 the notorious Kelly gang held up the National Bank, escaping with two thousand pounds and enticing the bank manager's wife to note that Ned was 'much better-looking' than his police description implied.

Farmers Arms Hotel Museum
25 Kirkland Avenue
Euroa, VIC 3666.
Ph: (03) 5795 2927 or (03) 5795 2064
1.00p.m. – 4.00p.m. Friday to Monday, public and school holidays.
Other times by appointment.
3 quilts.

The Museum has a large collection of period clothing which is exhibited in the 'Dress Room.' It includes wedding and evening gowns, christening dresses, nighties, camisoles, and heirloom underwear.

✷ The quilts are permanently displayed within the Museum and may be seen during the hours listed or at other times by appointment.

✂ These quilts provide an indication of the enduring popularity of the hexagon style. They were all created in Victoria by different makers at different times.

A beautiful quilt of Grandmother's Flower Garden design was made in 1932 by members of the local branch of the Country Women's Association. The work was inspired by the president of the group, Mrs Ian Currie, who taught the other members the traditional English method of piecing over paper templates. The quilt was finely hand stitched from beautiful chintz fabrics and when exhibited at the 1932 'State Home and Handcraft Exhibition' in Melbourne, it won a silver cup.

Another quilt of hexagons was made during the early 1900s by Mrs S. Hart of Strathbogie, near Euroa. This work was made in a pretty design of oval-shaped rows and was also a prize winning quilt.

An unfinished quilt of Grandmother's Flower Garden design was made by Mrs Helen Smith of Trawalla, near Ballarat. It features the embroidered date *'1896.'*

Milawa

The little village of Milawa is located in the picturesque countryside of north east Victoria, just a short drive from Wangaratta. It is the centre of a wonderful gourmet region renowned for its wine, home-made mustards, bread, cheeses, berry and nut farms.

Brown Brothers Winery
Bobinawarrah Road
Milawa, VIC 3678.
Ph: (03) 5727 3285
Viewing by appointment.
Approximately 12 quilts.

Brown Brothers is the perfect location for 'the man behind the quilter.' There are wine tastings at the cellar door and gourmet luncheons at the winery's Milawa Epicurean Centre. Just across the road, the corporate headquarters building provides a beautiful light-filled gallery in which many of June Brown's quilts are displayed.

✷ The quilts are hung on permanent display. Please telephone June in advance to arrange a suitable time.

✂ June is a prolific quiltmaker. Among the many quilts displayed at Brown Brothers are two works made in 1992 designed to tell the story of her family's winery and to celebrate its centenary.

Looking East depicts Mt Buffalo with green paddocks and layers of rich soil in the foreground. Trellised winter vines have been quilted over the strips and Pinot Noir grapes and leaves have been appliquéd around the border.

Looking West depicts the sun setting over the Warby Ranges, an old barn and St Paul's Church appliquéd to the centre. The two black vine leaves stitched to the foreground represent the frost of 1967 which completely blackened the vineyard. Appliquéd Sauvignon Blanc grapes and leaves feature around the border. Made from cotton fabrics, the quilts were hand and machine pieced, hand appliquéd and quilted. Details were added using hand painting and machine embroidery.

ABOVE: *Yarrawonga Community Quilt.* Made by the Yarrawonga-Mulwala Community with Susan Mathews, 1994. Collection Yarrawonga-Mulwala Pioneer Museum, Mulwala, Victoria.

Yarrawonga and Mulwala

The twin towns of Yarrawonga and Mulwala are set on the banks of the Murray River, a one hour drive from Albury and Wodonga. Picturesque Lake Mulwala stretches 15 kilometres east beyond Yarrawonga. Its banks are lined with towering red gums which create a haven for birds and wildlife as well as forming the focal point of recreation for the towns. A rich agricultural region of orchards, sheep, wheat and dairy farms, it is known as 'Sun Country' because of its beautiful climate.

Yarrawonga-Mulwala Pioneer Museum
151 Melbourne Street
Mulwala, VIC 3730.
Ph: (03) 5744 1402 Mrs Jacye Symes,
Easter to Christmas:
1.30p.m. – 5.00p.m. Wednesday to Sunday, public and school holidays.
Christmas to Easter:
9.30a.m. – 1.00p.m. Wednesday to Saturday, public and school holidays.
1.30p.m. – 5.00p.m. Sunday.
Other times for groups by arrangement.

The Museum collection includes displays of early farming, sport, and hobby activities, as well as toys dating back to the last century. There are two cross stitch samplers brought to Australia from England by Mary Webster c.1850.

✷ The quilt is hung on permanent display and may be seen during opening hours or by arrangement.

✂ This quilt (249cm x 284cm) was designed by Susan Mathews and made by members of the Yarrawonga-Mulwala community in 1994. Inspired by an aerial view of the town, it depicts Lake Mulwala as the focal point. It was made from 4,223 triangles pieced together by machine using the traditional American pattern with the appropriate name of Lady of the Lake. Photographs of important sites and activities were transferred to fabric and included amongst the triangles. They require close inspection to find, a deliberate feature of the design so that the more you look into the quilt, the more you will see. All the fabrics were dyed by hand and as the triangles were cut they were pinned onto two large design boards before being stitched. The work was machine quilted using metallic, rayon and invisible nylon threads.

Corryong

Corryong is set high in the mountains of Victoria's alpine country and is approximately 125 kilometres from Albury. It was here that Banjo Paterson met the legendary Jack Riley, an Irish immigrant whose tales of droving and hunting brumbies reputedly inspired the writing of one of Australia's favourite ballads, *The Man from Snowy River.*

The Man from Snowy River Museum
103 – 105 Hanson Street
Corryong, VIC 3707.
Ph: (02) 6076 1114 or (02) 6076 1363
or (02) 6076 1089
10.00a.m. – 12 noon and
2.00p.m. – 4.00p.m. everyday.
Other times by appointment.

The museum collection includes some beautiful items of period clothing made in London for the wedding of Miss Eliza Langhorn in 1818. There is an exquisite dress of pink and green striped silk with detachable sleeves and cape. It was brought to Australia by her daughter, Elizabeth, who wore it at her own wedding at Sutton Grange in 1857. Also displayed is Eliza's sun bonnet, a boned silk bodice, silk slippers, night cap and walking shoes.

✱ The quilt is framed and hangs on permanent display within the museum. The cushion cover is also permanently exhibited and may be seen during the hours listed or by appointment.

✂ This beautiful quilt of Tumbling Blocks was made in Carmarthen, Wales, by Miss Harriet Dixie c.1825. In 1831 Harriet married John Waters and the couple had four sons. Years later, following the death of John, Harriet re-married and the dislike felt by her sons towards their step-father led the boys to leave Wales. Edward and John migrated to Canada, Alexander and Thomas to Australia. Harriet died in 1856 and the quilt was sent to Thomas and his wife Alice who lived on a property named 'Gravels Plain' near Corryong.

A variety of silk, satin and brocade fabrics were used to create the quilt. It has no backing and many of the paper templates still remain behind the patches. The templates had been cut from docket books formerly used for the Great Northern Railway on which the famous steam train, the 'Flying Scotsman,' travelled north from London. The quilt remained with the family until 1980 when Harriet's granddaughter, Miss Winnifred Waters, donated it to the museum.

A tiny patchwork cushion (23cm square) was created from gold printed cigar band ribbons by a member of the Waters family c.1900. At this time, silk was relatively inexpensive and bundles of fine cigars were packaged using bright silk ribbon printed with the name of the manufacturing company. They were frequently collected to make cushion and table covers, as well as quilts. The ribbons used in this cushion have been stitched together by hand using feather stitch.

Bright

Bright is nestled in the foothills of the Victorian Alps about an hour's drive from Wodonga. During the 1930s, the local community planted hundreds of deciduous trees and today the poplars, himmalayan cedars, pin oaks, Dutch and English elms provide a spectacular display during Autumn. Bright is also a popular tourist destination because of its close proximity to the Victorian snow fields, excellent trout fishing and bush walking.

Alpine Shire Council
Churchill Avenue
Bright, VIC 3741.
Ph:(03) 5755 0555 Fax: (03) 5755 1811
9.00a.m. – 5.00p.m. Monday to Friday.

✱ The quilt is hung on permanent display in the Shire Council Chambers. Visitors are welcome to see it during office hours. It is advisable to ring in advance to ensure the Chambers are not in use.

✂ This quilt (289cm x 198cm) was made in 1988 by members of the Ovens Valley Patchwork and Quilters Group. It was created as a commemorative work of art for the Bicentennial. Designed and co-ordinated by Elaine Splatt, the focal point is a pictorial circle which depicts the rugged beauty of Mt Buffalo and the tree clad Ovens Valley. Swirling out from the circle is a progression of the history, people and activities that have taken place between 1788 and 1988. Sepia coloured fabrics add to the feeling of time passing through two centuries of history. The quilt was appliquéd, embroidered and quilted by hand.

Bright Historical Museum
Cnr Station Street and Railway Avenue
Bright, VIC 3741.
Ph: (03) 5755 1405 Historical Society.
2.00p.m. – 4.00p.m. Sundays
and school holidays between
September and May.
Other times by arrangement.

The museum collection includes examples of lacework, beading, cross stitch samplers, and costumes. There is a hand made christening gown, and a dress acquired from a local shop c.1880.

✷ The quilt is hung on permanent display and may be seen during opening hours or by arrangement.

✂ This quilt of random hexagon rosettes was created by Mrs Rene Rayner of Porepunkah, a few kilometres north west of Bright. Her husband, George, was a farmer and blacksmith, and Rene worked as a teacher at the Porepunkah School between 1917 and 1920. The quilt is believed to have been made during the 1930s and was stitched by hand over paper templates from printed cotton fabrics.

ABOVE: Detail of *Quilt of Tumbling Blocks*. Made by Harriet Dixie, c.1825.
BELOW LEFT: *Cushion Cover of Cigar Band Ribbons*. Made by a member of the Waters Family, c.1900. Collection The Man from Snowy River Museum, Corryong, Victoria.

Omeo

The secluded little town of Omeo is approximately 110 kilometres from Bright and a 40 minute drive from Mt Hotham. The discovery of gold during the 1850s drew thousands of miners to the area and most of the historic buildings remaining in the town today date from this period.

Omeo Historical Museum
Old Court House
Day Avenue
Omeo, VIC 3898.
Ph: (03) 5159 1550 or (03) 5159 1445
10.00a.m. – 2.00p.m. Saturday, Sunday
and public holidays.
Other times by appointment.

The museum is housed in the small court house c.1861 in which Alfred Howitt lived and presided as the first Magistrate of Omeo. The collection includes examples of drawn thread work, embroidered doyleys, a century old christening gown and other clothing.

✷ The quilt is permanently displayed and may be seen during opening hours or by appointment.

✂ A quilt of gathered hexagons (175cm x 195cm) was made c.1915 by Ada and Mary Pendergast. John and Elizabeth Pendagast married in 1868 and lived on their property 'Pender's Court' with their two sons and seven daughters, including Ada and Mary. The girls made the quilt from bleached flour bags which probably came from the old flour mill in Omeo. Each 'snow flake' was created by ruching a large hexagon over a smaller one and whip stitching the two together. A Pendergast relative still living in the town today, remembers 'the Pender girls' making little white puffs during the early years of World War I. The work was always referred to as the *Snow Quilt*.

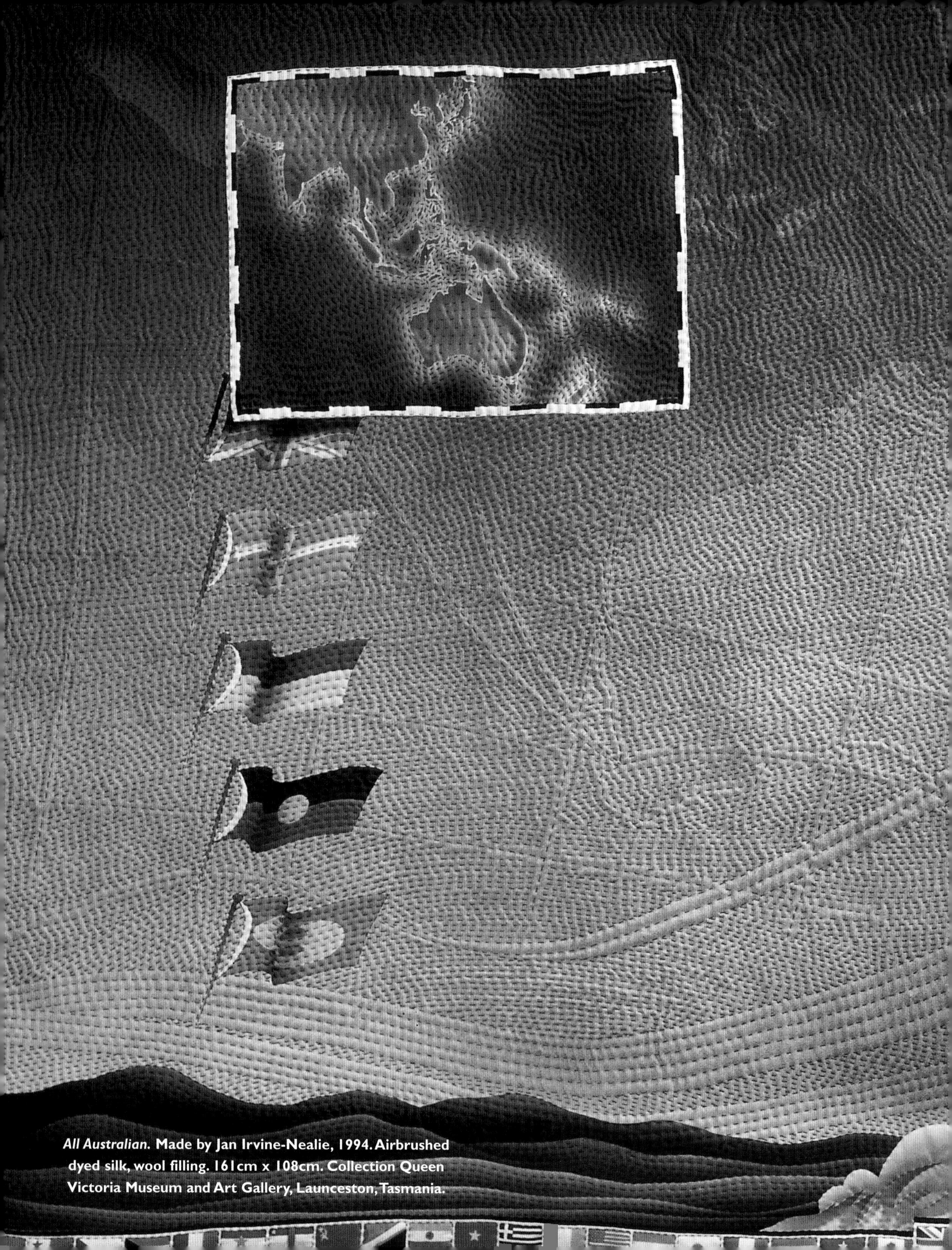

All Australian. **Made by Jan Irvine-Nealie, 1994. Airbrushed dyed silk, wool filling. 161cm x 108cm. Collection Queen Victoria Museum and Art Gallery, Launceston, Tasmania.**

QUILTS OF
TASMANIA

Hobart and Nearby Regions

The charming maritime city of Hobart was established in 1804 on the picturesque harbour of the Derwent River. During the early days it developed as a base for whalers and sailors as well as a ship building centre for the colonies. Much of the early character of the city has been preserved. The hilly area of Battery Point was first settled by fishermen and seafarers and its charming higgledy-piggledy lanes remain little changed from the 1830s and 40s. The buildings range from stately homes and historic pubs to tiny fishermen's cottages like those lining the village green of Arthur's Circus. There are numerous galleries, antique shops and restaurants. The National Trust conducts heritage walking tours every Saturday morning. Telephone (03) 6223 7371.

The Tasmanian Museum and Art Gallery

40 Macquarie Street
Hobart, TAS 7001.
Ph: (03) 6235 0777 Fax: (03) 6234 7139
10.00a.m. – 5.00p.m. daily.
Closed Christmas Day, Good Friday and Anzac Day.
3 quilts, appliquéd panels, and skin rugs.

The Tasmanian Museum and Art Gallery is located in the wharf area of Constitution Dock, just a short walk from the centre of the city. It is housed in a group of buildings which include three of the oldest remaining structures in Hobart. The collection of needlework encompasses items from the earliest days of the colony until the present and representing the prevailing fashions of each period. All the known social history has been recorded for each item and many provide a fascinating glimpse into the lives of their makers and the times in which they were created. There is also a large collection of craft magazines and other sources of patterns and designs.

✷ A Textile Study Room has been established to enable visitors to see items that are not currently on display. Please contact the Curator of Decorative Arts one week in advance.

✂ A delightful quilt of nursery rhymes (140cm x 93cm) was made in Sydney by Amy Amelia Earl in 1925. It was donated to the Gallery by her great niece, Margaret Kent, who remembers it being in constant use during her childhood. Amy was born in 1867 in Dronfield, Derbyshire, the daughter of Hennson and Mary Earl. She loved needlework from an early age and Margaret still has a cross stitch sampler made in 1880 and signed *'Amy Earl Aged 13 Years.'* Amy emigrated to Australia in 1883, settling first in Queensland but later moving to the Sydney suburb of Concord where the quilt was made.

Created for a loved child, it was used as a cot cover and play rug and depicts stories that have been favourites with children for many generations. They include *Little Miss Muffet, Puss in Boots, Hey Diddle Diddle, Baa Baa Black Sheep* and *There was an Old Woman who lived in a Shoe.* The scenes have been stitched in naive style and then applied to a background of Crazy patches cut from wool and cotton. Many of the motifs have been appliquéd using buttonhole stitch, others have been worked in cross stitch, and each patch has been outlined in coloured embroidery.

Numerous animals and birds feature among the stories and include an Australian kangaroo, emu, koala, and a parrot copied from the Arnott's Biscuit logo. This logo was very well known at the time and its motto *'Honesty is the best policy'* was symbolised by the parrot on his T-shaped perch – *'On his T is the best pol (parrot) I see.'* Margaret remembers her mother frequently drawing attention to these words as a good example by which to live. An image of King George V affirms the strong ties that still existed between Australia and Britain.

The work has a filling of hessian and has been finished with a gathered frill. Much of the appliqué has been padded and buttons have been used for eyes. The date and initials of the maker *'A.E. May 1925'* have been embroidered to a patch in the foreground. This delightful verse accompanies an appliquéd cat shown from the rear and peering back over his shoulder at the words:

'If ye want a thing
And can't have a thing
Turn your back on a thing.'

One of the country's most significant historical quilts, the remarkable *Fan Quilt,* (224cm x 228cm) was made in Tasmania by an unknown but skilled needlewoman in 1888. It is possible that a letter stitched within the large central medallion may present a clue. It has been embroidered with the name *'Miss Blyth'* along with her Tasmanian address of *'Formby,'* now West Devonport. Another inscription has the words *'Tina worked this,'* indicating that the maker was probably given some of the patches by friends or family members.

The quilt features an eclectic mix of motifs reflecting the life and customs in Australia at the time of its making. A dated inscription commemorates the Queen's Jubilee of 1888. Our allegiance to Britain is also reflected in the Prince of Wales feathers appliquéd to the centre. Australia was to celebrate the

ABOVE: *Embroidered and Quilted Rug*. Possibly made by Miss Blyth, 1888. 224cm x 228cm. Collection Tasmanian Museum and Art Gallery, Hobart, Tasmania.

centenary of European settlement the following year and numerous Australian motifs of wattle, gum leaves and flags are also included.

Dominant within the design is the Victorian love of oriental decoration and the social importance of 'the fan'. The appliquéd border features countless examples of this essential accessory which not only formed part of most social occasions of the day, but could also be used to indicate many different emotions. Quite possibly the quiltmaker saw the comical side to the language of fans. Certainly the depiction of two children playing grown ups with the caption *'Domestic Bliss,'* indicates her sense of humour. The work has been

finely appliquéd and embroidered by hand. Its lining of red twill is machine quilted in a diamond pattern.

An Hmong Story Quilt entitled the *People of Laos* was made in 1990 by Lou Xiong. Lou was born in Laos in 1955. She came to Hobart from a refugee camp in Thailand where members of her family still remain. Traditionally it is the men who draw the designs for the Story Quilts and the women who complete the stitchery. Lou was taught to sew by her mother. Her work is set on a fabric map of Laos and depicts the three unique groups of Hmong people, each group differentiated by the colours of white, green and blue. The quilt is accompanied by samples of prairie points, reverse appliqué and other techniques used by the artist in its creation.

The collection also includes a series of large appliquéd and embroidered altar panels originating from St John the Baptist Church, Hobart. One of the panels has been made from the Cathedral Window pattern, its circular effect created from folded and re-folded squares. There are also several skin rugs made from the pelts of emu, possum and platypus.

RIGHT: *Nursery Rhyme Quilt.* Made by Amy Amelia Earl, 1925. Presented by Mrs Margaret Kent. 140cm x 93cm. Collection Tasmanian Museum and Art Gallery, Hobart, Tasmania.

May
AE

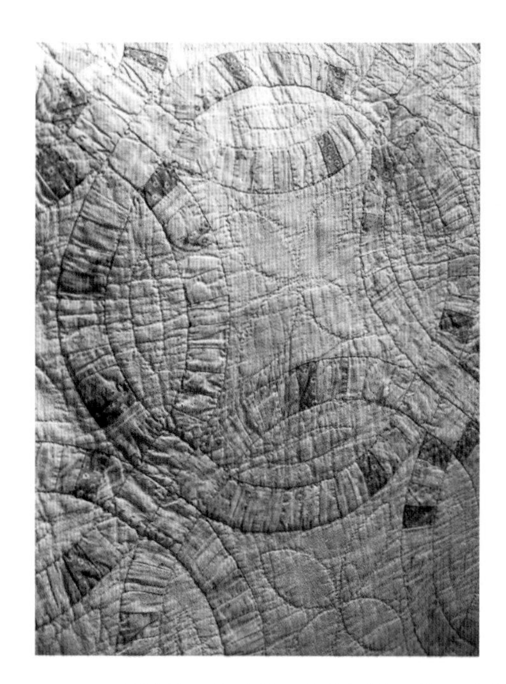

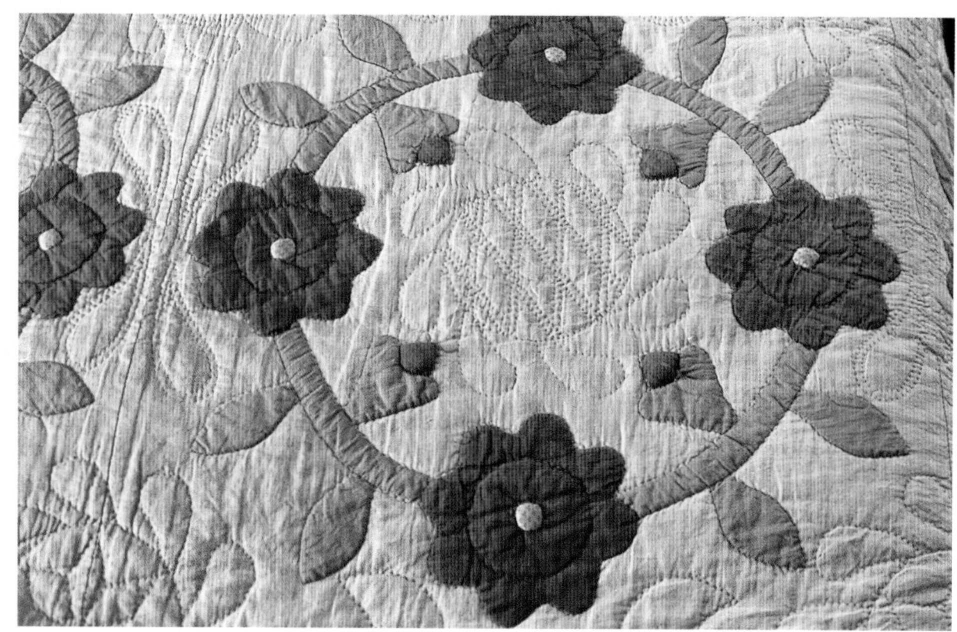

LEFT: Detail of *Double Wedding Ring Quilt*. Unknown Maker, c.1930. RIGHT: Detail of *Wreath of Roses Quilt*. Unknown Maker, c.1860. Collection Narryna Heritage Museum, Battery Point, Tasmania.

Migrant Resource Centre (South Tasmania) Inc.
49 Molle Street
Hobart, TAS 7000.
Ph: (03) 6234 9411 Fax: (03) 6231 1264
9.00a.m. – 5.00p.m. Monday to Friday.
3 panels.

The Resource Centre provides settlement support services to newly arrived migrants and refugees. It is located on the second floor of the building.

✷ The wall hanging is permanently displayed in the entrance foyer and may be seen during opening hours.

✂ A wall hanging entitled *Women of the World – Flowers of the World* was designed by Woodbridge artist Anna Maria Magnus. It was made in 1991 by women from more than seventeen different countries. Many could not speak English so that much of the communication was done in sign language. The work was divided into three separate panels (each one 54cm x 180cm) which symbolised the coming together of diversity within the city of Hobart. Using flowers as symbols, one side represented tropical areas of the world, the other side temperate regions, with the middle panel featuring Hobart. Techniques used to create the hanging included appliqué, embroidery, needlepoint and quilting.

Narryna Heritage Museum
103 Hampden Road
Battery Point, TAS 7000.
Ph: (03) 6234 2791
10.30a.m. – 5.00p.m. Tuesday to Friday.
2.00p.m. – 5.00p.m. Saturday, Sunday and public holidays.
Closed Christmas Day, Good Friday, Anzac Day and the month of July.
3 quilts, plus several smaller patchwork items.

Narryna was the first folk museum to be established in Australia. Its setting is a beautiful Georgian house built from local sandstone and brick in 1834. Huge elm trees shade the property and there is a walled courtyard and an original coach house. The museum is dedicated to preserving and displaying the art, furniture, clothing and textiles of the period between 1803 and 1900. It contains one of the finest and most significant collections of colonial treasures in Australia. There are more than thirty cross stitch samplers, some of them dating from the 18th century. The costume collection includes 250 dresses, wedding gowns, period children's wear, and accessories. Needlepoint, embroidery, stump work, beaded cushions and pole screens are displayed throughout the house. In addition to the patchwork quilts, there are also four hand knitted bedspreads and several Crazy Patchwork cushions from the 1890s. The textiles are displayed on a rotational basis and special exhibitions involving particular themes are arranged throughout the year.

✷ All three quilts are permanently displayed and may be seen during opening hours. Mary Harper's quilt is

LEFT: *Wreath of Roses Quilt.* Unknown Maker, c.1860. Collection Narryna Heritage Museum, Battery Point, Tasmania. RIGHT: *Crazy Patchwork Quilt.* Unknown Maker, c.1890. 155cm x 155cm. Collection National Trust of Australia (Tasmania) – Runnymede, New Town.

hung in a glass case in the upstairs hall of Narryna. The other quilts cover antique beds in the Cedar Bedroom.

✂ A lovely medallion quilt was made in County Dublin, Ireland, by Mary Harper c.1830. It travelled to Australia with Mary when she and her husband came to live in Van Diemen's Land in 1851. The central medallion of the quilt has been created from hexagon rosettes in softly coloured cotton fabrics of the period. Successive rows of Nine Patch blocks, strips and diamonds have been hand pieced and used to frame the centre. The work has been made using the English method over paper templates and some of the papers still remain in place.

An appliquéd quilt of unknown maker has been created in the traditional Wreath of Roses design and dates from the 1860s. It has been made from blocks, each one featuring roses and rosebuds applied to a background of cream cotton. The flowers have been padded to give a dimensional effect and a border of leaves and buds has been added around the edge. The appliqué has been shadow quilted by hand and circular motifs have been worked within the wreaths. The block design of the quilt, as well as the colours and quilting pattern, indicate that it is probably American in origin. Despite being more than a century old, it has been beautifully preserved and it seems likely that the quiltmaker always reserved the work 'for best.'

A quilt of Double Wedding Ring design was created by an unknown maker c.1930. This work is also likely to be of American origin. Controversy surrounds the beginnings of this pattern though quilt historians are generally of the view that it was not made prior to 1900. Certainly, it was one of the most popular and frequently made quilt designs in America during the 1920s and '30s. This quilt has been created from pretty pink, blue and yellow dress prints typical of the '30s era and has a scalloped border. It has been outline quilted and has a four petalled flower in the centre of each ring.

New Town

New Town was one of the first village settlements to be established on the outskirts of Hobart. Today it is an inner suburb located only a few minutes drive north of the city centre.

Runnymede
61 Bay Road
New Town, TAS 7008.
Ph: (03) 6278 1269 Fax: (03) 6278 1269
10.00a.m. – 4.30p.m. Monday to Friday.
12 noon – 4.30p.m. weekends.
Closed Christmas Day, Good Friday
and the month of July.
2 quilts.

The lovely colonial home of Runnymede was built in 1836 for Robert Pitcairn, the first lawyer to qualify in the colony and a leading advocate for the abolition of transportation. Captain Charles Bayley purchased the house in 1864 and named it 'Runnymede' after his favourite ship. The Captain's descendants lived in the house until it was acquired by the Government in 1967. It has since been restored and furnished by the National Trust to depict a gentleman's residence of the period 1840 to 1860. The picturesque grounds overlook New Town Bay and Risdon. The collection includes some beautiful examples of 'ladies' leisure pastimes' such as bobbin lace making, patchwork and tapestry. There are also 19th century toys and dolls and two cross stitch samplers, one of them made by a member of the Bayley family and dated '1791'.

✷ Both quilts are permanently displayed in Runnymede – the Crazy quilt in the Library and the child's sampler in the Morning Room. They may be seen during opening hours. It would be appreciated if groups would contact the Supervisor a few days before visiting.

✂ A Crazy quilt (155cm x 155cm) of unknown maker dates from the late 19th century. It has been created from richly coloured silk, brocade, moire and taffeta fabrics with a wide border of red velvet. Each random patch has been heavily embroidered using a diverse range of stitches. Spiders, horse shoes and other motifs have been added for additional decorative effect.

An unfinished patchwork quilt (85cm x 89cm) is believed to have been created by a child around the turn of the century. It consists of small squares of silk, satin and velvet, each one embroidered by hand with a variety of motifs, many of them floral designs. The squares have been appliquéd with blanket stitch onto a white cotton background. A large central square features an embroidered shield design with Latin motto and has been framed by a border of gold leaves.

Headway Day Care Centre
Alkoomi House
St John's Park
St John's Avenue
New Town, TAS 7008.
Ph: (03) 6228 8296
9.00a.m. – 4.00p.m. Monday to Friday.

Headway is a rehabilitation day care centre for victims of brain injury.

✷ The quilt is permanently displayed in the recreation room of Alkoomi House. Visitors are welcome. Please contact the centre a day in advance.

✂ A patchwork quilt of Variable Star design (150cm x 210cm) was made by the Huonville Quilters between 1989 and '90. It was donated to the new Headway organisation as a wall hanging for their refurbished building. The quilt was pieced by hand from squares and triangles, the stars being created from dark fabrics, the Four Patch blocks from medium fabrics, and the background from light tones. The work was hand quilted using outline stitching to surround each star and a double cable pattern for the border.

Also in Hobart

A pictorial tapestry of the city was created to celebrate the Bicentennial by members of the Embroiderers' Guild of Tasmania. It may be seen in the reception room of the Town Hall, Macquarie Street.

Bellerive

Bellerive and Rosny Park are suburbs of the Clarence Municipality which is located on the eastern shore of the Derwent River directly opposite Hobart. This is a 10 to 15 minute drive across the Tasman Bridge from the centre of the city.

Originally named Kangaroo Point, Bellerive was settled during the 1820s and many of the earliest buildings still remain. A delightful heritage walk explaining the history of some of the properties has been prepared by the City of Clarence.

Bellerive Community Arts Centre
The Old Watch House
17 Cambridge Road
Bellerive Village, TAS 7018.
Ph: (03) 6245 8742
10.00a.m. – 3.00p.m. weekdays.
3 quilts and 2 arpilleras.

In 1975 the Tasman Bridge collapsed after being rammed by a ship. This disaster meant that the suburbs on the eastern shore were cut off from the cultural centres of Hobart. The need for residents to have access to the arts became vital and the Bellerive Community Arts Centre was established in response. There is now an inspiring programme of changing activities, workshops, and exhibitions. The Arts Centre is based in the original Old Watch House which was built in 1842. The many lives of this lovely heritage building have been depicted on one of the quilts.

✷ The quilts are hung on permanent display within the Arts Centre. The building is in use most days but it is advisable to ring in advance. Weekend access is also possible.

✂ *A Stitch in Time* (176cm x 127cm) was designed by Judith Andrewartha in 1986 during her period as Artist-in-Residence at the Centre. It records the history of the Old Watch House building from the early planning stages to the 1980s, illustrating its many uses over 150 years. Even the original drawings made by the Director of Public Works in 1841 have been included. Appliquéd representations show the various alterations and additions made over time as the building served first as a watch house, then as a council, police office, library, and arts centre. The quilt also records the cursive handwriting that still remains clearly discernible on an old wooden door. *'Hedley Westbrook, son of Thomas Westbrook who built and gave the Hall of the Postal Institute to the people of Bellerive, 24 May 1867. Inclosed the door with plywood 1 May 1945. H.W.'* A gum tree represents a man named Stan Hill who continued to teach oil painting until well into his nineties. Techniques used in the making of the quilt included fabric painting, crayon and pen work, machine piecing, hand appliqué and hand quilting.

The Bellerive Arpillera (181cm x 110cm) was created by members of the Arts Centre in June 1991. It was made during a workshop with Chilean born artist, Elena Gallegos who introduced the group to the traditional appliquéd pictures or arpilleras of Chile. She told them stories of the women who had used this form of folk art to depict their lives under the Pinochet regime, bringing them to life with tiny figures. The arpilleras had helped the women to deal with their unresolved grief. Sometimes they chose to include fabrics cut from the clothes of missing relatives.

The Bellerive Arpillera also featured numerous little figures with each member of the group making a small doll of themselves. The charming background was designed to include a floor plan of the Arts Centre building. The rock wall in the courtyard garden was embellished with Suffolk Puff flowers and other cottage plants cut from floral prints. The board walk around the bay and the old shops of Bellerive Village were added to the foreground. At the conclusion of the

PHOTOGRAPHY GEOFF LEA.

ABOVE: *The Bellerive Arpillera.* Made by members of the Bellerive Community Arts Centre, 1991. 181cm x 110cm. Collection Bellerive Community Arts Centre, Bellerive Village, Tasmania.

ABOVE: Detail from the *Bellerive Arpillera.* Made by members of the Bellerive Community Arts Centre, 1991. 181cm x 110cm. Collection Bellerive Community Arts Centre, Tasmania.

workshop all the pieces were pinned together. Jill Cartwright then spent several weeks piecing the background by hand, stitching the figures to the scene and binding the edges.

Members of the Arts Centre wanted to help the women of Chile and were advised that the best means of doing this was to buy some of their work. During the next eighteen months a total of seventy eight arpilleras were purchased, including one to display at the Arts Centre. Depicting a Chilean community, it shows children going to school, women shopping at market stalls, a child on a swing, bread being baked. The sun shines on people who have survived harsh times and worked hard to restore dignity to their lives. Arpilleras are still available and may be ordered from Fundacion Solidaridad, Jose Miguel de la Barra # 456, Santiago, Chile. Fax: 56-2-6327532

A silk wall quilt entitled *Our Place* (150cm x 150cm) was made in 1992 following a visit to Hobart by Susan Clifford, the director of *Common Ground.* This British organisation works to prevent further loss or destruction of natural and cultural heritage by encouraging communities to work with artists in order to express the value of local places. A silk painting workshop held at the Arts Centre continued this theme. Nine of the resulting illustrations created by members depicted their own 'special places' and were pieced together to form a quilt. A huge sunflower beside a picket fence was painted from childhood memories of a Perth backyard. A view through a kitchen window showed the garden and beyond, to *'where the bandicoots play and black cockatoos screech.'* An image of a little shack at Port Arthur evoked twenty five years of holiday memories. Another cottage was described as *'the place of family, friends, neighbours and security – the happiest times and the saddest times.'* The pictures were pieced together by machine and hand quilted. All the stories were transferred to fabric and sewn to the backing.

Rosny Park

Rosny Park overlooks Kangaroo Bay towards Hobart and Mt Wellington, the scene depicted in the *Kangaroo Bay Quilt*. Here, adjacent to the Clarence City Council Chambers is the Rosny Historic Centre. This complex includes the Rosny Barn c.1815 with its displays illustrating the history of the area from the beginning of white settlement. There is also the Schoolhouse Gallery and an original cottage furnished to recreate the atmosphere of a Tasmanian home early this century. The Gallery provides a venue for changing exhibitions of community and contemporary art.

Clarence City Council Chambers
Bligh Street
Rosny Park, TAS 7018.
Ph: (03) 6245 8640 Fax: (03) 6245 8700
Mayor's Secretary.
(03) 6245 8600 Council Chambers.
8.30a.m. – 5.15p.m. Monday to Friday.
2 quilts.

✱ Both quilts are hung on permanent display – the *Kangaroo Bay Quilt* in the Mayor's Suite, the *City of Clarence Heritage Quilt* in the Council Chambers. They may be seen during office hours. It is advisable to ring the Mayor's Secretary before visiting to ensure the Chambers are not in use.

ABOVE: *Kangaroo Bay Quilt.* Made by members of the Bellerive Community Arts Centre, 1993. 102cm x 152cm. Clarence City Council Chambers, Rosny Park, Tasmania.

✂ *The Kangaroo Bay Quilt* (102cm x 152cm) was made in 1993 as a Tasmanian Arts Council project by members of the Bellerive Community Arts Centre. It was created during a week long workshop held with Judy Turner as Artist-in-Residence. Entitled *Special Places*, the project began with photographs being taken of the landscape around Bellerive. These were submitted to Judy in advance so that she could select the most suitable. The picture chosen depicted Kangaroo Bay at sunset with Mt. Wellington in the background. The pink and gold afterglow was shown reflected in the shimmering water of the river. It was perfect for interpretation into a quilt using Judy's special techniques of strip piecing and blending of colours.

Hundreds of fabrics were cut into strips and colour graded on a trestle table to create a palette from which to work. Using a graphed drawing of the scene together with the photograph, the strips were pinned onto flannelette, gradually building up the picture. It took several days of careful sewing to join them all together. Plain and printed fabrics were chosen to relate to the various design elements, particularly the hills, the sky and the bay. Dappled fabrics proved to be an inspired choice for the little boats on the river because they gave the impression of water reflections on the hulls. Once the scene had been completed, it was squared and trimmed before having a dark fabric border added on all sides. Finally, the work was machine quilted using wavy lines which softened the strip piecing and helped in the creation of a shimmering effect on the surface. The names of all contributors were sewn to the back.

The City of Clarence Heritage Quilt (200cm x 250cm) was made in 1988 by members of the Bellerive Community Arts Centre to celebrate the Bicentenary. The group was awarded a grant from the Council to create a quilt which represented the diversity of the municipality.

ABOVE AND OPPOSITE: *The Hobart Arpillera*. Made by members of the Risdon Vale Neighbourhood House, 1992. 88cm x 116cm. Risdon Vale Neighbourhood House, Risdon Vale, Tasmania.

Designed as a pictorial medallion, the work features a map of the region in the centre making it easy to follow the locations of every landmark included. Diverse views depict St Matthews Church, the Seven Mile Beach, the wreck of the *Otago* and the charming rose-covered facade of Lauriston Cottage. Most of the blocks were appliquéd and embroidered by hand. Others were hand painted. They were joined together with blue and yellow sashing and finished with hand quilting.

Risdon Vale

Risdon Vale is a 20 minute drive north of Bellerive. The Neighbourhood House and the Community Health Centre are situated beside the main shopping centre. A series of murals may be seen on the outside walls of the Community Centre, as well as shop fronts, the bus stop and other nearby sites. These were painted by women from the Neighbourhood House under the guidance of local artist, Caz Rodwell.

Risdon Vale Neighbourhood House
Sugarloaf Road,
Risdon Vale, TAS 7016.
Ph: (03) 6243 5752
10.00a.m. – 3.00p.m. weekdays.

✷ The work is hung on permanent display in the creche room and may be seen during the hours listed or at other times by appointment.

✄ This lively arpillera (88cm x 116cm) was made by a group of nine women

from the Risdon Vale Neighbourhood House in 1992. It was created during a workshop held with Jill Cartwright and was inspired by the appliquéd folk art pictures of Chile.

The work provides a whimsical glimpse of the small and beautiful city of Hobart. It captures its maritime atmosphere as well as the dominance of Mount Wellington on both the life and landscape. It features several quaint old houses from Battery Point, and just below them, Salamanca Place, its restored warehouses dating back to the days of sailing ships. The Botanic Gardens, city buildings and wharf area fill the centre, the Antarctic supply ship *Icebird* preparing for its next expedition. Towering over them all is the snow-tipped mountain, a bushfire raging on its lower slopes as a reminder of the ever present nightmare of summer. Little figures dot the countryside – walking, having a picnic, flying a kite. In the foreground the river is full of life. The big red yacht is first over the line in the Sydney to Hobart race. Like the traditional Chilean arpilleras, much of the appliquéd work was sewn to the background using buttonhole stitch. Each little figure was made individually from scraps of felt and cotton and then hand stitched in place. Tiny flowers were created in Broderie Perse appliqué and the work was finished with hand embroidery and quilting.

In the Nearby Region

The historic town of Bothwell is nestled in the beautiful Clyde River Valley, approximately 70 kilometres north of Hobart. Three tapestry wall hangings were made as a Bicentennial project by members of the local community. They now hang on permanent display in the Bothwell Historical Society Centre, Market Place. The Centre is open by appointment. Please contact Expressions of Interest Art Gallery. Telephone (03) 6259 5775.

PHOTOGRAPHY GEOFF LEA.

ABOVE: *Woodbridge Sesquicentenary Quilt.* Made by the West Winds Craft Group, 1995-'96. 3m x 2m. West Winds Community Centre, Woodbridge, Tasmania. OPPOSITE: Details of the quilt depicting the little village at the base of Woodbridge Hill, the jetty jutting out into the bay, numerous craft on the water, the old church and graveyard.

Huonville

The riverside town of Huonville is located in the lovely Huon Valley, a 25 minute drive south west of Hobart. Steeped in history, the first pioneers were attracted to the region because of its magnificent forests. In time, the most productive apple orchards in the world were to be established here. The area has now diversified to include sheep, cattle, and vineyards producing cool climate vintages. Huonville, along with many of the other townships nearby, features craft galleries, heritage museums, numerous art and wood turning centres, and antique shops.

Huon Valley Council
40 Main Road
Huonville, TAS 7109.
Ph: (03) 6264 1211
8.30a.m. – 4.30p.m. Monday to Friday.

✷ The quilt is hung on display in the upstairs hallway of the building and may be seen during office hours.

✂ This quilt (120cm x 180cm) was made by the Huonville Quilters to celebrate the Bicentennial in 1988. The bold design was divided into three sections and created using the Stained Glass appliqué technique. The work was stitched by hand using cotton fabrics in vibrant colours.

Woodbridge

The little seaside town of Woodbridge is located on the eastern shore of the boot shaped peninsula that extends south from Hobart and is encircled by the Channel Highway. The D'Entrecasteaux Channel separates it from Bruny Island and a regular ferry service from the nearby town of Kettering takes visitors back and forth. For many decades the waterways provided the only link with Hobart Town and the rest of the world. The early settlers became skilled in the construction of boats of all kinds, and this tradition has continued to the present day. Despite its close proximity to the city, it is still very much a rural area dotted with picturesque orchards and coastal farms. Many artists and craftspeople have made the region their home and their work can be seen in Hobart galleries.

West Winds Community Centre
3528 Channel Highway
Woodbridge, TAS 7162.
Ph: (03) 6267 4713 during school terms.
(03) 6267 4847 Caretaker during school holiday periods.
9.00a.m. – 3.00p.m. Monday, Tuesday and Thursday during school terms.
2 quilts.

The Community Centre is used for activities as diverse as line dancing, playgroup, wood chopping and weddings, and it was here that the Sesquicentenary Quilt was created. The building is located at the southern end of town, just past the school.

✷ The quilts are hung on permanent display within the Centre. During school term time they may be seen between the hours listed. During school holiday periods please contact the Caretaker at least 24 hours in advance.

POLICE
CALTEX

✂ The *Woodbridge Sesquicentenary Quilt* (3m x 2m) was made by the West Winds Craft Group during 1995 and '96. This large community project was co-ordinated by local quiltmaker, Sue Domeney. The design was carefully planned in order to create a pictorial history which recorded the heritage of the past and preserved it for future generations. The region was settled in 1847 and for more than a century it remained an agricultural area of apple orchards, timber forests and scallop fishing. During the last twenty years many changes have taken place. Though the rural tranquillity still remains, most of the farms have been subdivided and more and more families have sought work in Hobart.

To capture the essence of the town the background of the quilt was hand painted to depict Woodbridge Hill. The little village was appliquéd around its base and featured many of the original buildings – the school house, the lovely old churches, the post office, police station, hotel, and bakery. The quilters added the ship building and fishing industries along the shore, the timber forests, orchards and dairy farms on the hilltop beyond the houses. A multitude of techniques and materials were used to bring the quilt to life. The trees and bushfire smoke were created from hand dyed fleece and felt. Ribbons, buttons, leather pieces, wooden fish, feathered birds, and even plastic flies and ants were incorporated. Hand and machine embroidery provided intricate detailing to many tiny appliquéd pieces and the work was completed with hand quilting.

A large quilted hanging depicting the region was made in 1992 by members of the Woodbridge community. The project was initiated by local artist, Heather Creet, and the design evolved during a three day workshop tutored by artists Lorraine Hepburn and Sylvia Parr. The work focused on the life of the village within its maritime setting. The many craft that use the D'Entrecasteaux Channel were included – small fishing boats, pleasure yachts, and the white Bruny Island Ferry on its journey across the bay. The village of Woodbridge was depicted in the foreground with the picturesque harbour of Kettering tucked into the next bay. The brown hill of Bruny Island formed the background, its narrow isthmus crossing the horizon and joining up to the dramatic green outcrop of the Hummock to the right.

Much of the work was made using the hand dyed fleece and felt that had been created during the workshop. Hand made ceramic pebbles, along with shells collected from Woodbridge beaches, were stitched along the shore lines. The appliqué, embroidery, and quilting were done entirely by hand.

Port Arthur

Port Arthur is located on the Tasman Peninsula just over an hour's drive south east of Hobart. Established in the 1830s, it became the sole penal settlement in Van Dieman's Land and was renowned for its harsh discipline. When transportation of convicts was finally abolished in 1853 the buildings were used to house paupers and lunatics. In recent years, the historic importance of the site has led to the undertaking of major conservation work. The fascinating buildings and ruins include several restored houses, a museum, church, as well as the penitentiary. Currently a sad addition is being planned. This building will be a memorial and lasting tribute to the victims of the shooting tragedy that took place at Port Arthur in April 1996.

Port Arthur Historic Site
Tasman Peninsula, TAS 7182.
Ph: (03) 6250 2363 Fax: (03) 6250 2494
9.00a.m. – 5.00p.m. everyday.
Please note that the *'Junior Medical Officer's Residence'* and *'Trentham'* are open daily, though the hours vary in winter and summer and you may wish to telephone in advance.
4 quilts.

✷ The hexagon patchwork quilt and the wallaby skin rug are displayed in the *'Junior Medical Officer's Residence,'* corner of Champ and Bond Streets. The Crazy quilts can be seen in *'Trentham'* located on the opposite corner.

✂ A quilt of Grandmother's Flower Garden design (204cm x 178cm) was made in 1985 by Vanny Jackson and Ann Piesse. The work was created using the English method over paper templates, the rosettes cut from multi-coloured prints and the background from plain white cotton.

A wallaby skin rug (210cm x 137cm) dating from the late 19th century was purchased as an appropriate bed covering for the 1850s interior of the *Junior Medical Officer's Residence.* Skins of many Australian animals were used by early colonists to make patchwork rugs, an idea they copied from the Aborigines. This wonderful example has a carmen felt backing and a pink scalloped edging.

Two Crazy Patchwork quilts were made by Rose Solomon in 1997. Satin, velvet, brocade and cotton fabrics were used for the random patches of the double bed quilt, each patch edged with feather stitch. The little cot quilt (98cm x 136cm) was created from embroidered doyleys, lace and pastel coloured cottons. The edge of each patch was finished with embroidery using a wide variety of stitches.

Queenstown

Historic Queenstown, situated in the heart of the West Coast, is surrounded by a unique lunar landscape of barren hills – the legacy of copper tailings and logging operations from the past. The township was established more than a century ago, along with dozens of other small villages hastily founded following the discovery of rich mineral deposits throughout the region. Some of the settlements were little more than shanties. Others like Queenstown, Rosebery and Zeehan were substantial towns built with the wealth acquired during the boom. The charming little coastal village of Strahan is just a short drive away. Once a busy port serving the timber and mining industries, today it is the departure point for cruises to the World Heritage Area of the Franklin Gordon Wild Rivers National Park.

Eric Thomas Galley Museum
Cnr. Driffield and Sticht Street
Queenstown, TAS 7467.
Ph: (03) 6471 1483
After hours: (03) 6471 1758
10.00a.m. – 4.30p.m. Monday to Friday.
1.00p.m. – 4.30p.m. Weekends.
Opening hours are extended to
6.00p.m. between October and March.

The Eric Thomas Galley Museum is housed in a century old building which had served as the original hotel during the early days. More than 1000 photographs collected by Thomas provide a permanent record of the history of the West Coast region. Many pictures depict the harsh realities of life for the mining pioneers and their families. Several illustrate the tragedy of 1912 when forty-two men died after being trapped underground in the wake of a fire at the North Lyell mine. In addition, there is an interesting collection of commemorative china dating from Queen Victoria's Jubilee in 1887. There are also examples of lace work, crochet, and embroidery. The period clothing includes heirloom nighties, underwear, christening dresses, wedding gowns and other fine costumes dating from the turn of the century.

✱ The quilt is hung on permanent display at the top of the stairs and may be seen during opening hours.

✂ This beautiful pictorial quilt (300cm x 90cm) was made by a group of craftswomen from Queenstown and Strahan in 1992. It was created during a six week workshop organised for West Coast communities by the Tasmanian Crafts Council and tutored by textile artist Elena Gallegos. The group were taught many new techniques and skills including silk painting, hand appliqué, embroidery and quilting.

Elena introduced them to arpilleras – the traditional folk art pictures of Chile. Under her direction they made the naive little figures that formed such a major feature of the arpilleras. These whimsical characters were used to depict the towns people in all manner of activities – working, mountain climbing, playing, enjoying festivities with balloons aloft. Each figure was created individually and then hand stitched into position. Along with many other motifs, they were padded in order to give extra dimension to the quilt.

Many Chilean arpilleras were made during times of political upheaval and alluded to the desperation and anxiety felt by families who had missing relatives. By documenting these events the works also formed historical records. The Queenstown quilt was similarly designed to capture the life and history of the

TOP: *Crazy Patchwork Cot Quilt.* Made by Rose Solomon, 1997. 98cm x 136cm. Collection Port Arthur Historic Site, Tasmania. ABOVE: *Wallaby Skin Rug.* Unknown Maker, c.1890. 210cm x 137cm. Collection Port Arthur Historic Site, Tasmania.

THIS PAGE AND OPPOSITE: Details from *The Queenstown Quilt.* Made by Craftswomen from Queenstown and Strahan, 1992. 300cm x 90cm. Collection Eric Thomas Galley Museum, Queenstown, Tasmania. ABOVE: The Hills surrounding Queenstown. BELOW: Balloons aloft. OPPOSITE, TOP: The Mt Lyell Funeral. BELOW: Close-up of figures.

town, as well as the eerie beauty of the surrounding landscape. Like the Chilean arpilleras, not all the images reflected happy times – the sombre procession in black mourned the loss of so many loved ones following the Mt Lyell disaster.

The quilt was created from silk fabrics with threads of copper and tin wire couched to the surface to emphasise the huge influence of mining on the town. Symbols of copper wire were also used and included the Egyptian hieroglyphs for *'life'* and for *'tunnel.'*

An album of photographs was made to record the progress of the work and is displayed near the quilt. It has a hand painted silk cover with the names of all those who participated in the project embroidered to its surface.

Rosebery

The colourful town of Rosebery is less than an hour's drive north of Queenstown. Established more than one hundred years ago, it is still a major mining centre today. Dense and beautiful forest surround Rosebery and just five kilometres to the west are the spectacular Montezuma Falls.

Rosebery Library
Main Street
Rosebery, TAS 7470.
Ph: (03) 6473 1426
(03) 6473 1796 after hours.
4.00p.m. – 7.00p.m. Monday and Thursday.
1.00p.m. – 5.00p.m. Tuesday and Wednesday.
10.00a.m. – 1.00p.m. Friday.

✷ The quilt is hung on permanent display within the Library and may be seen during opening hours.

✄ *The Rosebery Quilt* (175cm x 80cm) was created in 1992 by a group of local craftswomen who attended the six week workshop tutored by Elena Gallegos. Like the *Queenstown quilt*, it was made from silk fabrics using the techniques of hand painting, appliqué and quilting. The work depicts the main street of Rosebery, its quaint buildings and their hand painted signs and awnings. The background features the distant hills and the zinc mine so much a part of the town's existence.

The group sketched the design on paper before transferring it to silk and hand painting the details. Little figures represent many of the local people and the characters are easily identifiable to those living in the town. All the figures were made from scraps of fabric, felt, wool and padding. The work was finished with a beautiful border of native wattle, each spray created from hand painted silk cut in tiny circles, gathered and padded. Yellow pom-poms were added here and there to enhance the textured effect.

Zeehan

Zeehan is a short drive south west of Rosebery. Classified as an historic town, it is also rich in mining history and heritage. Huge deposits of silver and lead were discovered just over a century ago. Many stately buildings remain in the town from the days of this boom when Zeehan was known as the Silver City. Local craftswomen also created a quilt during the workshop tutored by Elena Gallegos. It depicts the Zeehan Neighbourhood Centre and little children playing. It may be seen displayed at the Centre in Belstead Street between 10.00a.m. – 3.00p.m. Monday to Friday during school terms.

Launceston and Nearby Regions

The picturesque city of Launceston is the third oldest settlement in Australia having been founded in 1805, just one year after Hobart. Its charming Victorian streetscapes are nestled around the banks of the Tamar and Esk Rivers. Only a few minutes walk from the city centre is the spectacular Cataract Gorge, its beautiful old English trees planted more than a century ago. Just a short drive from Launceston in the rolling hills of the Tamar Valley, there are vineyards, strawberry farms and local historical museums. Several National Trust properties including Clarendon, Franklin House, Entally, and the White House are also within easy reach. All of these properties have quilts on display and their descriptions follow.

Queen Victoria Museum and Art Gallery

Wellington Street
Launceston, TAS 7250.
Ph: (03) 6323 3777 Fax: (03) 6323 3776
10.00a.m. – 5.00p.m. Monday to Saturday.
2.00p.m. – 5.00p.m. Sunday.
Closed Good Friday and Christmas Day.
12 quilts, other small items, and skin rugs.

The Queen Victoria Museum and Art Gallery was opened in 1891. Over the years it has developed as a nationally significant institution. Its collections include decorative arts, contemporary Australian craft and design, colonial and contemporary art, natural history, community history, geology and physical sciences. The textile collection includes substantial holdings of costumes, printed textiles, needlework and laces, some of the items dating back to the late 16th century. The needlework area contains examples of patchwork, quilting, embroidery and lace. Contemporary textile works by Australian artists are also held. The Museum plans to continue the acquisition of quilts for the collection. They are particularly interested in quilts made in Tasmania or having associations with the state, as well as the work of contemporary Australian quiltmakers. Acquisitions are determined annually by the funds available. Further information concerning donations or acquisitions can be obtained by contacting the Curator of Craft and Design.

✷ The quilts are not on permanent exhibition but are displayed from time to time. Visitors are welcome to see them by arrangement. Please contact the Curator of Craft and Design four weeks in advance. The collection is currently located off site from Wellington Street in a nearby building in Civic Square. From 2002, the Contemporary Craft and Design and Decorative Arts collections will be located at the Museum's new development within the Launceston Railway Workshops. These facilities will provide for vastly improved collection access and display.

The Historical Quilt Collection

✂ The collection includes a silk coverlet c.1860-'70 of unknown maker. It was possibly used as a table cover and features a centre of multi-coloured hexagons assembled in the form of diamonds. The hexagons are surrounded by a border of two rows of brightly coloured Tumbling Blocks which are set against a black background. A wide multi-coloured silk braid and fringe is used to edge the cover. The fabrics are silks, velvets and cottons of the period, hand pieced in the traditional English method over paper templates.

There is also a patchwork quilt made in 1898 by Rachel Louisa Raspin. It was made in Buckland on the east coast of Tasmania, where Rachel lived for most of her life. The square central medallion is embroidered with the initials *'R L R'* and the date *'1898'*. It is surrounded by diamonds made from Turkey-red cotton twill and white cotton, each one outlined in feather stitch. The quilt is edged with a deep scalloped border of white cotton crochet which provides an unusual contrast to the striking centre panel.

The Contemporary Quilt Collection

✂ *All Australian* was made by Jan Irvine Nealie in 1994. It is a dynamic quilt of dyed and stitched silk with a wool filling, the subject of which considers Australia's future nationhood. The work combines symbolic as well as representational imagery and depicts important historical events in Australia's development towards nationhood. These include the Southern Cross representing the flag of the Eureka gold miners' rebellion in 1854; the gold and purple flag for the women's suffrage movement; the Aboriginal flag – a symbol of our indigenous people's struggle for the right to vote and have freehold title to their traditional lands; and the flag denoting ecology. The quilt also refers to Australia's position within South East Asia and our cultural diversity. In addition, the Museum holds the companion piece to this work which is entitled *All Australian Now* and is stitched in fine filet crochet.

A contemporary wholecloth quilt of cream cotton was made by Sarah Lloyd in 1983. The work was hand stitched and features a central medallion detailed in chevrons and semi-circles. The centre is surrounded by a sinuous leaf and vine design and a double-stitched diamond pattern. This contemporary work can be compared with another wholecloth quilt held in the collection which dates from the 1880s.

Wave 24 – Blue Mirror was made by Barbara Macey in 1984. It features an

ABOVE: *Patchwork Coverlet*. Unknown maker, 1860-1870. Silk, velvet, cotton. 155cm x 158cm.
Collection Queen Victoria Museum and Art Gallery, Launceston, Tasmania.

ABOVE AND OPPOSITE: *Patchwork Quilt.* Made by Rachel Raspin, 1898. Cotton. 242cm x 174cm. Donated by Mrs C. Raspin. Collection Queen Victoria Museum and Art Gallery, Launceston, Tasmania. BELOW: *Launceston Bicentennial Quilt.* Made by Launceston Patchworkers and Quilters, 1986-'88. 160cm x 200cm. Launceston Town Hall, Launceston, Tasmania.

innovative adaptation of the traditional Log Cabin design and is part of a series examining relationships. Sombre shades of blue, charcoal and black give an intensity and depth to the surface. Movement is created through contrast in fabric texture as waves of blocks move in several directions across the quilt. The illusion of a mirror is fabricated by the shiny surfaces of some of the materials which reflect components of the design on a smaller scale.

The Museum collection also includes skin rugs and smaller items of patchwork such as tea cosies and bags dating from the late 19th and early 20th centuries.

Launceston Town Hall
St John Street
Launceston, TAS 7250.
Ph: (03) 6337 1111
8.00a.m. – 5.30p.m. Monday to Friday.

✷ The quilt is hung on permanent display behind glass in the Town Hall and may be seen anytime during office hours.

✄ This beautiful Bicentennial quilt (160cm x 200cm) was made between 1986 and '88 by the Launceston Patchworkers and Quilters. The design was developed from photographs, postcards and scenes of Launceston. Heritage buildings are clustered through the centre and include St John's Anglican Church, the Post Office and Clock Tower. The Tamar River in the foreground reflects the influence and involvement of the water on this riverside city. In the distance are the mountains of the valley – Mt Arthur, Mt Barrow and Ben Lomond. The fields depict the apple orchards, sheep, huge timber logs, and the local lavender farm in full summer bloom. The quilt was appliquéd, embroidered and quilted entirely by hand.

ABOVE: *Crazy Patchwork Quilt.* Made by Mary Price aged 14, 1892. 250cm x 102cm. Clarendon, Evandale, Tasmania. OPPOSITE: Details of embroidered motifs including wattle.

Clarendon

234 Clarendon Station Road
Evandale, TAS 7212.
Ph: (03) 6398 6220
Open daily between 10.00a.m. – 5.00p.m.
(4.00p.m. June, July and August)
Closed Christmas Day and Good Friday.
3 quilts.

Clarendon is reached by travelling through the charming and historic village of Evandale, just 20 kilometres south east of Launceston. A magnificent country estate of great historical and cultural significance, it is owned by the National Trust and has undergone extensive and meticulous restorations. The house was built in 1838 for James Cox, a wealthy wool and grain merchant, and today it provides a fascinating insight into the upstairs/downstairs lifestyle of the early 19th century. The service rooms are located in the basement, the grand reception rooms on the main floor, and the bedrooms upstairs. The house has been furnished with antiques of the era and the walls of the main rooms have been hung with beautiful paintings, some donated or bequeathed, others on loan to the Trust. There is an extensive costume collection and lovely examples of early clothing will always be seen on display.

✷ The quilts are permanently displayed in the bedroom that probably served as a night nursery and is now known as the 'Costume Room'. They may be seen during the opening hours listed.

✂ A quilt of Crazy Patchwork (250cm x 102cm) was made in 1892 by Mary Price. It won a *Special First Award* at the exhibition held in the Albert Hall during the same year. Mary was just fourteen years old at the time and today her quilt is a rare surviving example of work

completed by a child. It was created from multi-coloured brocades, velvets and satins, the patches outlined in a variety of stitches and embellished with motifs. They included horse-shoes, fish, fans, butterflies and flowers, both Australian and European. The design and stitchery display great skill in a needlewoman so young. The quilt remained in Mary's family for many years. It was donated to the Trust by her grandson, Mr R. Green.

A quilt of random patchwork hexagons (172cm x 106cm) was created during the 1950s by an unknown maker. The fabrics are believed to have been remnants from children's clothing and the work is known affectionately as the *wallaby rug*.

A quilt of Grandmother's Flower Garden design (212cm x 177cm) was made during the 1950s by Mrs Roy Crompton of Launceston. The rosettes were made from printed dress cottons and surrounded by a border of plain white hexagons. The edge of the quilt retains the shape of the rosettes and has been hand embroidered with satin stitch.

A lovely quilt of Grandmother's Fan design is currently on extended loan to the Trust and is displayed on the floor of the day nursery. It has been made from wool, wool gaberdine, thick gingham and velvet, the pieces of each fan and the seams between the blocks edged with herringbone stitch.

Franklin House
Hobart Road
Franklin Village, TAS 7249.
Ph: (03) 6344 7824
9.00a.m. – 5.00p.m. daily.
(4.00p.m. June, July and August)
Closed Christmas Day and Good Friday.

The beautiful colonial home of Franklin House is located 6 kilometres south of Launceston. It was built in 1838 for a local brewer and innkeeper, its thick walls constructed using convict labour during an era when bushrangers posed a very real threat of danger.

✷ The quilt is displayed on an early colonial bed in the upstairs bedroom and may be seen during opening hours.

✂ This coverlet of Suffolk Puffs (180cm x 240cm) is of unknown provenance. It consists of tiny circles of pale apricot and green cotton which have been hemmed, gathered around their edges and stitched together by hand.

Scottsdale

Scottsdale is set within the picturesque undulating country of north east Tasmania. Renowned for its beautiful gardens, many of which are open to the public, the region is especially lovely in Spring and early Summer when the rhododendrons, irises and lilies are in full bloom. The Rhododendron Reserve and the Pear Walk at nearby Lalla are spectacular, and from early December the lavender fields at Bridestowe Estate begin their flowering season.

Scottsdale Public Library
51 King Street
Scottsdale, TAS 7260.
Ph: (03) 6352 2300
11.00a.m. – 1.00p.m. & 2.00p.m. – 5.00p.m.
Monday to Wednesday.
11.00a.m – 1.00p.m. & 2.00p.m. – 6.00p.m.
Thursday and Friday.

✷ The quilt is framed in a protective case and hung on permanent display in the Library. It may be seen during opening hours or viewed through the glass doors on the driveway side of the building when the Library is closed.

✂ This quilt (200cm x 200cm) was made by the Dorset County Quilters in 1988 as a Bicentennial gift to the Scottsdale Municipality. The design was drawn by Robin Torzewski and depicts north east Tasmania, its landscape, history and culture. It features irregular shaped patches encased within the bright red outline of an apple. A large bite has been chomped from its side, creating an impression of the shape of Tasmania – the 'Apple Isle.' Images illustrate the mountains and the patchwork of rural paddocks in their varying shades of green, brown and yellow. Heritage buildings have been clustered through the centre and include one of the original homes of the district, 'Tucker's House,' nestled among the apple trees which surround it. There are blocks depicting the diverse rural pursuits of the region – the vegetables, hops, poppies, sheep, fishing, and vineyards, as well as the lavender in summer bloom.

Hand and machine appliqué and embroidery were used to create the quilt and each block was inset beneath the red border fabric in reverse appliqué.

St Barnabas Anglican Church
Cnr. King and Ada Streets
Scottsdale, TAS 7260.
Ph: (03) 6352 2389
The church is open everyday
between 9.00a.m. – 5.00p.m.
Services are held on Sunday at 9.30a.m.

The lovely old wooden church of St Barnabas was built in 1892. There is a contemporary leadlight window at the northern end of the church which depicts the story of St Barnabas and was made by Tasmanian master craftsman, Klaus Bruchsch. There are also several pieces of embroidery created by parishioners.

✷ The quilt is hung on permanent display and visitors are welcome to see it during opening hours or by arrangement with the rectory.

✄ This quilted hanging was made in 1992 by Lorraine Wootton and members of the Women's Fellowship Group. The project celebrated the Centenary of St Barnabas and was designed by Meredith Williams. Inspired by the architecture of the church, the front portico of the building was depicted within a circle at the top of the work. The theme used was 'Hands,' – those of help, friendship, work and prayer. Flowers were included as reminders of the garden walks held annually within the parish in order to raise much needed funds. Most members of the group are avid gardeners, contributing to the beauty of the church by arranging the floral displays. The hanging was made from cotton chintz, silk, satin, and metallic fabrics. It was appliquéd and quilted by machine, with the three dimensional flowers and buds being sewn by hand.

Hadspen

The little village of Hadspen is only a few minutes drive west of Launceston. It was first settled during the early 1820s on land granted to Thomas Reibey, the son of convict Mary Reibey who became a very successful business woman in Sydney. Hadspen has retained its old world charm and the original Red Feather Inn and other Georgian buildings still remain.

Entally House
Hadspen, TAS 7290.
ph: 03) 6393 6201
10.00a.m. – 5.00p.m. daily.
Closed Christmas Day and Good Friday.

ABOVE: *Crazy Patchwork Quilt.* Made by the Patchwork Sixteen Group, 1986-'87. 200cm x 260cm. Entally House, Hadspen, Tasmania.

Entally House was built by Thomas Reibey in 1819. It is the oldest and one of the most beautiful of the National Trust properties in Tasmania. Set on the banks of the South Esk River, it is surrounded by picturesque grounds which include a walled garden, stables and green house. Magnificent Regency furniture and silverware are displayed throughout. There is a charming collection of children's toys and a wonderful doll's house. There are also several rag rugs, cross stitch samplers and a cross stitch map dated 1810.

✷ The quilt is permanently displayed in an upstairs bedroom of the house and may be seen during opening hours.

✄ This quilt of Crazy Patchwork (200cm x 260cm) was made by the Patchwork Sixteen Group between 1986 and '87. It was presented to Entally House as a Bicentennial gift. The design was inspired by the quilt made by Mary Price in 1892 which is now displayed in the nursery at Clarendon. The work features sixteen separate blocks, each one created from multi-coloured silks, brocades, velvets, and taffetas. Many of the fabrics used by the makers were very old. The patches were embellished with beads, lace, charms, embroidery, and appliquéd motifs. Green chain stitched hearts were added to each corner. The blocks were separated by black velvet ribbon and surrounded by a black satin border. The layers of the quilt were tied and an inscription stitched to the back included the names of all those who had contributed to the work.

Westbury

Classified as an Historic Town, Westbury is to be found on the Bass Highway, a half hour drive west of Launceston. Many of its colonial buildings have been clustered around a picturesque village green and it is here on a prominent corner that White House is located. One of Australia's most significant quilts originated in Westbury where it was hung in the dining room of the Fitzpatrick Inn for many years. Known as the *Westbury Quilt,* it illustrates family life at the turn of the century and is now included in the collection of the National Gallery of Australia, Canberra.

White House
Village Green
Westbury, TAS 7303.
Ph: (03) 6393 1171
10.00a.m. – 4.00p.m. Tuesday to Sunday.
Closed July and August.
Quilt plus matching curtains.

Built for Thomas White in 1841, this former store and dwelling includes an original bakery, coach house and stables. Neglected for many years, the property was purchased and restored by the Clemons family who opened it to the public in 1971. The fascinating collections include horse drawn vehicles, early bicycles and cars, antique furniture, toys and an extraordinary doll's house. Large glass display cases contain everything from a miser's purse to Victorian fans. There are beautiful cross stitch samplers made by children during the late 18th century and a variety of lacework.

✷ The quilt is permanently displayed on a 17th century oak bed and may be seen during the opening hours listed.

✄ This quilt of Tumbling Blocks was made during the early 1970s by Felicity Clemons. It features clusters of coloured blocks which have been surrounded by a background of plain white hexagons. Three rows of Tumbling Block stripes form the borders. The work has been made from cotton fabrics using the English method over paper templates and each piece has been meticulously cut so that the pattern in every diamond is identical. Mrs Clemons also made patchwork curtains for the attic using the same pattern and fabrics to match the quilt.

Longford

The historic town of Longford is set in rich agricultural country on the banks of the Esk River, approximately 25 kilometres south of Launceston. First settled in 1813, it is one of the oldest towns in northern Tasmania. Several of its buildings were constructed more than 150 years ago using convict labour. Christ Church, built of sandstone in 1839, overlooks the village green. It is renowned for its stained glass window which was designed by William Archer of Woolmers Estate. Hawthorn hedges and European trees, along with the legacy of stately homes, colonial cottages, inns and shops, provide a strong reflection of the English and Irish heritage of Longford.

Woolmers Estate
Longford, TAS 7301.
Ph: (03) 6391 2230 Fax: (03) 6391 2270
10.00a.m. – 4.30p.m. everyday.
Closed Christmas Day.
House tours: 11.00a.m., 12.30p.m., 2.00p.m. and 3.30p.m.
2 items.

Woolmers Estate is set in magnificent grounds overlooking the river. It is only a 5 minute drive south east of the town. Built by Thomas Archer in 1819, it is one of the earliest properties in the region and has been occupied by descendants of the family for more than 180 years. Thomas's son, William Archer, was the first native born Tasmanian architect and designed the 1843 addition to Woolmers Estate. The house, along with its collections of beautiful antique furniture and personal possessions, presents a remarkable window into the past and a time capsule of colonial Tasmania.

✷ The chair and work box may be seen during tours of the house and bookings may be made by telephone or fax. Accommodation is also available and light meals are served in the servants' kitchen.

✄ This delicate Victorian chair is a rare Australian example of the use of patchwork for soft furnishings. The custom of making small decorative items and domestic furnishings from Tumbling Blocks or hexagon mosaic patterns was extremely popular in Britain during the Victorian era. Covered boxes, sachets and evening bags, cushions, work-box lids, small chairs and stools were all created this way. The examples that remain today indicate the remarkable ingenuity of their makers. This chair covering was made c.1890 by a member of the Archer family. The Tumbling Blocks have been created in the traditional English style over paper templates and the family still have the maker's work-box in which additional silk diamonds remain.

Deloraine

The picturesque town of Deloraine is set on the banks of the Meander River, 50 kilometres south west of Launceston. Deloraine was settled during the 1830s and has been classified by the National Trust as a town of historical significance. Many lovely Georgian and Victorian buildings still remain and have been meticulously restored.

Thousands of visitors travel from far and wide to attend the annual craft fair held in the town every November. The surrounding countryside is rich and green, dotted with dairy cows, fat lambs and mixed farms. Nearby, there are rainforest walks, limestone caves and cascading waterfalls.

Deloraine Community Complex

Alveston Drive
Deloraine, TAS 7304.
Ph: (03) 6362 2844 Fax: (03) 6362 3272
10.00a.m. – 4.00p.m. Monday to Wednesday all year.
1.00p.m. – 5.00p.m. Sundays between December and April.
4 panels plus a Commemoration Quilt.

✷ The panels are permanently displayed on either side of the stage within the Community Complex. They may be seen during opening hours or at other times by arrangement. A booklet telling the story of the *YARNS Project* is available and there is a 10 minute audio visual presentation. The Commemoration Quilt is mounted on a blackwood stand nearby.

✂ The superb *YARNS Artwork in Silk* tells the pictorial story of the Meander Valley, its history, mountains, rivers, rural industries and lifestyles. Created between 1992 and '95, it was the inspiration of retired farmer and Tasmanian Tiger searcher, Ned Terry. Ned had seen the wonderful theatre curtain displayed in the Griffith Regional Theatre during a holiday in western New South Wales. He realised that Deloraine's picturesque countryside and rich heritage could be illustrated in a similar way. He hoped that the work would provide a drawcard for visitors and at the same time bring together the people of the valley. From its very beginning the *YARNS Project* was envisaged as an opportunity for the community to develop culturally by bringing together disparate groups to learn about each other. Everybody was encouraged to participate, to share ideas, to teach and to learn.

Niecy van der Elst-Brown was appointed as artistic director and a long list of subject matter for inclusion in the design was compiled. Niecy began by producing a set of working drawings. Local engineer Tony Imison developed an ingenious method of enlarging them by using an overhead projector and transparencies.

The four panels (3.5m x 4.00m each) depict the region from settlement to the present, each one reflecting a different season and taking approximately 2,500 hours to create. Local artist Harry Eyles provided many of the drawings for the exquisite birds, animals and old buildings. Workshops were held in a variety of techniques including machine embroidery, appliqué, and silk dyeing methods. Spinning, weaving, crochet, beading and quilting were also used in the creation of the panels.

Niecy chose silk as the dominant fabric because of its beauty, versatility and archival qualities. Some of the silk was hand painted to achieve realistic tree trunks, rocks, snow, foliage and animals. Many other fabrics, including tulle, wool, velvet, cotton and lace were used for different effects.

More than five hundred people were involved in the *YARNS Project* with hardly a family in the district not participating in some way. From this large group, three hundred women

ABOVE: *Victorian Chair covered in Silk Tumbling Block Patchwork.* Made by a member of the Archer family, c.1890. Woolmers Estate, Longford, Tasmania.

Yarns Artwork in Silk. Made by the community of Deloraine, 1992-'95. 3.5m x 4.00m. Deloraine Community Complex, Deloraine, Tasmania.

ABOVE: Winter. BELOW: Spring. OPPOSITE, ABOVE: Summer. OPPOSITE, BELOW: Autumn

contributed to the sewing and making. The work was therefore a powerful mecca for the enrichment of community life. It also resulted in the creation of a lasting treasure and heirloom for future generations living in Deloraine.

During 1997 a commemoration quilt was made depicting the women at work on *YARNS* and recording each of their signatures. The town was also the proud recipient of Tasmania's 'Premier Tourist Town' award. A history of the project is currently being compiled and will include a photograph of each person or group involved, along with details of the piece they worked on.

In the Nearby Region

In the town of Sheffield, a short drive north west of Deloraine, artists from Tasmania as well as interstate have created an amazing series of murals that illustrate significant events in the history of the region.

Further north at Devonport, there is an embroidered and woven banner hung on permanent display in the office of the Tasmanian Arts Council in Best Street. It was a collaborative work made in 1986 by two north west coast artists, Annie Bell and Angela Trambas, and combines hand weaving with traditional Greek embroidery.

Stanley

The oldest settlement in Tasmania's north west, the little fishing village of Stanley is nestled beneath the huge rocky outcrop known as the Nut. The town was established during the 1820s by the Van Diemen's Land Company and their original bluestone store can still be seen today on the sea front. 'Highfield,' an historic home built by the company, is open to the public as a house museum and provides a fascinating insight into the early colonial era.

Lyons Cottage
14 Alexander Terrace
Stanley, TAS 7331.
Ph: (03) 6458 1145 Hon. Secretary.
10.00a.m. – 4.00p.m. daily.
11.00a.m. – 3.00p.m. during Winter.

Stanley was the birthplace of Australia's only Tasmanian Prime Minister, Joseph Lyons, who was born in this humble cottage in 1879 and spent his childhood years here. Today the house is open to the public and is managed by a small committee of local volunteers.

✷ The quilt is permanently displayed on an old iron bed and may be seen during opening hours.

✄ A small counterpane of Crazy Patchwork (160cm x 110cm) is believed to have been made c.1980 by Mrs Nell Cartledge. Nell was a keen needlewoman and a regular volunteer at Lyons Cottage. The quilt was made by hand from scraps of cotton fabric and the edge of each patch was embroidered with feather stitch.

Nearby, at the Stanley Discovery Museum in Church Street, there is a cushion of Crazy Patchwork created by an unknown maker. It may have been made by Nell Cartledge as a very young woman. It features a top of velvet patches outlined with feather stitch and a backing of hand crocheted work. The crochet design depicts a ship, flags, and the inscription *'Our Heroes Dardanelles 1915.'* This was typical of the many patriotic patterns published in books and magazines at the time commemorating the heroism of Australian soldiers during the 1914-'18 War. The museum also has a wonderful collection of shell work on display. It is open daily except during June and July.

King Island

Rugged and picturesque, King Island guards the western entrance to Bass Strait – that turbulent area of water separating Tasmania from the mainland. It is serviced by aircraft from both Victoria and Tasmania and is less than an hour's flight from Melbourne and only 30 minutes from Launceston. The first white settlers to inhabit the place were tough and lawless sealers whose relentless quest for oil ended in the devastation of the seal colonies. Today, the island's undulating hills support the rich green pastures of the many beef and dairy farms which are renowned throughout Australia for the excellence of their produce.

King Island Historical Museum
The Light Keeper's Cottage
Currie, King Island 7256.
Ph: (03) 6462 1360 Trend Tourist Information Centre.
2.00p.m. – 4.00p.m. everyday.
Closed July and August.

The King Island Museum is housed in the former Currie lighthouse keeper's residence. Situated high on the hilltop overlooking the harbour, it was built in 1880, the heyday of the noble lighthouse tradition. The house has been classified by the National Trust and is typical of the homes provided for light keepers in Australia during this period. In addition to the quilt, there is a fascinating collection of memorabilia, photographs, old farm implements, and relics from some of the tragic shipwrecks suffered throughout the 19th century.

✷ The quilt is housed in a specially designed frame and hangs on permanent display in the museum. An album of photographs recording its making is kept nearby.

✄ *The King Island Quilted Wall Hanging* was made for the Bicentenary in 1988 by sixty five ladies from this small and closely knit community. The work was co-ordinated by Charlotte Denton and drawings and templates were made by local artist Lisa Fitzhardinge. The design depicts the historical development of the island over 200 years, the large central panel featuring the beautiful structure of the Cape Wickham Lighthouse. It was here that the first settlement really began and the keeper was virtually in charge of the whole island. Supplies came only once a year and because of the isolation, gardens and crops were nurtured and pastures grown for livestock.

The Aborigines had not lived on King Island since the land bridges were drowned during the ice age. Seals knew no fear and were easy prey for the sealers whose grisly work is depicted at the top. The tragic history of shipwrecks is symbolised by the '*Netherby*' which had been bound for Brisbane in 1866 when it struck a reef. John Parry, the First Mate, is still recognised today as one of the island's great heroes. Agriculture, the main-stay of the island, is represented by herds of beef, dairy cattle, sheep and turkeys. The Currie Lighthouse and the old residence housing the museum are also included. Flying above them is the muttonbird, part of island folklore and a source of food since the earliest days. To the left is the little white church at Yambacoona, used by all denominations and shown surrounded by the abundant animal life and wild flowers of the island.

ABOVE: *King Island Quilted Wall Hanging*. Made by a community group, 1988. King Island Historical Museum, Currie.

The wall hanging was appliquéd and embroidered entirely by hand. Long forgotten items of clothing and old curtains provided the myriad of patterns, textures, and colours. One poor husband found himself minus a shirt tail! Quilting was also done by hand using a large floor frame. An album of photographs recording the many months of making is to be seen beside the quilt. The delightful story of the project was written by Patricia Partridge and is available at the museum.

Durham Quilt of Yellow and White Cotton Sateen, Made by Matilda Clish, 1913. Collection Embroiderers' Guild of South Australia.

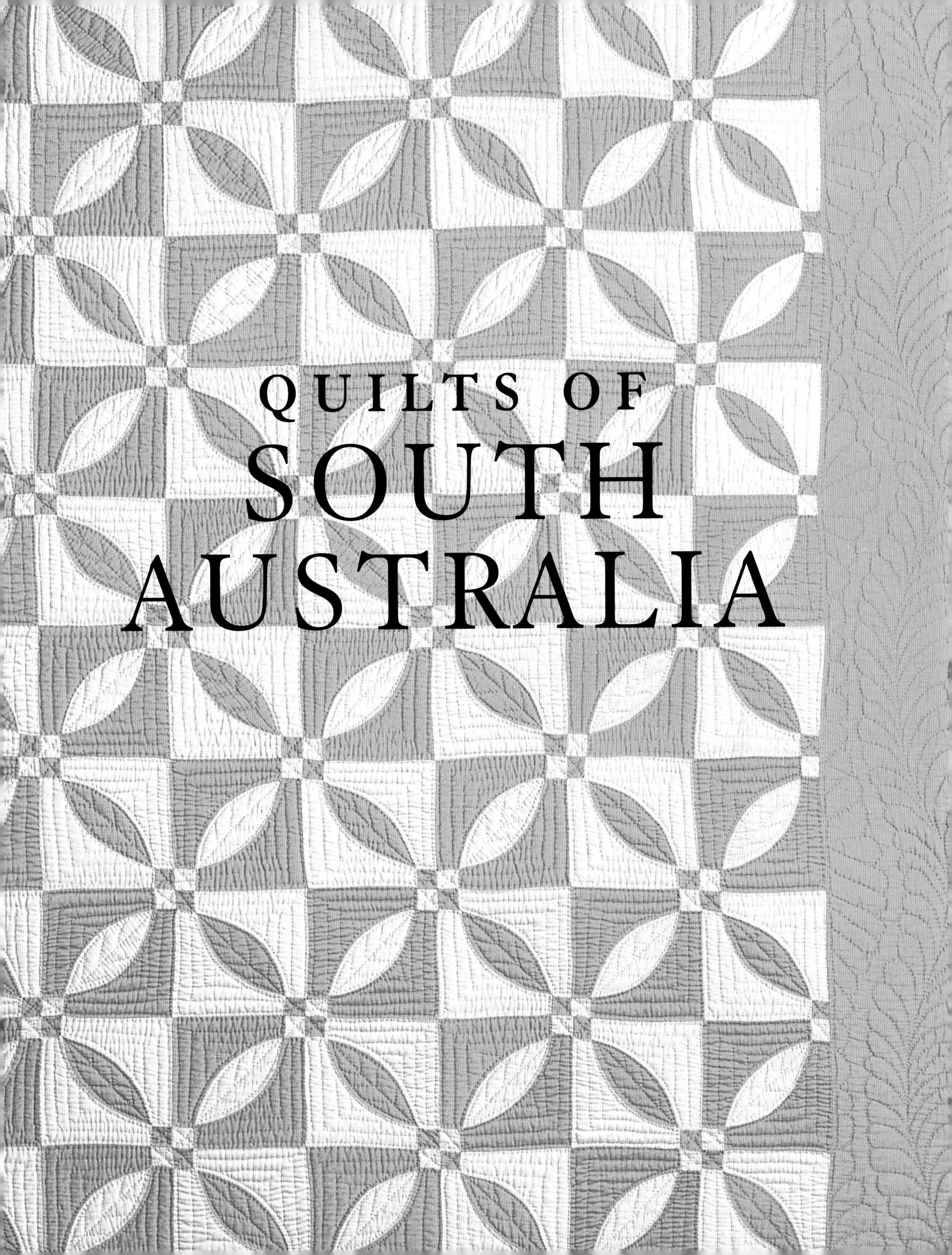

QUILTS OF SOUTH AUSTRALIA

Art Gallery of South Australia

North Terrace
Adelaide, SA 5000.
Ph: (08) 8207 7000 Fax: (08) 8207 7070
10.00a.m. – 5.00p.m. daily.
Closed Christmas Day.
9 quilts and smaller quilted textiles.

The Art Gallery of South Australia acquired its first quilt by donation in 1972. Several more have been given since and it is hoped to acquire additional examples of these beautiful textiles. All the historical quilts in the collection have been held by the maker or the maker's family and descendants until their donation to the Gallery. Their provenance forms an interesting and important aspect of their documentation and enjoyment. Five of the quilts are Australian, three were made in England and one in the United States. However, it is through South Australian connections that all have come to the Gallery. The quilts form an important part of a wide-ranging collection of textiles which spreads from the late 16th century to the present day. Special strengths include works from the British Arts and Crafts Movement, especially those produced by Morris and Company, and works by Australian artists.

✷ The quilts are displayed occasionally with exhibitions planned to coincide with other major quilting events. They may also be seen by appointment. Access is limited however, and requests must be made in writing 2 - 4 weeks in advance to the Curator of Decorative Arts.

✄ The collection of quilts held by the Gallery includes some splendid examples. A beautiful Australian Crazy Patchwork quilt (202cm x 268cm) was made by Rebecca King between 1890 and '95. Rebecca had been born at Morphett Vale, South Australia in 1859 and lived most of her life on a farm at Aylesbury, near Georgetown. The quilt was made as a wedding present for her sister. It was created from silk and cotton fabric pieces placed at random over the entire surface. It was beautifully embroidered with many entertaining motifs including tennis rackets, a kettle, horseshoes, butterflies, and an Australian emu and kangaroo. Rebecca married Thomas Hynes in 1901. She was a talented painter as well as a quiltmaker. Ref. 726A4A

Another quilt of Australian origin (105cm x 77cm) was made by Elizabeth Magarey in Adelaide c.1870. This pieced coverlet of printed cotton squares, rectangles and triangles has a border of red twill. It is thought to have been made when Elizabeth was quite young as some of the hand stitching is finely worked while some indicates less care. Ref. 772A32A

A table cover and cushion (140cm x 147cm and 70cm x 70cm) were created c.1900 from gold printed cigar band silk by Annie Percival (nee Tait). Annie had been born in Silverton, New South Wales in 1887 and lived with her family in Broken Hill until they moved to Adelaide around 1905. Her father, Thomas Tait, built and managed hotels where she was ideally placed to collect the cigar silks. Annie created these items around the turn of the century when silk was relatively inexpensive and bundles of fine cigars were packaged using bright yellow silk ribbon printed with the name of the company. Quilts and cushion covers were often made using these ribbons by women who must surely have endured a great deal of cigar smoke to obtain them. Annie carefully arranged her collection of silks and secured them with herringbone stitch. Ref. 874A5A and 874A6A.

Two beautiful silk quilts were created in England by Henrietta Stanton c.1860-'70. Henrietta had been born in London in 1840, the daughter of a jeweller, and she married William Stanton around 1862. She and her husband both died in 1925. The two quilts were made in Norfolk, England and donated to the Gallery by the maker's granddaughter, whose mother was the youngest of Mrs Stanton's ten children. Both were made by hand in the traditional English method over paper templates and indicate a brilliant eye for colour and design. One was intended to be used as a table cover and features multi-coloured pieced silk stars. It has a black silk background and a border of Tumbling Blocks. The second quilt is of Tumbling Block design and was made as a bed cover. Ref. 772A74 and 772A75

The oldest quilt in the collection is a coverlet of Broderie Perse (223cm x 163cm) made in England by Jane Judd during the late 18th or early 19th century. It remained in the family of the maker until it was donated to the Gallery and is believed to have been brought to South Australia during the 19th century by Katherine Helroyd, a great granddaughter of the maker. Ref. 947A60

A memory quilt of Crazy Patchwork squares (190cm x 150cm) was made in Bethany, Virginia, United States

OPPOSITE: *Crazy Patchwork Quilt,* c.1890-'95. Made by Rebecca King, (1859-1915) Georgetown, South Australia. Silk, cotton. 202cm x 268cm. Gift of Dr A.W. Wall, 1972. Collection Art Gallery of South Australia, Adelaide.

ABOVE: Detail of *Patchwork and Appliqué Medallion Coverlet showing the whimsical border of 19th century ladies*. Unknown Maker, c.1830. 270cm x 240cm. Ayers Historic House, Adelaide.

by Virginia Huntington Barclay, who died aged only twenty one. Beautifully embroidered in red cross stitch is the poignant inscription *'In Most Loving Memory Of My Darling. 1883. VHB'.* A great variety of embroidery stitches have been used to embellish the work and even the backing shows careful selection and arrangement of fabrics. It was given to the donor's mother, Mary Barclay (nee Magarey) who had married the maker's brother. Ref. 832A4

A contemporary work by Sarah Crowest is entitled *Luxury Quilt* (181 cm x 152cm) and was made in 1996. Sarah designs and prints her own fabrics and this quilt was machine pieced from dyed, screen printed and painted cotton. Just as traditional patchwork quilts document significant events in their makers' lives, so Sarah collects together images and ideas from her own life, and from a chaotic state attempts to create something coherent. This quilt includes some of that chaos as well as much of the maker's humour. Ref. 972A9A

Ayers Historic House

288 North Terrace
Adelaide, SA 5000.
Ph: (08) 8223 1234 Fax: (08) 8359 2494
10.00a.m. – 4.00p.m. Tuesday to Friday.
1.00p.m. – 4.00p.m. Weekends and public holidays.
2 quilts.

One of Adelaide's architectural treasures, Ayers Historic House was originally the home of Sir Henry Ayers, his wife Anne and their large family. One of the last grand 19th century homes remaining on North Terrace, Ayers House reflects the status of its owners and its interior is one of the most beautiful in Adelaide. The hand painted ceilings and stencilled woodwork are believed to date from the 1870s. There is a beautiful collection of cross stitch samplers dating from 1744 and an antique work box made from walnut. There is also a variety of small sewing items which includes silver thimbles and a Victorian pin cushion embroidered with ribbon work.

✷ The cot quilt is permanently displayed and may be seen during opening hours. The antique medallion quilt is not always displayed but may be seen by prior arrangement. Please contact the house manager one week in advance.

✂ A beautiful patchwork and appliqué medallion coverlet (270cm x 240cm) is of unknown maker and history. Dating from the 1830s, its central square of chintz flowers has been stitched to the cream background using the technique of Broderie Perse. A strip of chintz fabric printed with a design of passion flowers has been used to frame it. The centre has been surrounded by rows of hexagon rosettes, stars and circles, each one made in the English method over paper templates. The work has no filling or lining, the fine hand stitching being clearly visible on the reverse side. The whimsical border of 19th century ladies, hands joined as they dance around the edge of the quilt, is reminiscent of paper cut-outs made by children.

The little cot quilt displayed in the upstairs nursery originally belonged to the Ayers family. It has been made from blue linen and features white daisies meticulously embroidered using satin stitch, stem stitch, and colonial knots. It has no filling and has been finished with a gathered silk ruffle and a backing of silk. Five of the eight Ayers children lived in the North Terrace house and the youngest child, Lucy, was born there. It is likely that this quilt, along with the stuffed toys made from flour sacks, belonged to her.

Adelaide Town Hall
128 King William Street
Adelaide, SA 5000.
Ph: (08) 8203 7777 Fax: (08) 8203 7575
9.00a.m. – 5.00p.m. Monday to Friday.

✷ The quilt is housed in a specially built glass case and hung on permanent display in the foyer of the building. Tours of the Town Hall and its civic collection are held regularly by prior appointment.

✄ This Bicentennial quilt entitled *Adelaide: The Years Between 1836 – 1988* (170cm x 122cm) was designed by Alison Verrier and made by members of the Quilters' Guild of South Australia. It includes scenes depicting the early settlement of the state as well as the present day. There is the famous Old Gum Tree where the proclamation of Adelaide was first read in 1836. There is also the lovely Holy Trinity Church, the oldest church in the state. Founder and town planner of Adelaide, Colonel William Light whose bronze statue appears at the top, overlooks his city from Montefiore Hill. The quilt was made from cotton, cotton blends, silk, satin and lace. It was hand appliquéd, embroidered and quilted. (Civic Collection no. 1914).

Also in the City

There are several examples of work on public display made by members of the Embroiderers' Guild of South Australia. A magnificent series consisting of five panels may be seen in the foyer of Telstra House, 30 Pirie Street. There is also an appliquéd banner commemorating the fifty years since the end of the war which is displayed in the Naval, Military and Air Force Club, 111 Hutt Street. Telephone (08) 8223 2422.

Two hand woven tapestries (250cm x 150cm) were created between 1993-'94 to celebrate the centenary of Women's Suffrage. The work was designed by Kay Lawrence, co-ordinated by Elaine Gardner, and assisted by Lucia Pichler. The weaving was undertaken by the Adelaide Community Weavers and the tapestries now hang on permanent display in the House of Assembly, Parliament House, North Terrace. They may be seen from the public gallery during weekdays (except sitting days) between 9.00a.m. and 5.00p.m. Telephone (08) 8237 9100.

The South Australian Country Women's Association
Mary Walker House
30 Dequetteville Terrace
Kent Town, SA 5067.
Ph:(08) 8332 4166 Fax: (08) 8364 3050
9.00a.m. – 5.00p.m Monday to Friday.
Closed public holidays.

Kent Town is an inner suburb of Adelaide located approximately 2 kilometres east of the city centre.

✷ The quilt is hung on permanent display in a specially designed case and visitors are welcome to see it during the opening hours listed.

✄ An embroidered and appliquéd quilt (210cm x 150cm) was designed and made by members of the South Australian Handicraft Committee as a project to commemorate the Bicentennial in 1988. The pictorial centre depicts a profusion of Australian native birds perched on the branches of an old gum tree. The side borders illustrate many species of native flowers, all of them finely embroidered using a great variety of stitches and threads.

The Embroiderers' Guild of South Australia Inc.
16 Hughes Street
Mile End, SA 5031.
Ph: (08) 8234 1104 Fax: (08) 8234 1513
10.00a.m. – 2.30p.m. Monday to Thursday.
5 quilts plus other small items.

The suburb of Mile End is located approximately 3 kilometres west of the city centre.

The Embroiderers' Guild of SA was formed in 1965 and has grown to a membership of approximately 600 throughout the state. The lovely old house in Hughes Street was purchased for use as a headquarters in 1987. There is a separate exhibition gallery at the rear in which classes are held and a changing exhibition of members' work is displayed. Formal certificate courses are offered for those wishing to achieve an advanced level of expertise. A monthly newsletter is published and special interest groups have been formed, one of which is for members involved in patchwork and quilting.

✷ The Guild is happy to share their beautiful collection with members of the public provided appointments are made in advance. Please contact the Secretary by letter or telephone 2 weeks in advance.

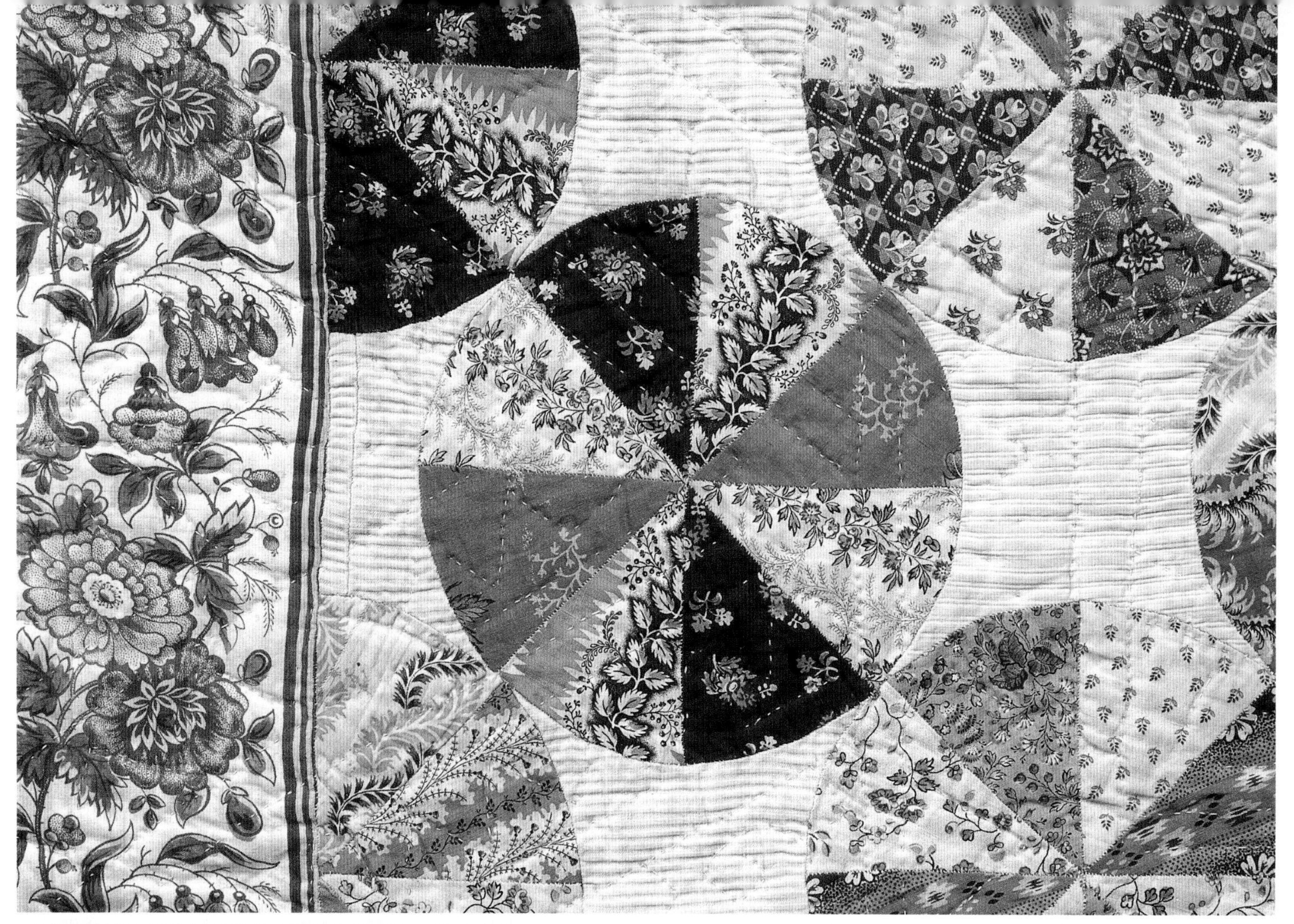

PHOTOGRAPHY EDWIN NICZYNSKI.

TOP: *Patchwork Quilt of Chintz.* Made by Anna Blackmore, 1828; BELOW: *Patchwork 'Jug,'* c.1890. Donated to the Guild by Elizabeth Silsbury and formerly belonging to her grandmother, Jane Elizabeth Norris. OPPOSITE: *Crazy Patchwork Cushion of Ribbons* completely covered with embroidery. Made by Mary Moore, 1892. All Collection Embroiderers' Guild of South Australia, Mile End, S. A.

✂ The museum was established to enable members to study embroidered needlework that represented all styles, periods and countries. The collection includes a magnificent Durham quilt (212cm x 172cm) created in 1913 by Matilda Clish of Annfield Plain, County Durham. It was made as a wedding gift for Mrs Clish's daughter who told the Guild that *'mother made lots of quilts, all of her own design.'*

This quilt has a top featuring blocks of yellow and white cotton sateen arranged in fours. The blocks form a pattern having chequerboard centres surrounded by appliquéd leaves. The border of yellow cotton has a white square in each corner to complement the central design. The work has a backing of plain yellow sateen, a filling of cotton, and has been finely quilted by hand in the traditional style of Durham quilts. A second quilt of the same design but of different colouring was made by Mrs Clish for another daughter and is now part of the collection of the renowned Beamish North of England Open Air Museum. This quilt is featured in Janet Rae's book, the *Quilts of the British Isles*.

A medallion quilt top was created c.1840 by Elizabeth Hardy who arrived in South Australia on the ship *Kangaroo*. The centre features a Square-on-point highlighted by a black background. Within the square there is an encircled hexagon rosette of printed chintz. The Broderie Perse flowers surrounding it have been applied with buttonhole stitch. Successive pieced and appliquéd borders frame the medallion and feature lovely fabrics dating from the 1820s. Several hexagons have been made from minute pieces joined together by hand. It is believed that Elizabeth had a very large family and this may have been the reason the quilt remained unfinished.

PHOTOGRAPHY EDWIN NICZYNSKI.

A patchwork quilt of chintz was obviously treasured for many years but sadly cut into two lengths at some later time. Its maker was Anna Blackmore whose brother, Robert, was a gentleman farmer of Somerset, England, and the author of *Lorna Doone*. The quilt was created from hand pieced blocks, each one featuring a segmented circle of eight individual wedge-shaped pieces. It was made over paper templates, finished with a border of floral chintz, and lined with wool from the family's flock of sheep.

ABOVE: *Durham Quilt of Yellow and White Cotton Sateen.* Made by Matilda Clish, 1913. 212cm x 172cm. Collection Embroiderers' Guild of South Australia, Mile End, S.A. OPPOSITE: Detail of quilt; Matilda Clish with her husband, William.

The initials and date *'A.B. 1828'* were embroidered onto a front panel in very fine red cross stitch. After her death, the quilt was sent to a relative of Anna's, Mr George Webber Tazewell, who had emigrated to Australia. It was Mr Tazewell's daughter who donated it to the Guild.

There are three quilts that were created using patterns published by the *Adelaide Chronicle* between 1933 and '34. Two of the quilts were made by Miss Elsie Blake of Rocky Farm, Bulls Creek, South Australia. The first features Australian wildflowers, the second Australian birds. The Guild also owns a beautiful quilt embroidered with wildflowers by Ida Summers in 1933. Ida had been a needlework teacher and made this delicate quilt on white cotton voile with a yellow lawn backing.

There are some fascinating small items in the Guild's collection. A cushion of Crazy Patchwork was made by Mary Moore in 1892. Mary later married Percy Nicholls who was Principal of Pulteney Grammar School from 1901 to 1942. Most of the cushion top has been created from ribbons including one commemorating the golden jubilee of Queen Victoria in 1887. The patchwork has been completely covered with embroidery. The motifs include a moon, lighthouse, spider's web, flags, and an early version of the Australian Coat of Arms.

A quaint three dimensional 'jug' of velvet patches c.1890 was donated to the Guild Museum by Elizabeth Silsbury and had belonged to her grand-mother, Jane Elizabeth Norris (nee Russell). The jug features Australian wattle on one side, a beaded daisy on its base and was probably used as a needlework bag.

There is also a lovely gown of hexagons with pink lining made by Elsie Horseman during World War II.

PHOTOGRAPHY CHRISTOPHER SPROD.

ABOVE: *Celebratory Amalgamation Wall Hanging.* Made by members of the Women's and Children's Hospital Craft Group, 1991-'94. Women's and Children's Hospital, North Adelaide. OPPOSITE: Unfinished *Medallion Quilt.* Made by Elizabeth Hardy, c.1840. Collection Embroiderers' Guild of South Australia, Mile End, S.A.

Women's and Children's Hospital

72 King William Road
North Adelaide, SA 5006.
Ph: (08) 8204 6779
24 hours a day.

The suburb of North Adelaide is located approximately 2 kilometres north of the city centre.

In March 1989 the Adelaide Children's Hospital and the Queen Victoria Hospital amalgamated to become the Women's and Children's Hospital. The Celebratory Amalgamation Wall Hanging was created to commemorate the amalgamation of the two hospitals on the same site in North Adelaide.

✷ The hanging is permanently displayed in the main gable-roofed walkway of Level One (between the new building and the Ronald McDonald Children's Clinic). It may be seen at any time.

✂ The *Celebratory Amalgamation Wall Hanging* was made by a craft group of hospital staff and supporters between 1991 and '94. The project was designed by Meg Douglas and co-ordinated by Rosemary Boucaut. Members of the group pieced and appliquéd individual sections and held lunch time meetings as well as weekend workshops. The hanging was made in three panels. Those on the outside illustrated the past history of the Queen Victoria and Children's Hospitals while the centre depicted the future and the new Hospital. Complementary design elements were used in the outer panels to balance and connect the two together. The rainbow in the central panel symbolised joy and clear days ahead. The work was made by hand and machine. The background was pieced from 'tiles' of fabric. Hospital figures and buildings were appliquéd. Other techniques included fabric dyeing, hand and machine embroidery, stumpwork, and quilting.

PHOTOGRAPHY EDWIN NICZYNSKI.

Old Government House
Belair National Park
Upper Sturt Road
Belair, SA 5052.
Ph: (08) 8278 5477
12.30p.m. – 4.00p.m. Sundays and public holidays. Groups by appointment.
4 quilts.

The picturesque town of Belair and the adjacent National Park are set in the rolling foothills on the southern outskirts of Adelaide, approximately 11 kilometres from the city centre.

Old Government House was built in 1859 on the site of the original Government Farm and is a fine example of colonial Georgian architecture. Constructed of local stone, it features a huge bay window with turret and flagpole and was used as the official vice-regal summer residence by the early governors of South Australia. Today it is cared for by the Friends of Old Government House and is furnished in a manner befitting a wealthy Victorian gentleman. A quaint stone cottage within the grounds depicts the more modest surroundings of the servants' quarters and it is here that the quilts are to be seen. Textile heritage tours are now available and have been designed to enable many of the fine textile items normally kept in storage to be enjoyed.

✱ The quilts are permanently displayed on beds in the cottage and may be seen during opening hours. Textile heritage tours may be arranged by appointment.

✂ A beautiful pieced mosaic quilt (165cm x 264cm) was made by Louisa Fanny Catt of Meadows, South Australia, for display at the Adelaide Jubilee International Exhibition in 1887. Louisa had been born in 1841, just five years after the founding of the colony. She came from a pioneering family who lived at Magill, now a suburb of Adelaide. One of her twelve children owned a drapery business and it is very likely that it was from this source she obtained the printed and ribbed silks, striped and checked taffetas, and silk brocades used for her work. The quilt pattern was created from squares and elongated lozenge shapes and was included in S.F. Caulfeild's *Dictionary of Needlework* published in 1882. Patches in the centre of the work were pieced from darker fabrics to create a diamond within the design. The diamond was highlighted by the use of lighter colours to surround it. The quilt was hand stitched using the English method over paper templates. It has a silk backing, cotton batting, and has been quilted by machine. It was treasured by the family for many years until being donated to Old Government House in the early 1960s by Mrs Catt's grand-daughter, Mrs J Steuart.

A small Log Cabin cot quilt was made c.1870 by Mrs Sarah Keen. Sarah was born in 1830 in Somersetshire, England and arrived in South Australia in 1855. She was then the wife of Reverend Thomas Keen, a Bible Christian whose ministry was to lead them to many different towns throughout South Australia. The quilt was made from very narrow strips of velvet, cotton, taffeta and brocade. The strips were pieced around black velvet squares onto blue and white striped ticking. It was edged with a green cotton frill and backed with green cotton. On her death in 1910, Reverend Keen paid a wonderful tribute to Sarah, as his *'constant help in all things, whether it was his studies, his ministry or in the maintenance of their home, often in difficult circumstances.'*

A Crazy Patchwork cot quilt was created c.1885 by Mrs Esther Lewis, the wife of the Post Master General of South Australia. Mrs Lewis took over the full time care of her grand-children when her daughter, Bessie, died in 1883 leaving six children under the age of twelve. It was during this time that the quilt was created. The work features random patches of velvet, brocade and satin and has a border of peach velvet. It is backed with floral cotton and the edges of each patch have been embroidered with feather stitch using silk threads.

There is also a large Crazy Patchwork quilt which was made by Mrs Pridmore c.1920. Little is known of the history of this work which features many triangular patches believed to have been obtained from fabric sample books.

Lobethal

The little town of Lobethal is nestled in the picturesque Onkaparinga Valley of the Adelaide Hills. It is approximately 50 kilometres east of Adelaide and only about an hour's drive from the wine district of the Barossa Valley. One of the earliest settlements to be established in South Australia, Lobethal was founded by Prussian immigrants in 1842 and the legacy of their architectural heritage remains in the town today. The oldest Lutheran Church in Australia is to be found just off Main Street. The town is well known for its annual Christmas Lights Festival when local businesses and homes create beautiful illuminated displays.

PHOTOGRAPHY EDWIN NICZYNSKI

OPPOSITE TOP AND BELOW RIGHT: *Mosaic Quilt.* Made by Louisa Fanny Catt, 1887. BELOW LEFT: Detail of *Crazy Patchwork Cot Quilt.* Made by Mrs Esther Lewis, c.1885. Collection Old Government House, Belair, South Australia

LEFT: Detail of *Hexagon Quilt.* Made by Thelma Hill, c.1950. RIGHT: *Bed Jacket.* Made by Miss E. D. George, 1951. Collection National Costume Museum, Lobethal, South Australia.

The National Costume Museum
1 Lenswood Road
Lobethal, SA 5241.
Ph: (08) 8389 5730 or (08) 8389 6157
2.00p.m. – 4.00p.m. Tuesday to Sunday and public holiday Mondays.
Other times by arrangement.

The National Costume Museum was established in 1995 to accommodate the Helen Hughes Collection of period costumes and accessories. Housed in the original 'Blanket Room' of the old Onkaparinga Mill building, this remarkable collection includes items dating from 1810 to the 1980s. It began with a chest of clothes that had been handed down through generations of Helen's family. The chest originally belonged to her great grandmother who arrived in South Australia in 1839, having made the long sea voyage aboard the Zebra with Captain Dirk Hahn. Helen used the heritage clothing to raise money for charity by conducting parades throughout the state. Today her collection has grown to include christening and wedding gowns, heirloom underwear, children's clothes, tea cosies dating from the 1870s, and many other items of historical memorabilia including the quilt.

✷ Approximately 80 complete costumes are exhibited at any one time. The quilt is not always displayed but visitors are welcome to see it by arrangement. Please notify the Museum in advance if groups will be visiting.

✂ A patchwork quilt of random hexagons was made by Mrs Thelma Hill during the 1950s. Mrs Hill lived in the *White House* overlooking the Onkaparinga Racecourse and the quilt was one of two that she created for her daughter on the occasion of her marriage. The work was made by hand in the English method over paper templates using cotton dress prints in Autumn colours. It has a warm filling of cotton and has been finished with a border of gold cotton sateen.

There are several lovely quilted dressing gowns. One was made by Helen Hughes in 1941 for her trousseau and was finished just before ration coupons were introduced. Helen machine quilted the pink silk-satin fabric in one inch squares before laying and cutting the pattern. The machine she used was one of the last three electric Singer sewing machines imported into South Australia before the war. It had been ordered by her mother some months earlier and was in transit by ship when World War II broke out.

A magnificent reversible wrap-over gown of pure silk taffeta was created by an unknown maker in 1949. It was probably made for a trousseau and features pale blue on one side and pink on the other. The work has been so finely stitched that it is impossible to say which was considered the principal layer. It has a waist-length shawl collar and huge cuffs which feature very fine hand quilting of twelve to fourteen stitches to the inch. The quilted design of daisy sprays has been raised by trapunto work and has been done so invisibly that it is difficult to detect the points through which the wadding has been stuffed. Blue silk mules or slippers, their tops embroidered in cross stitch, have been made to match the gown.

A beautiful pink silk-satin bed jacket featuring fine hand quilting and trapunto was made by Miss E. D. George in 1951. The fronts of the work were quilted, the edges finished with both quilting and trapunto. It won first prize for *Italian Quilting* at the Royal Adelaide Show of 1951 and the certificate that was awarded to Miss George can also be seen in the Museum.

Three baby's bibs of cream silk were quilted by hand and edged with silk crochet for Herbert Schubert, born on the 1st January, 1900. Each bib has a different quilting design and crochet trim. Herbert's father had been sent from Germany to become the first engineer of the nearby Bird-in-Hand gold mine which had opened in 1879. In addition to the bibs, a christening gown and bonnet made for Herbert are also part of the collection.

Goolwa

The historic port of Goolwa is located on the Fleurieu Peninsula near the mouth of the Murray River. It is approximately 80 kilometres south of Adelaide and a short drive from Victor Harbour. The town was originally intended to become the New Orleans of Australia and between 1850 and '80 it was a thriving port for river trade between South Australia and the eastern colonies. The densely spaced cottages found in the residential precinct known as *Little Scotland* were once home to the many Scottish riverboat employees. The excellent fishing in the nearby Lakes area and close proximity to the Coorong National Park have made Goolwa a popular tourist destination. It is also renowned for its historical significance and the centre of the town along with the original wharf area, has been declared a State Heritage Area.

Goolwa National Trust Museum
11 – 13 Porter Street
Goolwa, SA 5214.
Ph: (08) 8555 2221, (08) 8555 3767
or (08) 8555 2117
2.00p.m. – 4.30p.m. Tuesday to Thursday, Saturday, Sunday, public and school holidays. Other times by arrangement.
2 quilts.

PHOTOGRAPH COURTESY DIANNE FINNEGAN.

ABOVE: Detail of *Patchwork Quilt.* Made by Augusta Hutchinson, c.1852. 192cm x 140cm. Collection Goolwa National Trust Museum, Goolwa, South Australia.

The National Trust Museum is sited opposite the picturesque Memorial Gardens and is housed in a former blacksmith's shop dating from the 1870s. The diverse collection ranges from relics that have been salvaged from shipwrecks to domestic objects. There are some lovely examples of period clothing. A glass case displays a black wedding dress worn by a Goolwa bride in 1901, and along side it, the suit that belonged to the groom. There is also a delicate cape with intricate lace insertion work.

✷ The quilts are permanently displayed within the Museum and may be seen during the opening hours listed or by appointment.

✄ A beautiful hand pieced patchwork quilt (192cm x 140cm) was made by Augusta Hutchinson c.1852. Early in that year, Mr Young Bingham-Hutchinson married Augusta Emily Kingdon at Heavitree in Devon. Shortly after their marriage the couple came to live in Australia and it is believed that Augusta made the quilt during the long sea voyage from England. Young Bingham-Hutchinson was destined to become a prominent and respected man in South Australia and one of his great friends was Governor Hindmarsh. A street within the Heritage Precinct of Goolwa commemorates his name and descendants of the family still live in the nearby Hindmarsh Valley.

The quilt was made from forty eight pieced blocks, each one containing a segmented circle of ten individual wedge-shaped pieces. The wedges were formed over paper templates and the completed circles appliquéd to background squares of calico. The fabrics include a wide variety of dress cottons and each square is only 16cm in diameter. The quilt has a thin cotton batting and has been heavily quilted. It was in constant use by the

PHOTOGRAPHY MARGARET PATTERSON.

LEFT: *Patchwork Quilt depicting the historic McLaren Vale Hotel.* Made by Quenby Sinclair and Deb Nichol, 1995. 200cm x 140cm. McLaren Vale Hotel, McLaren Vale, South Australia. RIGHT AND OPPOSITE: *Log Cabin Quilt c.1910.* The maker, Eunice Strawbridge's mother, had worked as a dressmaker and the silk and velvet fabrics used for the quilt were remnants from her sewing. Collection Hope Cottage National Trust Museum, Kangaroo Island, S.A.

family for more than one hundred years before being donated to the Museum.

A sofa cover of random hexagons was made by Val Lawrence. Val stitched the pieces together while working one afternoon a week as a volunteer at the Museum. She began the cover in 1967 and it took six years to complete. The materials are cotton dress fabrics from the 1950s and '60s. There are more than 600 hexagon pieces, every one of them cut from a different fabric.

McLaren Vale

The pretty township of McLaren Vale is set in the rural wine growing region of Southern Vales, approximately 40 kilometres south of Adelaide. Many of the local wineries are open for tastings and cellar door sales. There are numerous restaurants and galleries dotted throughout the area, often to be found in historic buildings. Every year during July and August, acre upon acre of pink and white blossom come into full bloom and the Almond Blossom Festival is held in the nearby township of Willunga.

McLaren Vale Hotel
Main Road
McLaren Vale, SA 5171.
Ph: (08) 8323 8208
10.00a.m. – 12.00p.m. Monday to Saturday.
11.00a.m. – 8.00p.m. Sunday.

The McLaren Vale Hotel is a restored bluestone building dating from 1857. The hotel cafe and courtyard overlook the beautiful gardens of Hardy's Winery. Nearby stands a huge Moreton Bay Fig tree which is listed on the National Trust Register of significant trees.

✷ The quilt is permanently displayed in the hotel restaurant *Magnums* and visitors are welcome to come in and see it.

✂ This quilt (200cm x 140cm) was made in 1995 by Quenby Sinclair and Deb Nichol. It was commissioned by the hotel management to reduce noise levels in their new restaurant. The large central panel depicts the historic hotel building, framed across the top and bottom by a variety of images sewn to a background of striped tea towels. The lower pictures depict the food and beverages of the restaurant, the top illustrate scenes of the region – the vineyards, cows, South Australian magpie, and the ever popular 'ute' complete with three dogs in the back. Each pictorial scene was appliquéd by machine and the work was machine quilted and tied. Tie-dyed fabric was used for the blue sky background and very thick batting was chosen as a noise insulator.

Kangaroo Island

Kangaroo Island is separated from the coast of South Australia by Backstairs Passage and is only a 30 minute flight from Adelaide. Ferries take an hour and leave from Adelaide or Cape Jervis. The island is renowned for its wonderful seafood, cheese, and honey. Much of the land is conserved as National Park and its isolation has made it a haven for many species of wildlife now extinct or seldom found on the mainland. Colonies of penguins live around the coast, sea lions laze on the beach at Seal Bay, and each Spring heralds the blooming of masses of wildflowers.

PHOTOGRAPHY MARGARET PATTERSON.

Hope Cottage
National Trust Museum
47 Centenary Avenue
Kingscote
Kangaroo Island, SA 5223.
Ph: (08) 8553 2656 or
(08) 8553 2151 after hours.
2.00p.m. – 4.00p.m. daily.
1.30p.m – 5.00p.m. January only.
July and August open Saturday only,
except by appointment.
3 quilts.

Hope Cottage was one of the earliest dwellings on the island. It was built in 1859 by Charles and Michael Calnan who had made their fortunes on the Victorian goldfields. They returned to build three identical houses on a beautiful site overlooking Backstairs Passage. Over the years the cottages became known as Faith, Hope, and Charity. Hope Cottage has now been restored and furnished to depict the pioneering history of the island. Displays tell of the sealers and escaped convicts, the tragic shipwrecks, and the ingenious ways in which early settlers supported themselves. There are numerous examples of needlework. A family sampler stitched by Mrs Littley between 1876 and '92 records the names of the children of George and Mary Turner. There is also a lovely hand knitted cotton quilt, one of three made by Lucy Turner c.1908.

✱ The quilts are permanently displayed within the cottage and may be seen during opening hours.

✂ This lovely old quilt of Log Cabin design was donated to the National Trust by Mrs Eunice Strawbridge. It had been made by her mother who worked as a dressmaker in England during the early 1900s, and the beautiful silk and velvet fabrics were remnants from her sewing. The quilt is a traditional Light and Dark design with blocks arranged to form large diamonds of alternating pale and dark shades. The work remains unfinished and has no backing, the fine hand stitching clearly visible on the reverse.

A second patchwork coverlet is believed to date from the late 19th century. It was donated to the National Trust by Margaret Bruick and had been made by her great grandmother, Mrs Susan Gillett. The work was sewn by hand from squares, triangles and rectangles of cotton fabric. It has no filling or backing.

There is also a little Log Cabin cot quilt which was created in 1985 by Kangaroo Island quiltmaker, Judith Morris.

Angaston

Angaston is set in the beautiful Barossa Valley, approximately an hour and a half's drive north east of Adelaide. From the 1830s onwards, prominant early colonist George Fife Angas, (after whom the town was named) encouraged German immigrants to settle on his large holdings of land. Today their influence can be seen in the vineyards, churches, cottages, bakeries and restaurants dotted throughout the valley. Angaston is also the home of two of the Barossa's oldest wineries, Saltram and Yalumba, the later having been planted on land originally purchased from George Fife Angas.

PHOTOGRAPHY DOUGLAS COATS.

RIGHT: *The Barossa Heritage Quilt.* Made by the Vine Patch Quilters, 1997-'99. 350cm x 250cm. Barossa Council, Angaston, SA.

Barossa Valley

Barossa Council
Washington Street
Angaston, SA 5353.
Ph: (08) 8564 2042 Fax: (08) 8563 8461
9.00a.m. – 5.00p.m. Monday to Friday.

✷ The quilt is hung on permanent display in the foyer of the council building and may be seen during office hours.

✂ This beautiful heritage quilt of the Barossa Valley (350cm x 250cm) was created between 1997 and '99 by thirty nine members of the Vine Patch Quilters. The Barossa Wine and Tourist Association had approached the group in 1996 concerning the possibility of making a commemoration quilt to mark the 50th anniversary of the Barossa Vintage Festival. While a quilt could not have been finished in time for the anniversary, this proposal was to inspire the quilters to embark on a project that would take three years to complete and result in the creation of a magnificent community work of art.

Co-ordinated by Joyce Brooker, the work focuses on the life, the history, and the people of the valley from the earliest days. In contrast to the convict colonies of New South Wales, Victoria and Tasmania, from its earliest beginnings South Australia was planned as a free settlement. From 1838 onwards, English free settlers along with Lutheran pioneers, began to establish villages in the valley. Beautiful music, the making of bread, cheese, and wine were part of the culture from the beginning. The quilt depicts these picturesque villages with their heritage of German architecture – early stone cottages, barns, churches and shops. They are set against a background formed by the undulating hills, the slopes covered by acre upon acre of lush green vines.

A myriad of fabric colours, textures and techniques were used in the creation of the work. Curtain and upholstery fabrics, cotton, wool, velvet, silk, satin and organza were all included and when prints featuring musical instruments could not be found, an internet request resulted in eighteen perfect fabrics being sent from all over Australia! At one point, when the magnitude of the project dawned on the makers, they appliquéd galahs and a laughing kookaburra into the huge eucalypt that framed the left hand side. Both hand and machine appliqué and embroidery were used in creating the quilt. Fabric overlays provided shadowing effects. Much of the work was padded to provide a realistic three dimensional appearance. Lace, beads and ribbons were all incorporated. Finally, the name of every quiltmaker who had contributed to the project was embroidered beneath the vine leaves clustered in the foreground.

Collingrove Homestead
Eden Valley Road
Angaston, SA 5353.
Ph/Fax: (08) 8564 2061
1.00p.m. – 4.30p.m. Monday to Friday.
11.00a.m. – 4.30p.m. Weekends.

Collingrove Homestead is to be found 6 kilometres south east of Angaston. Built in 1856, this magnificent country estate originally belonged to the Angas family and was bequeathed to the National Trust in 1976 by Ronald Angas. Furniture and memorabilia from several generations of the family are displayed throughout the house. Collingrove is now used as an historic museum and to provide heritage bed and breakfast accommodation.

✷ The quilt may be seen during opening hours or at other times by appointment.

✂ This large pieced medallion quilt (208cm x 185cm) is of unknown maker c.1901. Sadly, it cannot be ascertained whether it was made, or acquired, by a member of the Angas family, though much of the contents of the house formerly belonged to them. The colours of red and black have been used to give focus to different sections of the quilt. A red Square-on-point is featured in the centre and its shape and colour has been echoed throughout the quilt in successive blocks, borders and binding. Hundreds of tiny squares and triangles form a complex pattern which has been stitched by hand. The outside border features squares which have been surrounded by red triangles and carefully cut to show their fabric patterns. A horse can be seen in several. Others feature prints with the Roman numbers and letters *'V11R,'* issued to commemorate the ascension to the throne of King Edward VII in 1901. All the fabrics are prints except the red. A light blanket has been used as a filling and the work has been hand quilted in a diamond pattern.

Kapunda

The historic village of Kapunda is nestled in gently rolling countryside just a short drive from the Clare and Barossa Valleys. Australia's oldest mining town, it was first settled by pastoralists in 1839. It was the discovery of copper three years later however, that was to lead to the rapid development of Kapunda. Several original miners' stone and mud cottages can still be seen, along with other heritage-listed buildings dating from the 1840s. Many include diverse and beautiful examples of decorative iron lacework, designed and made by local foundries at the turn of

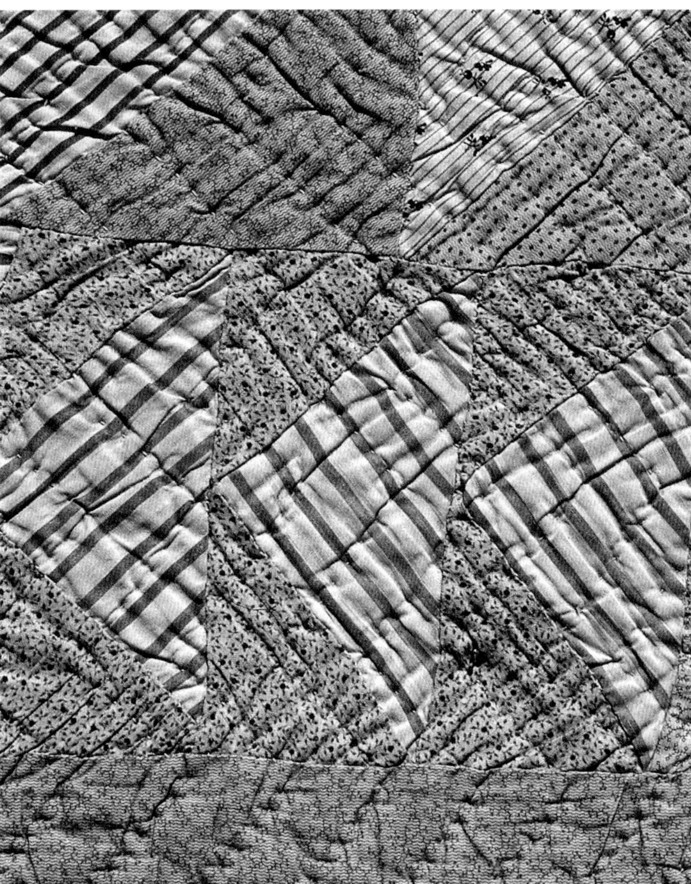

PHOTOGRAPHY PETER SWANN.

ABOVE: Detail of Irish *Pieced Medallion Quilt*. Made by Miss Donnelen, c.1820. 218cm x 193cm. Collection Kapunda Museum, Kapunda, South Australia.

the century. In Kidman Square, an interesting mural depicts the life of the town's most famous pioneer, Sir Sidney Kidman, known as the Cattle King.

Kapunda Museum
11 Hill Street
Kapunda, SA 5373.
Ph: (08) 8566 2021 or (08) 8566 2603
September to May: 1.00p.m. – 4.00p.m.
daily except Friday.
June, July and August: 1.00p.m. – 4.00p.m.
weekends, school and public holidays.

The Kapunda Museum is housed in a magnificent stone building of Romanesque design, the front of which has two distinctive towers. Displays provide a detailed insight into the lives of the miners from Cornwall and Wales who flocked to the settlement. The rich history and some of the folklore surrounding the life of Sidney Kidman is also recorded. In addition to the quilt there is a collection of period costumes, a cross stitch sampler dated 1838 and a macrame mantle-shelf fringe.

✷ The quilt is permanently displayed within the Museum and may be seen during the opening hours listed.

✄ This pieced medallion quilt (218cm x 193cm) was made in Ireland c.1820 by a young woman named Miss Donnelen. The traditions of patchwork and quilting were already very firmly established in Ireland. Many quilts originating there accompanied their makers when they came to live in Australia. Miss Donnelen emigrated to Kapunda during the 1840s and the quilt travelled with her. It remained in the family for more than 150 years before being donated to the Museum by descendants of the maker.

The central medallion of the work features rows of alternating red and cream triangles. Strips of Flying Geese pattern form successive borders and the final frame of Squares-on-point is edged with Turkey-red. The fabrics are all dress cottons, many plain and striped with a few small floral prints. The work is a true scrap quilt and the tiniest snippets of material have been added here and there to complete a patch. It has been sewn entirely by hand over paper templates. A woollen blanket has been used as a warm filling and the quilting has been worked in simple diagonal lines to create an overall diamond pattern.

PHOTOGRAPHY DICK CLELAND.

OPPOSITE,TOP: *Patchwork and Appliquéd Quilt.* Unknown Maker, 1829. Malowen Lowarth Cottage, Burra, South Australia. OPPOSITE, BELOW: Details showing border pattern and appliquéd motifs on patchwork. ABOVE: Detail of cross stitch initials.

Burra

The picturesque town of Burra is set in undulating hills approximately 160 kilometres north of Adelaide. Listed on the Register of the National Estate, it is one of Australia's oldest mining towns and one of South Australia's most beautifully preserved. It was the discovery of copper by a shepherd in 1845 that was to lead to the establishment of the Burra Mine, a mine which along with Kapunda was to bring a huge influx of wealth to the fledgling colony. Large numbers of Cornish miners flocked to the town and numerous heritage buildings remain from these times. The mine closed in 1877 but by then a strong agricultural industry had been established and today Burra is renowned for the quality of its merino sheep studs.

A lovely mural depicting the countryside was painted by local artist Allyson Parsons. It may be seen at the Regional Council of Goyder in Market Square.

Malowen Lowarth Cottage

11 Paxton Square
Burra, SA 5417.
Ph: (08) 8892 2154 Visitor Centre
1.00p.m. – 3.00p.m. Saturday.
10.30a.m. – 12.30p.m. Sunday, public and school holidays.
Other times by arrangement.

Paxton Square, near the centre of Burra, contains thirty three cottages which were built to house the Cornish miners between 1849 and 1852. At this time Burra had the largest metal producing mine in Australia with more than 1800 men and boys employed. The cottages were unique in the mining history of the country, providing the first decent accommodation to miners and their families. Previously they had lived in dwellings called 'dugouts' which may still be seen today, excavated into the creek banks where disease and lack of sanitation led to many deaths. Most of the original cottages have undergone restoration and are now used for visitor accommodation. Malowen Lowarth, which is a Cornish name meaning 'Hollyhock Garden,' has been restored and opened to the public by the National Trust.

✷ The quilt is displayed on the double bed in the cottage and may be seen during the hours listed or at other times by arrangement with the Burra Visitor Centre.

✂ This delightful patchwork quilt was made in charming naive style almost 170 years ago. The initials and date *'A.N. to S.N. 1829'* have been neatly embroidered in cross stitch in the top left corner, indicating that the work was made as a gift from one member of a family to another. While the letters *'A'* and *'S'* were very clear and easy to decipher, the surname letter had the curious appearance of the Roman number *'II.'* It remained a mystery until quilt historian Annette Gero matched it to the letter *'N'* in the alphabet of an antique cross stitch sampler dating from the same period. It is probable that the quilt originated in England and came to South Australia with one of the early settlers.

A counterpane with no filling, the work has been entirely sewn by hand. It is a true scrap quilt, the background made from squares, rectangles and triangles in a variety of dress fabrics dating from the early 19th century. A border of cream cotton frames the patchwork, its sides plain, its top and bottom featuring a design of naive flowers and moon motifs. Numerous motifs have also been sewn to the pieced background, all of them irregular pieces which have been cut randomly from printed cottons. There are hearts, circles, crosses, and hexagons sewn in no apparent order.

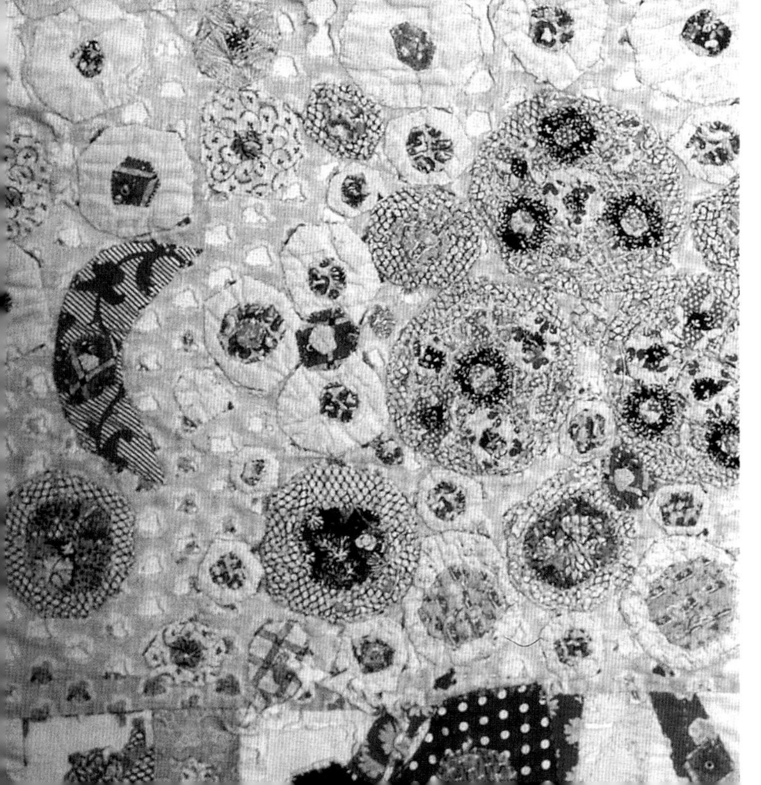

The shapes have not been formed over templates but simply had their edges turned under before being applied to the top. The colours are predominantly blue and pink, with browns in all shades – from pale to dark chocolate and terracotta. The prints are mainly florals of both small and large scale, several featuring the undulating stripes typical of the period.

Regional Council of Goyder
1 Market Square
Burra, SA 5417.
Ph: (08) 8892 2100
9.00a.m. – 4.30p.m. Monday to Friday.

✷ The quilt is hung behind glass in the foyer of the Council building and may be seen during opening hours.

✂ This work, entitled *Burra through the eyes of a Quilter,* was made in 1995 by the Burra Quilters Group to celebrate 150 years settlement of the town. The pictorial centre was drawn by local artist Leonard Bence and depicts several historic landmarks. Silhouetted against a blue sky is the Burra Mine Chimney and Morphetts Enginehouse, now a museum with displays and relics of Cornish mining equipment. A rural cottage has been surrounded by paddocks, its boundary marked by post-and-wire fencing and merino sheep grazing in fields nearby. The central oval has been framed by blocks of Crazy Patchwork, each block made from velvet, silk and taffeta and embellished with embroidery, beads and lace. Historic images have been transferred to fabric from old photographs and stitched amongst the Crazy patches. The work was pieced, embroidered and quilted entirely by hand.

In the Nearby Region

The small rural township of Saddleworth is to be found midway between Kapunda and Burra. A pictorial medallion quilt was made by the Saddleworth Quilt Group to celebrate the Bicentennial in 1988. The work was hand appliquéd, embroidered and quilted and now hangs on permanent display in the foyer of the Clare and Gilbert Valleys Council, Belvidere Road. It may be seen between 9.00a.m. and 5.00p.m. Monday to Friday. Telephone (08) 8847 4096.

Balaklava

The Mid North town of Balaklava is set on the banks of the Wakefield River less than an hour's drive south of Clare. It became a favoured stop over for bullock teams during the 1840s and by the turn of the century had developed as the centre of a thriving wheat region. A walking trail has been prepared to guide visitors past historic sites and along the river bank. The historical museum in May Terrace opens on the 2nd and 4th Sunday of each month or by appointment. Its collection includes a Crazy Patchwork tea cosy c.1900. Telephone (08) 8862 1467.

Wakefield Regional Council
10 Edith Terrace
Balaklava, SA 5461.
Ph: (08) 8862 1811 Fax: (08) 8862 1115
9.00a.m. – 5.00p.m. Monday to Friday.

✷ The quilt is permanently displayed in the Council Chambers and may be seen during opening hours. It is advisable to telephone in advance to ensure the room is not in use.

✂ This quilt (132cm x 132cm) was designed by Valerie Veitch and made by the Balaklava Patchers on the Plains. The project celebrated the state's Jubilee 150 in 1986 as well as the Australian Bicentennial in 1988. Set against a background map of the Wakefield Plains, it depicts the native flora and fauna of the region. It also includes the rural activities and history from the time of earliest settlement to the present.

The bullock team portrays the early passage of copper-ore through the district on its journey to Port Wakefield. The animals were stitched by a quiltmaker whose great grandfather had left the family farm to join the bullockies at the age of only fourteen in order to help support his family. The old red brick flour mill shown in the centre of the work dominated the town of Balaklava for one hundred years. Demolished in 1975, the appliquéd mill encompasses both history and humour with its embroidered cat in determined pursuit of a very well fed mouse.

The quilt was constructed in nine separate pieces which were then sewn together to form the picture. The work was appliquéd, embroidered and quilted entirely by hand.

In the Nearby Region

A short drive north of Balaklava is the village of Snowtown. A pictorial medallion quilt was made by the Snowtown Quilters to celebrate the Bicentennial in 1988. Its centre features a commemorative banner worked in cross stitch and outlined with finely detailed hand quilting. Pictorial images surround the centre and illustrate heritage buildings, native birds and animals and the rural fields of the surrounding countryside.

The work was appliquéd, embroidered, and quilted entirely by hand and now hangs on permanent display in the Snowtown Area School Library, Glen Davidson Drive. It may be seen between 9.00a.m. and 5.00p.m. Monday to Friday and 8.30a.m and 11.30a.m. Saturday. Telephone (08) 8865 2006.

Jamestown

Set in rich agricultural and pastoral country, Jamestown is only an hour's drive north of the Clare Valley. The picturesque Belalie Creek winds its way through the centre of the town, many lovely trees along its banks floodlit in the evenings. Jamestown was named after an early Governor of South Australia, Sir James Fergusson, who had emigrated from Scotland. Many of the street names are of Scottish origin. Heritage murals in Ayr Street were painted for the town's centenary by local artist Ian Walker and illustrate the stories of early pioneers.

Jamestown National Trust Museum
Mannanarie Road
Jamestown, SA 5491.
Ph: (08) 8664 0026 Museum Caretaker.
10.00a.m. – 4.00p.m. Monday to Saturday.
2.00p.m. – 4.00p.m. Sunday.

The National Trust Museum is housed in the Old Railway Station buildings which date from 1885. The collection brings to life the early years of settlement, the development of the forest, the flour mill and other businesses. One enterprise that began many years ago in Jamestown and still prospers to this day is that of Haig's Chocolates. One of Adelaide's most famous specialties, they were first sold by a young Mr Haig from his mother's Ayr Street shop. The Museums's textile collection includes three white linen Signature cloths embroidered in red thread, a wool embroidered sampler c.1890, tray cloths, doyleys and embroidered pillow cases. There are also embroidered aprons from the 1940s and a book of tatting samples made c.1900 by Mrs Lamb, wife of the local butcher.

✷ The unfinished quilt and small block of Crazy Patchwork are permanently displayed in a glass cabinet. The sachet is not always exhibited but may be seen by request. Please contact the Museum a day in advance.

✄ These little items of patchwork were made around 1910 by Mary Elizabeth Floyd Perren (nee Honeychurch). Mary had been born in England in 1875 and married Ed John Perren at Baldina, South Australia in 1907. Ed worked as a blacksmith and railway ganger and the couple lived for many years in a railway cottage in Jamestown. Mary died in 1957 at the age of 82.

Mary's unfinished quilt of Crazy Patchwork (152cm x 76cm) was made from multi-coloured silks and satins dating from the late 19th century. The fabrics were probably remnants from her dresses and it is likely that the work was intended for use as a small sofa or table cover. The Crazy patches were stitched

LEFT: Detail of the *Balaklava Heritage Quilt* showing the bullock team travelling 'the copper run.' Made by the Balaklava Patchers on the Plains, 1988. 132cm x 132cm. Wakefield Regional Council, Balaklava, South Australia. RIGHT: Unfinished *Crazy Patchwork Quilt*. Made by Mary Elizabeth Floyd Perren, c.1910. 152cm x 76cm. Collection Jamestown National Trust Museum, Jamestown, South Australia.

PHOTOGRAPHY BEV ARGENT.

ABOVE and OPPOSITE, TOP: *Log Cabin Quilt.* Made by a Port Pirie milliner, c.1890. 147cm x 147cm. OPPOSITE, BELOW: Detail of *Wholecloth Quilt of Italian Origin.* Unknown Maker, c.1920-'30. Both quilts Collection Port Pirie National Trust Museum, Port Pirie, South Australia.

around a hexagon-shaped centre made from narrow strips and each seam was embroidered with herringbone stitch. The Museum also has a small block of unfinished Crazy work (46cm x 46cm) which may have been made as a cushion cover or possibly another section of the little quilt. Certainly some of the same silks and satins have been used to create it.

There is also a small bag of Tumbling Blocks pattern which was probably made as a pyjama or handkerchief sachet. The work has been hand stitched over paper templates from cotton dress materials and has a lining of white cotton.

Port Pirie

The thriving commercial and industrial centre of Port Pirie is located on the eastern side of Spencer Gulf where it overlooks the Port Pirie River harbour. It is approximately 230 kilometres from Adelaide and only a short drive from the southern slopes of the Flinders Ranges. The first settlers were pastoralists and graziers and today the undulating rural countryside surrounding the town is dotted with sheep properties, wheat farms and market gardens.

Port Pirie National Trust Museum
Ellen Street
Port Pirie, SA 5540.
Ph: (08) 8632 2272 Branch Chairman, National Trust.
10.00a.m. – 4.00p.m. Monday to Saturday.
1.00p.m. – 4.00p.m. Sunday.
Closed Christmas Day.
2 quilts.

The Port Pirie National Trust Museum is situated close to the harbour in historic Ellen Street. It occupies two splendid buildings – the grand Victorian pavilion style railway station c.1902 and the fine old Customs House c.1882. The textile collection includes beautiful examples of embroidered linen, pulled thread work, heirloom nighties and underwear. There is also a hand crocheted coverlet made of white cotton with a bobble design c.1890.

✷ The quilts are permanently displayed within the Museum and may be seen during the hours listed. It is possible to arrange a closer inspection by prior appointment. Please contact the Museum several days in advance.

✂ This Log Cabin quilt (147cm square) was made during the late Victorian era by a Port Pirie milliner whose business was located in Ellen Street. It has been created in the design known as Barn Raising and features light and dark concentric diamonds surrounding the centre. Fabrics of taffeta, brocade, silk, and velvet have been used for the work and it has been edged with a wide border of dark burgundy velvet.

A wholecloth quilt c.1920-'30 is believed to have originated in Italy and was owned by an Italian family who lived in Port Pirie for many years. Made from plum coloured cotton sateen, the

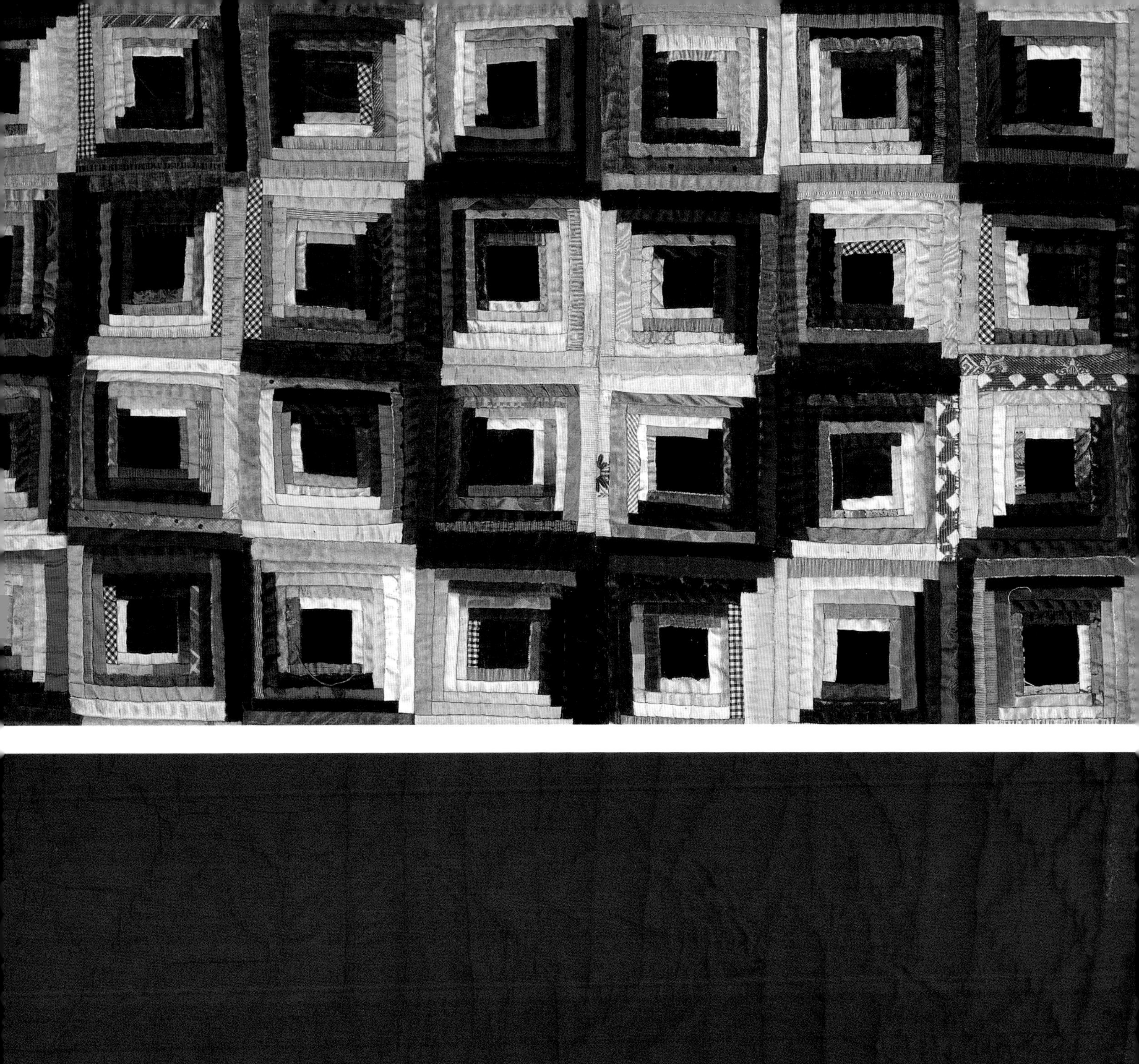

quilt has a thick filling and has been finely hand quilted in a diamond pattern incorporating floral motifs. A similar quilt, also of Italian origin, is held in the collection of Griffith Pioneer Park Museum in New South Wales where it is thought that such work was created to mark a special occasion, such as a marriage. Both these Italian quilts resemble the wholecloth quilts of Durham, Northumberland and Wales.

Quilts hold a unique place in the Italian heritage of Port Pirie. Molfettesi migrants, mainly fishermen and seamen, began to arrive in the town towards the end of the 19th century. A devout Catholic community, they settled in King Street, Solomontown, bringing with them their devotion to Mary as well as their Molfettesi tradition of holding special celebrations in her honour. In 1956 Italian fishing boats assembled in the Port Pirie harbour for the first *Blessing of the Fleet* ceremony. Afterwards, a procession carried the statue of Mary from the wharf along King Street to St Anthony's Church. The homes along the route of the procession were gaily decorated with flags, bunting, and lights. Brightly coloured quilts and bedspreads were draped over chairs, verandahs, and fences and competitions were held for the best decorated homes and boats. Fireworks were lit on the wharf and outside the church and thousands of people came to watch the colourful displays. In Molfetta, quilts are used to this day to adorn the streets for the procession. The *Blessing of the Fleet* ceremony is still held in Port Pirie every September, though quilts no longer form part of the display. Many Italians have now moved away from King Street and although the boats are still festooned, the street itself is not decorated as it was in the early years.

Renmark

The centre of the oldest irrigation area in Australia, the Riverland town of Renmark is approximately 250 kilometres north east of Adelaide. Founded by the Chaffey Brothers just over a century ago, the town has seen many changes. Once a thriving river port for paddle steamers, the river trade was to give way to rail and then to road transport. Irrigation has led to the establishment of thriving orchards of citrus and stone fruits, vegetable farms, and numerous wineries. A pepper tree on the corner of Renmark and Ral Ral Avenues is the last of many planted by the Chaffey Brothers to line the main street of the town.

Olivewood

Cnr. Renmark Avenue and 21st Street
Renmark, SA 5341.
Ph: (08) 8586 6175
10.00a.m. – 4.00p.m. Thursday to Monday.
2.00p.m. – 4.00p.m. Tuesday.
Closed Wednesday.
4 quilts.

✷ *The historic home of Olivewood was built in 1889 for Charles Chaffey and his family. Chaffey was Canadian and had come to South Australia with his brothers to establish the Renmark Irrigation Colony, Australia's oldest irrigation settlement. Olivewood was built in the style of a*

PHOTOGRAPHY ITALO VARDARO.

LEFT: *Patchwork Mosaic Quilt.* Unknown Maker, c.1880. RIGHT: Detail of *Pieced and Appliquéd Quilt.* Made by Mrs Charles Warren and still containing templates cut from newspapers dated 1869. National Trust of Australia (South Australia) – Olivewood, Renmark, S.A.

TOP: Detail of *Quilt of Tumbling Blocks*. Made by Mrs Coulter c.1880. 195cm x 195cm. ABOVE AND LEFT: *Pieced and Appliquéd Quilt.* Made by Mrs Charles Warren, c.1869. National Trust of Australia (South Australia) – Olivewood, Renmark, S. A.

ABOVE: *Art in Textiles.* Made by Northern Yorke Peninsula Quilters, 1993 - '95. 310cm x 110cm. District Council of the Copper Coast, Kadina, South Australia.

log cabin, similar to those of Chaffey's home-land. The property was extensive and included an olive grove, citrus and stone fruit orchards, vineyards, and fields of wheat and lucerne. Today it is owned by the National Trust and a museum of local history has been established in the original olive-oil house. The collection includes photographs and memorabilia of early Renmark as well as some beautiful examples of needlework. Enter the house from the 21st Street approach.

✷ The quilts are permanently displayed within the house and museum and may be seen during the opening hours listed.

✂ A beautiful quilt of Tumbling Block design (195cm x 195cm) was made by Mrs Coulter c.1880. Mrs Coulter lived at Yorketown on the southern end of Yorke Peninsula and it is believed that she was in her eighties when she created the quilt. Made from silk fabrics in plains, stripes, florals and plaids, the work has a cotton filling and a loosely woven cotton backing. It has been finely hand quilted in a grid design.

A frail but lovely pieced and appliquéd quilt is displayed behind glass in the museum. It was made by Mrs Charles Warren and still contains templates cut from newspapers dated 1869. The patchwork has been hand pieced from hexagons of silk, satin, brocade and velvet. Many of the patches feature embroidered and appliquéd flowers. A large spray of Australian wattle has been created from tiny pom poms and stitched to a background patch of black silk.

A patchwork mosaic quilt of unknown provenance was made in medallion style c.1880. It features a large central square of pieced stars with wide borders of hexagon rosettes, pieced diamonds and stars.

A quilt of printed cotton hexagon rosettes c.1960 is displayed in the nursery. It is of unknown maker and history.

Orroroo

The historic town of Orroroo is set in picturesque countryside on the edge of the southern Flinders Ranges. It is approximately 260 kilometres north of Adelaide. Many of the heritage buildings and original village shops still remain from the earliest days. The first house was built of pine in 1876 and is open to the public by appointment. Telephone (08) 8658 1219 or (08) 8658 1084.

Yesteryear Costume Gallery

50 Second Street
Orroroo, SA 5431.
Ph: (08) 8658 1032 Beth Catford.
10.00a.m. – 5.00p.m. most days.

The Yesteryear Costume Gallery has a collection of items dating from 1830 to the present. It was begun by Theresa Innes who used the heritage clothing to stage fashion parades in order to raise funds during World War II. Since the 1960s Beth Catford has continued her work, raising thousands of dollars for charity. The collection now comprises hundreds of items depicting the history of fashion through the years. It includes dresses, wedding gowns, bathers, heirloom underwear, nighties, and accessories. There are also examples of embroidery, lace, beading, and several Marcella and crocheted coverlets.

PHOTOGRAPHY NEIL RUSSACK.

✷ The items are displayed within the Gallery and may be seen during opening hours or by appointment.

✄ Two little Crazy Patchwork bags of unknown maker c.1890 were used to carry and protect prayer books. They were hand made from tiny remnants of silk, satin, velvet, and ribbons and each patch was outlined with herringbone stitch. They were lined with pale blue cotton and finished with scalloped lace and braided handles. There are also two patchwork cushion covers of unknown maker c.1890. One has been hand pieced from squares of plain and printed silks and edged with wide red fringing. The other features hand pieced squares, triangles and rectangles cut from printed cotton dress scraps.

In the Nearby Region

At Booleroo Centre, a half hour drive from Orroroo, a quilt of pictorial blocks was made by members of the Booleroo Centre of Quilts and donated to the new Medical Centre, 60 Stephens Street. The work was appliquéd, embroidered and quilted by hand and may be seen between 8.00a.m. and 8.00p.m. Monday to Friday and 8.00a.m. and 11a.m. Saturday. Members of the group recently completed a heritage quilt depicting buildings of the town. It hangs on permanent display in the Civic Centre, also located in Stephens Street.

Hawker

The outback town of Hawker is set in the central Flinders Ranges and is an important focal point for the many tourists visiting the area. During the 1870s and '80s it was the hub of a large wheat growing area but frequent and devastating droughts forced farmers from the land. Several historic buildings remain from this time including the old railway station, the Hawker Hotel and the Institute in which the quilt now hangs.

Hawker Institute
Elder Terrace
Hawker, SA 5434.
Ph: (08) 8648 4014 Hawker Motors
Service Station.
7.30a.m. – 6.00p.m. everyday.

✷ The quilt is hung in the foyer. It can be seen at any time through the front glass doors but for closer viewing the key is available from the service station.

✄ The Constitution Act Amendment was passed in December 1894 making South Australian women among the first in the world to be given the right to vote and stand for parliament. The *Women's Suffrage Centenary Quilt* was made in 1994 to commemorate this historic event. The work was initiated by Sharon Pippos and designed by Pam Watkins and Jo Naismith. Quiltmakers from far and wide participated in its creation. The centre features the women's suffrage centenary logo in its distinctive colours of purple and gold. Silhouettes of the makers frame the centre and are surrounded by pictorial blocks illustrating diverse aspects of the region's history. Many images pay tribute to the women, both past and present, who have worked so hard to make their world a better place. The work was pieced, appliquéd and embroidered by hand and machine.

Kadina

The largest town on Yorke Peninsula, Kadina is located 150 kilometres north west of Adelaide. It forms one of

LEFT: Detail of *Art in Textiles.* Made by Northern Yorke Peninsula Quilters, 1993 - '95. 310cm x 110cm. District Council of the Copper Coast, Kadina, South Australia.

the three corners making up the Copper Triangle with Wallaroo and Moonta. Also known as *Little Cornwall,* the region proudly guards its mining heritage. Each town has its own National Trust museum with displays illustrating the lifestyle of the Cornish miners of the 1860s. A Kernewek Lowender festival is held every two years to celebrate this rich heritage and special events are spread between the three towns. There are exhibitions of antiques, crafts, and quilts, as well as museum displays, open gardens and countless Cornish pasties.

District Council of the Copper Coast
Taylor Street
Kadina, SA 5554
Ph: (08) 8821 1600 Fax: (08) 8821 2736
9.00a.m – 5.00p.m. Monday to Friday.

✷ The quilt is hung on permanent display in the foyer of the Council building and visitors are welcome to see it during office hours.

✂ The magnificent *Art in Textiles* community quilt (310cm x 110cm) was designed and stitched by members of the Northern Yorke Peninsula Quilters between 1993 and '95. Photographs were applied to fabric to illustrate the diversity and development of the region. The virgin scrub, natural coastline, and the important industries of shipping, mining and farming were depicted across the top. Many of the heritage buildings of *Little Cornwall* were included, along with a photograph of Kate Cocks who epitomised the spirit and tenacity shown by so many of the early pioneering women. A dramatic black strip and bright stylised fish were used to separate the historic buildings on one side of the quilt from the industries depicted on the other. A ship being loaded with wheat was sewn next to silos and shearing sheds, mine shafts and miners. Even the sulphurous smog over the Wallaroo smelters was included. The quilt involved a multitude of techniques including hand and machine piecing, quilting, appliqué, embroidery and cyanotype. The fabric for the background was specially hand dyed. Each technique was chosen to suit the era being depicted, with traditional embroidery used on historic segments and machine embroidery on those representing life today.

Northern Yorke Peninsula Library
Graves Street
Kadina, SA 5554.
Ph: (08) 8821 2704
9.00a.m. – 5.00p.m. Tuesday to Friday.

✷ The quilt is displayed in the foyer of the Library and may be seen during the hours listed.

✂ The *Copper Triangle Heritage Quilt* (250cm x 200cm) was made in 1986 by the Northern Yorke Peninsula Quilters. The project celebrated 150 years of South Australian settlement. It featured pictorial blocks depicting aspects of community life, both past and present and was pieced, appliquéd and quilted by hand.

Moonta

It was near the site now occupied by Moonta that copper was first discovered. According to local folklore, a shepherd named Paddy Ryan noticed the ore in the diggings of a wombat burrow. Many of the town's original stone buildings still remain from the days of the mining boom. The old primary school now houses the National Trust Museum and contains countless relics from the early Cornish settlers. Included in the collection is a hand crocheted bedspread c.1900.

RIGHT: *Contrasts 3 Metamorphosis.* Made by Pam Jones, 1997. 130cm x 88cm. Collection Copper Triangle Gallery, Moonta Town Hall, Moonta, South Australia.

Moonta Town Hall
George Street
Moonta, SA 5558.
Ph: (08) 8825 2622
9.00a.m. – 5.00p.m. Monday to Friday.
1.00p.m. – 4.00p.m. Saturday and Sunday.

The Kernewek Lowender Art Collection is housed in the Copper Triangle Gallery upstairs in the Moonta Town Hall. During business hours the Council of the Copper Coast have a branch office on the ground floor and will direct you to the Gallery. It is also opened on weekend afternoons by volunteers.

✷ The quilt is hung on permanent display in the gallery and may be seen during the opening hours listed.

✄ This quilt, entitled *Contrasts 3 Metamorphosis,* (130cm x 88cm) was made by South Australian textile artist Pam Jones in 1997. It was exhibited at the biennial Kernewek Lowender Exhibition where it won the Local Artist Award. The quilt was the third in a series made by Pam exploring the contrasts in the environment. The Copper Triangle region in which she lives was almost completely cleared of native vegetation during the early days of white settlement. This was largely a result of the mining boom in the 1870s when trees were used as fuel for the stacks. Pioneering farmers also cleared the rural areas.

The quilt contrasts the environment of the past with its tailing heaps and dry barren landscape with the recent greening that has taken place. The mining areas have now been regenerated, sustainable farming has been promoted, and thousands of native trees and shrubs have been planted. The treeless plains are being replaced with a new green environment. The quilt has been made entirely from triangles, some representing the tailing heaps, others the trees and golden fields of grain in the regenerated landscape. The work was machine pieced and quilted and hand embroidered. It has a cotton batting and most of the fabrics were hand dyed.

Wallaroo

Wallaroo is the major port on the western coast of Yorke Peninsula. Like the other towns of the Copper Triangle, its history is closely linked with the discovery of vast deposits of copper ore. Many of the buildings constructed during the 1860s still remain. They have been listed by the National Trust who also conduct guided walking tours of the heritage precinct.

Wallaroo Heritage and Nautical Museum
The Old Post Office
Jetty Road
Wallaroo, SA 5556.
Ph: (08) 8823 2366 or (08) 8823 2843
10.30a.m. – 4.00p.m. Wednesday.
2.00 p.m. – 4.00p.m. Saturday, Sunday and school holidays.
10.00a.m. – 4.00p.m. Public holiday weekends. Other times by appointment.

The Museum is housed in the original post office c.1865 and has extensive displays illustrating the town's maritime history. Its collection includes a white embroidered tablecloth c.1900 from the Methodist Church and an embroidered cap made by nuns for the Catholic Church choir.

✷ The banner is hung on permanent display and may be seen during the opening hours listed.

✄ The large banner (240cm x 120cm) in the collection of the Museum was made in

1941 for the Wallaroo Fighting Forces Comforts Fund. Like those in Red Cross Collections, it was made to commemorate the names of soldiers as well as for fundraising. A 'Queen Competition' for queen of the Army, Navy and Airforce, was held at the same time. The banner features a large *'V'* for Victory appliquéd in red cotton. The signatures of all the men going off to war, as well as the name of each queen and many local townspeople surround the *'V'*. There are between three and four hundred signatures in total and each person paid a small donation for the privilege of being included.

Northern Yorke Peninsula Regional Health Service
Ernest Terrace
Wallaroo, SA 5556.
Ph: (08) 8823 2100
11.00a.m. – 8.00p.m. everyday.

✷ The quilt is permanently displayed in the foyer of the hospital and may be seen during the hours listed.

✄ This pictorial quilt (205cm x 105cm) was made between 1986 and '88 by the Northern Yorke Peninsula Quilters. The central oval depicts a rural scene featuring an appliquéd cottage, trees, and birds stitched to a strip pieced background. The borders of Australian iris and Crazy Patchwork were made from silk and satin using the technique of Stained Glass appliqué. The work was pieced, appliquéd and quilted entirely by hand.

Maitland

The township of Maitland is located in the centre of Yorke Peninsula just a short drive from Moonta. It is surrounded by a rich grain growing region and local residents say the countryside looks like a patchwork quilt during harvest time – the colours of the ripening wheat and barley contrasting dramatically with the brown earth bordering the fields.

Maitland National Trust Museum
Cnr. Gardiner and Kilkerran Terrace
Maitland, SA 5573.
Ph: (08) 8832 2220
2.00p.m. – 4.00p.m. Sundays, public and school holidays. Other times by appointment.

The National Trust Museum is housed in the original Maitland school building c.1877. The collection includes period clothing, christening gowns and hand made underwear. A crocheted bedspread is more than a century old. There are numerous examples of embroidered work and two cross stitch samplers of German origin dated 1892.

✷ The quilt is hung on permanent display within the Museum and may be seen during the opening hours listed.

✄ This *Farm Life Quilt* of embroidered squares (204cm x 142cm) was made in 1932 by one of the Misses Zacher of South Kilkerran, near Maitland. The Zachers were born in Australia of German descent and came to Yorke Peninsula around 1890. There were ten children in the family, including five girls, all of whom made a farm life quilt using these designs. Each quilt featured embroidered blocks alternated with plain squares which were embellished with a horn of plenty design. This work was either made by Meta or Hilda. The designs depicting farm animals, buildings and activities were published in regular instalments in the women's pages of the weekly newspaper, the *Adelaide Chronicle*. The quilts were exhibited at the Adelaide Show with prize money of twelve pounds for the best work.

Ceduna

The seaside town of Ceduna is located on the far west coast of Eyre Peninsula, approximately 780 kilometres from Adelaide. The centre of a farming and fishing community, it is nestled on the shores of Murat Bay and is the last stopping point of any size before crossing the vast Nullarbor Plain to Western Australia. Its sheltered bays, sandy coves, and nearby islands make it a popular holiday destination. An Oyster Festival is held during the long weekend in October and includes special entertainment, stalls, fireworks, and a colourful street parade of floats created by the local community.

The Old Schoolhouse National Trust Museum
Park Terrace
Ceduna, SA 5690.
Ph: (08) 8625 2210 or (08) 8625 3936
10.00a.m. – noon Monday, Tuesday, Friday and Saturday.
2.00p.m. – 4.00p.m. Wednesday.
10.00a.m. – noon and 2.00p.m. – 4.00p.m. Thursday.
Closed Sundays and public holidays.

The Museum occupies the original school house dating from 1912. Other heritage buildings have been relocated to the site and include the first Ceduna post office, gaol and a blacksmith's shop. The collection includes a large number of household items, clothes, and 'fancy work' done by women around the turn of the century. In addition to the patchwork quilt, there is a hand crocheted coverlet of white cotton made by Mrs Annie Edwards of Penong during the 1920s.

✷ The quilt is permanently displayed within the Museum and may be seen during the opening hours listed or at other times by arrangement.

✂ This Log Cabin quilt was made by hand during the early 1930s. It was created by the step-mother of Mrs A. J. Marchant who lived on a farm with her husband in the Maltee area, east of Ceduna. The design is known as Courthouse Steps and features blocks divided into four sections, strips of the same colour being placed on opposite sides of the central square. The fabrics used include silk, satin, cotton, lurex, and taffeta, and most are plain with a small number of plaids, stripes, and floral prints. The quilt has a heavy filling believed to be a blanket. It has been finished with a wide border of plain scarlet satin and backed with floral cretonne.

Port Lincoln

Port Lincoln overlooks the huge natural harbour of Boston Bay at the southern tip of Eyre Peninsula. It is nestled in picturesque rolling countryside dotted with sheep and grain farms and is the centre of a large fishing fleet. Its proximity to both rugged coastal areas as well as sheltered beaches makes it a popular tourist destination.

Port Lincoln Country Women's Association Hall
7 Hallett Place
Port Lincoln, SA 5606.
Ph: (08) 8682 3962 or (08) 8682 3474
10.00a.m. – 3.00p.m. Thursdays
or by appointment.
24 banners.

✷ The banners are hung on permanent display and may be seen during opening hours or at other times by arrangement.

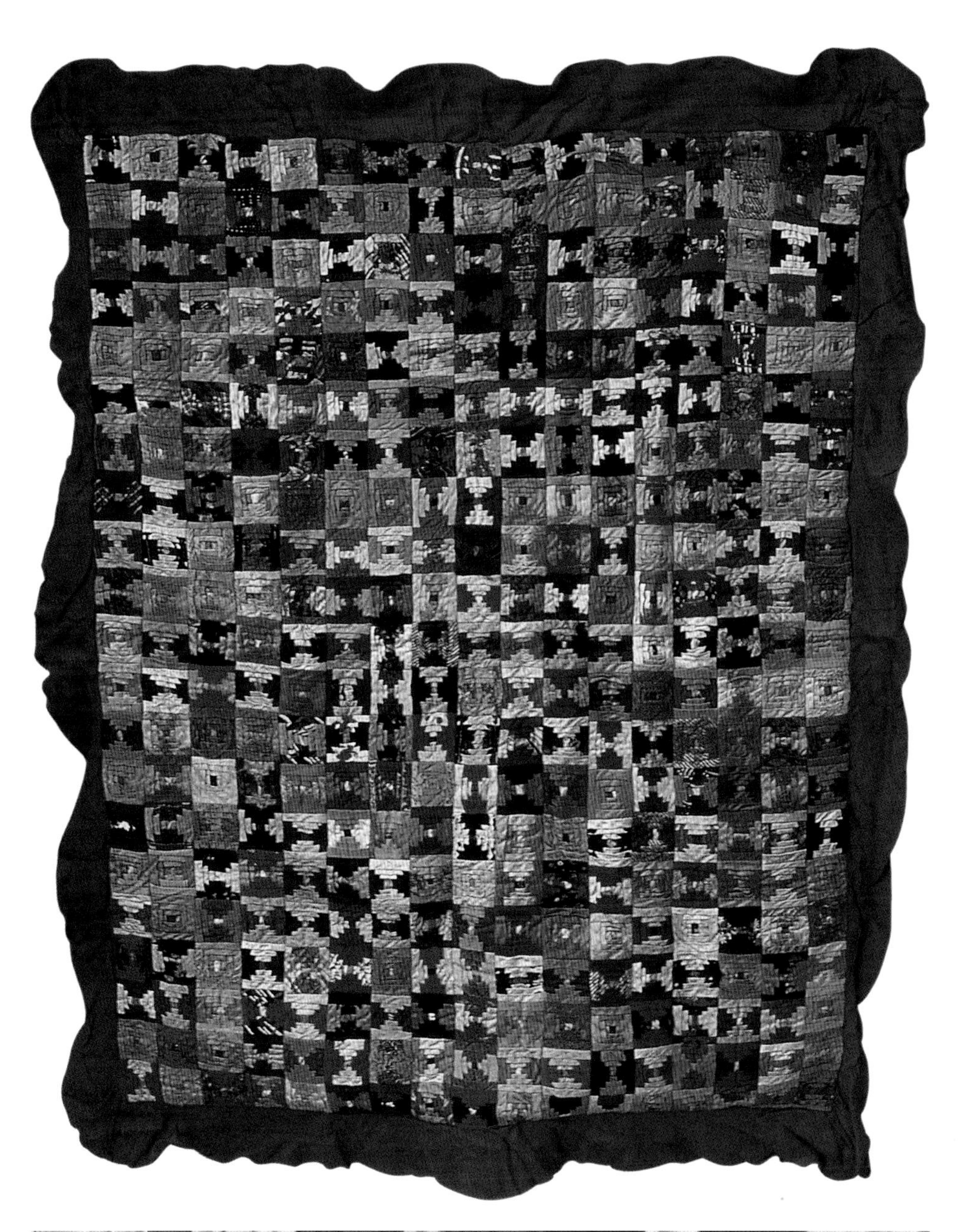

PHOTOGRAPHY CAROL SUTER.

RIGHT: *Log Cabin Quilt.* Made by Mrs A. J. Marchant's step-mother, c.1930. Collection Old Schoolhouse National Trust Museum, Ceduna, South Australia.

✂ This series of 24 banners (100cm x 65cm each) was created by the Country Women's Association and the Women's Auxiliary Branches of Eyre Peninsula. The project was designed to celebrate Jubilee 150 in 1986 and depicts the history of the Peninsula from earliest European settlement. The panels focus on the role played by pioneering women, presenting a unique pictorial story which details the harsh realities of their lives. Diverse images depict the tragedies they endured and the hardships they overcame with courage, spirit, and humour. Each banner was designed and made by a different group, some appliquéd by hand, others by machine. Faces were hand painted and many details were added with embroidery.

Tumby Bay

The picturesque little port of Tumby Bay, just 50 kilometres north of Port Lincoln, is an important centre for the vast inland grain properties of Eyre Peninsula. Its sheltered bays, excellent fishing, and beautiful offshore islands make it a popular tourist destination.

C.L. Alexander National Trust Museum

Cnr. West Terrace and Lipson Road
Tumby Bay, SA 5605.
Ph: (08) 8688 2574 (08) 8688 2501
(08) 8688 2050
2.30p.m. – 4.30p.m. Friday and Sunday.
Other times by appointment.
2 quilts and an embroidered net coverlet.

The Museum occupies an old wooden schoolhouse and separate rooms depict a kitchen, bedroom and parlour of the 1880s. In addition to the patchwork quilts there are many items of hand made crochet work.

✷ The quilts are not permanently displayed but visitors are welcome to see them by prior arrangement.

✂ A single bed coverlet of white Suffolk Puffs was made in 1914 by Mrs Fanny Creasy (nee Barber) of Lockiel, South Australia. Mrs Creasy created the quilt while recuperating from an accident, stitching the puffs by hand using fabric given to her by friends.

A large double-sided patchwork quilt of random cotton hexagons was made in Tumby Bay by Mrs Gladys Charlton c.1975. It is believed that Mrs Charlton was in her late 80s when she created it.

A net coverlet and matching pillow shams were hand embroidered with gold perle thread in 1916 as a wedding present for Mr and Mrs Don Stewart of Butler Tanks, near Tumby Bay. The maker is known only as a close friend of the Stewart's.

Kingston

The pretty coastal town of Kingston overlooks Lacepede Bay at the southern end of Coorong National Park. It is approximately 300 kilometres south east of Adelaide. Proximity to the shallow lakes and lagoons of the Coorong create a haven for an enormous variety of bird life, and the safe beaches and excellent fishing make the town a popular holiday location. The port serves the local lobster fishing industry and it is a charming site to watch the fleet returning to the jetty each afternoon between October and April with the day's catch.

Lacepede Bay District Council

29 Holland Street
Kingston S.E., SA 5275.
Ph: (08) 8767 2033 Fax: (08) 8767 2937
8.30a.m. – 5.00p.m. Monday to Friday.

✷ The quilt is hung on permanent display in the foyer of the building and may be seen during the hours listed.

✂ This unique wall hanging (240cm x 240cm) was made in 1986 by a group of local women to celebrate South Australia's Jubilee 150. Meg Douglas and Peg Sadler travelled to Kingston from Adelaide several times to provide guidance and work as artists-in-residence. The design was based on an aerial view of the town and surrounding countryside. The placid waters of Lacepede Bay, the sweep of coastline, the little township and rural properties were created in fabric to look just as they would from an aeroplane flying overhead.

The blocks of the town were machine embroidered, gaps left between them to represent streets. Grey bias binding was used for sealed roads with main roads edged with fine white cord to make them stand out. Upholstery materials were chosen to achieve the realistic landscape texture of the rural farmlands. Machine embroidery was used to blend the pieces together. A woolly merino sheep was created by looping threads through tapestry canvas and then clipping them to different lengths to achieve the wrinkly folds beneath the neck. Unravelled threads from upholstery fabrics were used to form seaweed, each one sewn to the calico sand using zig zag stitch. The Cape Jaffa Lighthouse was appliquéd to the foreshore and the ketch *Falie* to the water.

PHOTOGRAPHY JOHN PALUMBO.

OPPOSITE CENTRE: *Kingston Jubilee 150 Wall Hanging.* Made by local women, 1986. Lacepede Bay District Council, Kingston, S.E., South Australia. OPPOSITE, TOP: Details illustrating the woolly merino and the ketch *Falie.* OPPOSITE, BELOW: the Cape Jaffa lighthouse and the lobster.

PHOTOGRAPHY JOHN PALUMBO.

OPPOSITE: *Log Cabin Quilt.* Made by Pearl Toop, 1954. Collection National Trust Pioneer Museum, Kingston S.E., South Australia.
ABOVE: Pearl Toop and a detail of her quilt.

A hand embroidered lobster was stitched into the ocean, tiny red beads providing the life-like shine. This beautiful quilt took thousands of hours to complete. The finished top was stab quilted onto canvas, mounted to a timber backing and hung for the enjoyment of the entire community.

Cape Jaffa Lighthouse
Marine Parade
Kingston S.E., SA 5275.
Ph: (08) 8767 2050 Kingston Caravan Park.
(08) 8767 2114 Kathleen White.
2.00p.m. – 4.30p.m. daily during school and public holidays.
3 quilts.

The historic Cape Jaffa Lighthouse was build in 1867 on Margaret Brock Reef, eight kilometres offshore. In 1975, the National Trust dismantled the building from this rocky platform and re-erected it on the foreshore at Kingston. The lighthouse structure contained a small house and was one of the few in Australia in which people actually lived. It is now open to the public and provides a fascinating insight into the lives of the keepers and their families.

✷ The quilts are displayed on beds within the lighthouse and may be seen during opening hours or at other times by arrangement.

✂ These three quilts were created by members of the Kingston Branch of the National Trust especially for display in the lighthouse. The first, a quilt of random hexagons, was made between 1975 and '80 by Mrs Nancy McInness. Nancy stitched the work by hand using a variety of colourful cottons, sewing the patches together whilst working as a guide at the lighthouse. A quilt of Log Cabin design was made from scrap fabrics by an unknown member of the Trust during the 1970s. It has been finished with a pleated frill and backed with a cotton lining. The third quilt was made from random squares and rectangles by Kathleen White in 1988.

'Old and ugly' fabrics in colours of black, grey, and purple were combined effectively to create the work which is now to be seen on one of the original lighthouse beds.

National Trust Pioneer Museum
15 Cooke Street
Kingston S.E., SA 5275.
Ph: (08) 8767 2114 Mrs Kathleen White.
2.00p.m. – 4.00p.m. during school holidays or by request.

This folk museum is housed in a building constructed in 1872 and formerly used as part of the original timber mill. The collection includes photographs, clothing, and nautical items from the earliest days of the settlement of Kingston. There are examples of old crochet work, two 19th century wooden sewing boxes and a bobbin lace maker. A lovely wedding dress made c.1860 for Anne Maria Batten was never worn. It arrived from Scotland too late for the occasion and Anne was married in her riding-habit.

✷ The quilt is displayed on a bed within the Museum and may be seen during opening hours or by arrangement.

✂ This Log Cabin quilt was made by Mrs Pearl Toop in 1954. Pearl lived at Reedy Creek, about 19 kilometres from Kingston, and was a member of the Reedy Creek Methodist Church. Members of the Church Guild worked hard all year to make goods for the annual fete. Pearl created her quilt by machine, using colourful scraps and remnants from dresses. Some of the strips are extremely tiny and it is believed that she cut them from sample swatches sent out to the country by the big city stores. The work was backed with pink floral cotton and finished with a pleated frill of the same fabric. A blanket was enclosed between the layers for warmth. When Pearl arrived at the fete with her patchwork quilt, the other Guild members decided that it was

PHOTOGRAPHY JOHN PALUMBO.

ABOVE: *St Andrew's Jubilee 150 Quilt.* Made by members of St Andrew's Church Guild, 1986-'88. St Andrew's Anglican Church, Lucindale, South Australia. OPPOSITE: *Silk Mosaic Quilt.* Made by a member of the Chester Family, c.1870. 211cm x 223cm. Collection Millicent National Trust Museum, Millicent, South Australia. (Left) Detail of scalloped border with pieced star design. (Right) Detail of Prince of Wales feathers on central hexagon of pink fabric, reputed to have come from Queen Victoria's trousseau.

too difficult to put a price on it. Instead, it was sold by raffle for seven pounds ten shillings to Mr Alan Curkpatrick who presented it to his wife, Una. Alan and Una owned the quilt for more than forty years before donating it to the National Trust in 1995 when they sold their Reedy Creek farm.

Also in Kingston

There are two quilts hung on permanent display in the Uniting Church, Holland Street. The first was made in 1994 by thirty four women from the Parish. The theme was 'The drum-beats of His army are the heart beats of our love.' The quilt featured an army of hearts, each one made using a different technique. These included strip piecing, Crazy Patchwork, appliqué, tatting and cross stitch. Colours of burgundy and beige were chosen to co-ordinate with the stencilled wall decoration featured around the interior of the Church.

The second quilt was created in 1996 by eighteen members of the congregation. Using the theme 'Have I told you lately that I love you?,' it featured twenty blocks of patchwork, appliqué, embroidery and cross stitch. The quilts may be seen during Sunday morning services held at 9.30 and 11.00a.m., or at other times by arrangement. Please contact Mrs Katherine Lisk, (08) 8767 2597.

Lucindale

The little township of Lucindale is 40 kilometres west of Kingston and less than an hour's drive from Millicent. This small rural community is intensely proud of its town, and over the years Lucindale has been a consistent winner of the prestigious Tidy Town awards. It is also the home of the South East Field Days, held during the third weekend in March and including an exhibition of country quilts. The museum of local history is housed in the former railway station and is open by appointment. The collection includes a hand crocheted coverlet made by Hilda Thompson c.1900. Contact (08) 8766 2198 or (08) 8766 2367.

PHOTOGRAPHY JOHN PALUMBO.

St Andrew's Anglican Church

Cnr. Wattle and Sheoak Roads
Lucindale, SA 5272.
Ph: (08) 8766 2125 Mrs Phyll McDowell.
(08) 8768 9056 Mrs Julie Ewer.

Services are held on Sundays at 11.15a.m. except the first Sunday of each month when the time changes to 9.15a.m.

✷ The quilt is mounted on a timber frame and hung on permanent display at the back of the church. Visitors are welcome to see it. Please telephone in advance to make a time.

✄ This beautiful quilt (225cm x 196cm) was created between 1986 and '88 by the members of St Andrew's Church Guild. Made as a contribution to South Australia's Jubilee year celebrations, the design was created by Bessie Williams and Hazel Redway. The work depicts St Andrew, patron saint of the church, fishing in the Sea of Galilee. Above him, attached to the mast and billowing in the wind, is the flag bearing the St Andrew's Cross. The background of land and sea was made by hand piecing together the arched strips of fabric. The realistic colour variation in the sky was achieved by over laying with different shades of tulle. St Andrew's boat was appliquéd and embroidered by hand, darker thread being used to delineate the timber panels. The sail was made of furled material tied to the mast with cord. Actual fishing net was sewn to the base of the quilt and gathered to fit St Andrew's hands. His face was hand painted. The luminous fish were created from silver and red silk and satin, trimmed with sequins and stitched in place beneath the net. The work took more than two years to complete and Guild members went on to make two sets of beautiful vestments for the church.

Millicent

Founded in 1870, the town of Millicent is set in a prosperous pastoral region about an hour's drive south of Lucindale. It is surrounded by pine and blue gum plantations and the renowned wineries of the Coonawarra region are only a short distance away. The magnificent Millicent Community Tapestry, woven by forty weavers from the district, now hangs on permanent display in the Millicent Library. It may be seen daily except Monday. Telephone (08) 8733 2602.

Millicent National Trust Museum

1 Mount Gambier Road
Millicent, SA 5280.
Ph: (08) 8733 1192 Museum.
(08) 8733 3205 Tourist Centre.
(telephone and fax are the same)

9.30 a.m. – 4.30 p.m. daily.

The award winning Millicent National Trust Museum is housed in the original primary school c.1873. It is adjacent to the Tourist Information Centre and Admella Gallery. Displays are grouped within themes and the collection includes pioneer relics, household appliances, costumes and beautifully restored horse drawn vehicles dating from the 1840s. There are two framed cross stitch samplers, one of which is believed to have been made in Scotland during the early 18th century.

✷ The quilt is permanently displayed and may be seen during opening hours.

✄ This beautiful silk mosaic quilt (211cm x 223cm) dates from the second half of the 19th century. It is believed that the patchwork was begun by a member of the Chester family who was employed at Balmoral Castle, though where the work was completed is unknown. Dates and initials have been embroidered around the central star and record the births and deaths of family members. The work has been made from hexagons, diamonds and triangles in the English method over paper templates. The central hexagon features the Prince of Wales feathers and the fabric is reputed to have come from Queen Victoria's trousseau. The quilt is lined with pink muslin and backed with ivory glazed muslin. The lovely scalloped border features a star design.

Mount Gambier

Mount Gambier is set on the slopes of an extinct volcano and is surrounded on all sides by pine forests. The Blue Lake lies within the crater of the volcano, its colour changing mysteriously to a deep blue every November and reverting back to grey-green the following April. Heritage walks take visitors past the many historic buildings remaining from the 1860s, most of them built of the distinctive white Mount Gambier stone.

District Council of Grant

324 Commercial Street West
Mount Gambier, SA 5290.
Ph: (08) 8721 0444 Fax: (08) 8721 0410
9.00a.m. – 5.00p.m. Monday to Friday.

✷ The quilt is hung on permanent display in the foyer of the building and may be seen during office hours. Weekend viewing is also possible by appointment with the District Manager. Telephone (08) 8725 6691.

✄ This heritage wall hanging (220cm x 236cm) was designed by local artist Bev Puckridge, convened by Jan Tregoweth, and made by the Pine Tree Quilters in 1990. Pictorial blocks depict the rural industries and historic buildings of Mount Gambier and the surrounding countryside. Members of the group toured the region, photographing all possible areas of interest to be included on the quilt. Every rural industry was represented and native birds and animals were embroidered within triangular blocks across the top and bottom. The quilt was appliquéd, embroidered and quilted by hand.

Riddoch Art Gallery

6 Commercial Street
Mount Gambier, SA 5290.
Ph: (08) 8723 9566 Fax: (08) 8723 9161
10.00a.m. – 4.00p.m. Tuesday to Friday.
10.00a.m. – 2.00p.m. Saturday.
12.00noon – 3.00p.m. Sunday.

The Art Gallery is housed in the 19th century Old King's Theatre. Its collection includes traditional and contemporary works and features art in wood, works of local significance, as well as a touring exhibition programme.

✷ The quilt may be seen by appointment. Please contact the Curator by telephone or letter one week in advance.

✄ A medallion quilt entitled *Lancaster* (143cm x 143cm) was created by Jan Tregoweth and acquired by the gallery in 1990. Made using traditional Amish materials and designs, its centre features a Lancaster County Diamond-in-a-square. The fabrics are purple, black and grey cottons purchased by Jan in Pennsylvania. The work was hand quilted in feather and pumpkin-seed flower designs.

Penola

The charming town of Penola is approximately 50 kilometres north of Mount Gambier and only a short drive from the Coonawarra district. The oldest town in the region, it has retained much of the original 19th century character. There are fine examples of slab and hewn-timber houses which were built by settlers in the 1850s. The picturesque Heritage Area of Petticoat Lane is renowned for its quaint cottages, red gum kerbing and roses. The Blessed Mary MacKillop, anticipated to become Australia's first Saint, lived in Penola 130 years ago. The Woods MacKillop Schoolhouse, the first in the country to cater for students regardless of income or social class, can still be seen today in Petticoat Lane.

Penola War Memorial Hospital

Church Street
Penola, SA 5277.
Ph: (08) 8737 2311 Fax: (08) 8737 2505
24 hours a day.

✷ The quilt is hung on permanent display in the foyer of the hospital and may be seen at any time.

✄ This heritage quilt (152 x 102cm) was made in 1990 by the Penola Quilters. Ten appliquéd and embroidered blocks have been framed within red borders and depict the historic buildings and rural activities of the region. Many of the blocks illustrate the stone and timber cottages for which Penola is renowned. One of them, Sharam's Cottage, was built in 1850 and is the oldest house in Petticoat Lane. Beef cattle, pine plantations and the Wynn's Coonawarra Estate are also included. The quilt was made from cotton fabrics using hand and machine appliqué, embroidery and quilting.

PHOTOGRAPHY JOHN PALUMBO.

ABOVE: *Silk Mosaic Quilt.* Made by a member of the Chester Family, c.1870. 211cm x 223cm. Collection Millicent National Trust Museum, Millicent, South Australia.

Mundulla

Mundulla is found in the heart of the Tatiara Region about a 10 minute drive south west of Bordertown and less than 3 hours from Adelaide. First settled by Scottish pastoralists in 1846, the area is known as *Big Gum Country* because of the huge and majestic Red Gums, many of them 300 years old. It is particularly beautiful in Spring when the canola crop transforms the paddocks to a bright yellow patchwork. Many of the original buildings of Mundulla remain just as they were when built in the 1880s and a walking tour has been prepared for visitors.

Old Mundulla Hotel
Kennedy Street
Mundulla, SA 5270.
Ph: (08) 8753 4044
After hours: (08) 8752 1346
10.00a.m. – 5.00p.m. Thursday & Sunday.
10.00a.m. – midnight Friday and Saturday.
Closed Monday to Wednesday.

The Old Mundulla Hotel has had many lives. Built in 1875, it opened first as a general store, serving later as a hotel, hardware shop, and then a residence. It was saved from demolition by the local Rotary Club who raised a deposit enabling its purchase by the National Trust in 1974. It is now run as a restaurant, pioneer museum and art gallery. Museum pieces are displayed throughout the building, and in addition to the quilt there is a variety of embroidered linen, old clothing, and a large collection of hand crocheted items.

✷ The quilt is permanently displayed on an old iron bed in the upstairs bedroom and may be seen during the opening hours listed.

✄ This patchwork quilt of hexagon rosettes is of unknown maker and history. It came to the museum from the National Trust during the early 1970s. The work dates from the turn of the century and has been hand stitched in the English method over paper templates. The design is unusual. It features hexagon rosettes contained within square blocks. The blocks have been created from hexagons of brown printed cotton and separated from each other by a sashing of hexagons. Cotton dress and shirting materials from the period have been used for the work, each rosette carefully cut to show the same fabric print. The quilt has no backing and the honeycomb of hand stitching is clearly visible on the reverse.

Pieced and Appliquéd Quilt. Made by Sarah Evans, c.1806. 226cm. x 251cm.
National Trust of Australia (W.A.) – Woodbridge Historic Home, Guildford, W.A.

QUILTS OF
WESTERN
AUSTRALIA

Art Gallery of Western Australia
Perth Cultural Centre
James Street Mall
Perth, WA 6000.
Ph: (08) 9492 6600 Fax: (08) 9492 6655
Registration Department.
10.00a.m. – 5.00p.m. daily.
Approximately 12 quilts.

The State Art Collection at the Art Gallery of Western Australia contains 211 textile works. These have been acquired within the Gallery's main collection areas of Western Australian, Australian, and International Art. The majority of works are post 1960 and reflect the main streams of textile and fibre art practice of the past thirty years. They have been acquired to illustrate excellence and innovation in technique, use of material, development of form, strength of narrative content and formal presentation. There are examples of weaving, tapestry, embroidery, appliqué, quilting, printing, thread constructions and assemblage. While quilts do not form a separate category of the collection, many of the processes of quilting appear as key elements in a number of textile works. This reveals the importance and accessibility of the practice within the broader field of contemporary Australian textile art.

✷ Quilts that are not on current display are housed on site in the collection store. Supervised public access is permitted by appointment on Wednesday only of each week. Requests should be made by letter or telephone to the Registration Department two weeks in advance. Appointments are generally limited to 30 minutes and to a maximum of six people at any one time.

✄ The collection includes a quilt entitled *Dust to Dust* made by Western Australian textile artist Elsje van Keppel in 1996. This contemporary work of two panels(200cm x 96cm each) takes as its underlying structure the traditional

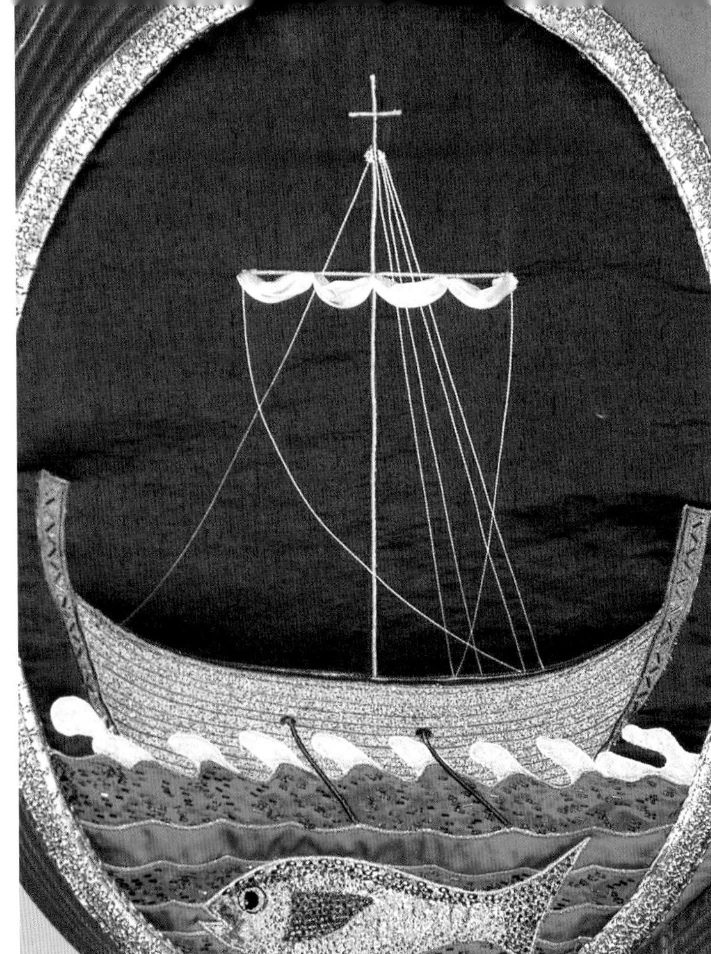

ABOVE: Details of *St Mary's Altar and Lectern Frontals.* Made by Ivy O'Sullivan, 1996. 270cm x 100cm and 120cm x 72cm. St Mary's Catholic Cathedral, Perth. OPPOSITE: *Dust to Dust.* Made by Elsje van Keppel, 1996. Silk, dyed and stitched, 200cm x 96cm. Collection Art Gallery of Western Australia, Perth.

Log Cabin design, described by Elsje as *'a metaphor for women's practicality, resourcefulness and frugality.'*

The fabrics used for the work were dyed in bush leaves and bark collected during a camping trip to the desert. The batik images were printed by Indonesian friends using designs based on the scarred walls Elsje had noticed in a building undergoing renovation. The many layers of paint had been removed to expose the red dust from which the bricks had originally been made. The artist says of *Dust to Dust* that it *'speaks of our compulsion to build and of nature as an unfolding process.'*

Eclipse of the Son (117cm x 91cm) was made in 1990 by Victorian textile artist Rose Marie Szulc. This work combines religious imagery with a personal, diary-like assemblage of ideas. It has been created using a combination of appliqué, machine stitchery, printing and paint on fabrics of cotton, silk and acetate.

Quilt Cover (282cm x 220cm) was made in 1984 by Western Australian textile artist Kate Weedon-Jones and was designed for either horizontal or vertical use. Its large scale geometric designs and strong colours present a unique work of contemporary art while at the same time continuing the tradition of the pieced quilt. It was created from cotton fabrics using silk screen printing, appliqué and quilting.

The Road to Nowhere (165cm x 165cm) was made by Queensland textile artist Ruth Stoneley in 1986. The work formed part of her series of black quilts and was made from a variety of black cottons, silks and chintz. It depicts a theme of confusion, of not knowing where to go or how to get there. The central wholecloth panel is covered with quilted lines that do not join together. It is surrounded by a pieced border which has been heavily quilted and beaded.

Wave 1 (132cm x 132cm) was made by Victorian textile artist Barbara Macey in 1980 and was the first of a series illustrating abstract wave forms. Barbara created this highly individual work of contemporary art entirely from black materials. It features many waves running diagonally across its surface, the clear distinction between them apparent because of the variety in sheen and texture in the different cotton lawns, taffetas and satins.

St Mary's Catholic Cathedral

Victoria Square
Perth, WA 6000.
Ph: (08) 9325 9177 Fax:(08) 9221 1716
The office is open between
9.00a.m. and 5.00p.m.
Monday to Friday.
Services are held daily. Please contact the office for times.
Altar and lectern frontals.

✷ The frontals are always displayed in the Cathedral during the Easter and Christmas seasons, as well as for special celebrations held throughout the year. They may be viewed at other times by appointment. Please contact the church office one week in advance.

✂ These stunning altar and lectern frontals were designed and made by Western Australian textile artist Ivy O'Sullivan in 1996.

The colours are richly symbolic, the images based on ancient symbols. The pelican and her chicks depicted in the central oval of the altar frontal were inspired by the illustration on a floor tile in the Blessed Sacrament Chapel. The sailing ship on the lectern frontal was also based on a floor tile, this time from the St Therese Chapel. Originally the image of the pelican feeding her babies with her own blood was a pagan symbol. Over time within the church, the five drops of blood came to represent the five wounds of Christ and was widely used to typify the Lord's redeeming work. The peace and quiet of the nest in which the pelican tends her young became a metaphor for the nurturing of the congregation through prayer. The ship was also used in early religious symbolism. The word *'nave'* was used to refer to *'the aisle of a church'* just as it was to *'a sailing ship'*. Both it seems, were considered a means by which the faithful were guided into a safe haven.

The red, blue, and green fabrics reflect the shades of the stained glass in the windows above the Sanctuary and all the colours embody strong religious meaning. Paper mock-ups of the designs were made before the work was transferred to fabric. It was essential that the frontals be bold enough to be clearly visible at the back of this very long building. The colours had to match the church windows and also provide an illuminating focal point in the dark Sanctuary area. Fabrics of silk and satin were chosen for their richness and brilliance. Each piece was created separately and then hand stitched to the background. The golden wing of the pelican was heavily machine embroidered and beaded. The nest was made from a variety of yarns which were stitched together to create a wide braid and then manipulated into place. The frontals were finished with machine quilting and then mounted onto specially crafted wooden frames.

West Australian Quilters' Association

Nedlands Yacht Club
The Esplanade
Nedlands, WA 6009.
Ph: (08) 9447 6840 President.
(08) 9330 1603 Secretary.
Regular meeting days are:
7.30p.m. 1st Wednesday of the month.
10.00a.m. – 3.00p.m 3rd Tuesday.
7.30p.m. 3rd Wednesday.
9 quilts.

The suburb of Nedlands is a short drive south west of the city centre.

The West Australian Quilters' Association began in 1976, one of the earliest to be formed in the country. Its aims were to advance the craft of patchwork and quilting in the state, provide information for members and arrange exhibitions. Today there are approximately 800 members and more than eighty home groups. The Association has a very comprehensive library of books and magazines, runs regular workshops, retreats and symposia, and has introduced a teacher accreditation programme. Major biennial exhibitions are held and the Quilters' Quarterly newsletter keeps both city and country members notified of forthcoming events and developments.

✷ Visitors are welcome to attend meetings of the Association and quilts may be viewed by prior arrangement with the President. Please contact in advance by telephone or letter. Postal address: PO Box 188, Subiaco, WA 6904.

The Contemporary Quilt Collection

✂ *Birds in Flight* (150cm x 250cm) was made in 1977, the first group work created by WAQA members. A scrap quilt of triangles, it was quilted by hand using a design of Prince of Wales Feathers.

The *10th Anniversary Celebration Quilt* (107cm x 140cm) was designed by Marjorie Coleman and made by members in 1986. An appliquéd quilt with sky blue background, it features ten stylised Bull Banksias symbolising the Association's 10th Anniversary.

Amethyst Magic (82cm x 98cm) was designed and made by Mignonne Marsh in 1991. Celebrating the Association's 15th Anniversary, it depicts crystals in many shades of soft mauves and pinks and was strip pieced by machine.

From the Country to the City (100cm x 120cm) was made by members of the Mount Magnet Craft Group for WAQA's 20th Anniversary in 1996. It was designed by Catherine Jensen and reflects the bond that develops through quiltmaking between women living in an urban environment and those from distant places. The work depicts the long journey undertaken by quilters living in the mining towns and farming communities to the north of the state as they travel the vast distances to reach Perth. A message on the back explains

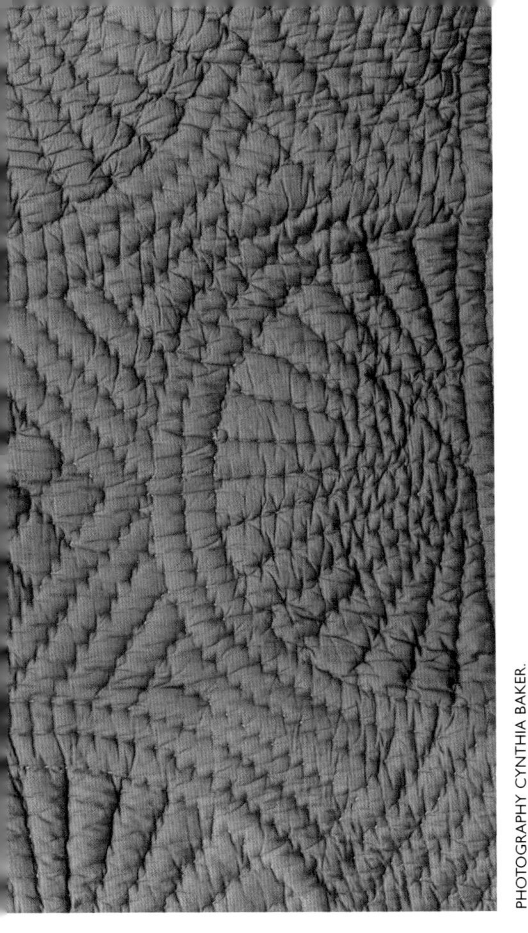

PHOTOGRAPHY CYNTHIA BAKER.

LEFT: *Greek Wholecloth Quilt.* Unknown maker, c.1945. Donated to the West Australian Quilters' Association by Katerina Marino. 186cm x 202cm. Collection WAQA, Nedlands, W.A. RIGHT: Detail of *Festal Frontal* showing Honeyeater. Made by Ivy O'Sullivan, 1997. 180cm x 90cm. All Saints Church, Greenwood.

that it is quiltmaking that provides *'the binding thread that will increase our understanding and compassion for each other, wherever we live, and our resulting awareness that will enhance and influence Australia's future direction.'* The work was machine pieced, hand appliquéd and hand quilted. The fabrics were hand dyed and painted.

The Historical Quilt Collection

A beautiful Greek wholecloth quilt (186cm x 202cm)of deep blue chintz was donated to the Association by Katerina Marino. It was a Greek tradition that parents must provide a quilt for the glory box of each daughter. These quilts came in various thicknesses depending on the warmth required. The thicker quilts were sometimes put on the floor and used as mattresses because many people did not have beds and others required extra bedding for guests. Some of the quilts were made large enough to cover six people as occasions arose when whole families would sleep together. This quilt was made on the island of Rhodes in the mid 1940s. It was stitched entirely by hand and the padding of wool was scoured by hand. Mrs Marino purchased it in 1948 and brought it with her to Australia four years later. It has been in storage for most of the past fifty years as the Australian climate negated the need for such a heavy cover.

A doll's quilt of medallion design (56cm x 56cm) was made by Kathleen Hada of California. It features a central Square-within-a-square and was donated to the Association by American quilter, Ruth Briggs.

An early 20th century Durham quilt (202cm x 222cm) is of unknown maker. It has been pieced from strips of deep green polished cotton and hand quilted in a traditional English pattern.

A silk patchwork table-runner (28cm x 138cm) is of unknown maker, c.1890. It features a row of eight-pointed stars surrounded by a border of triangles and squares. The work has been meticulously hand sewn over paper templates.

Royal Western Australian
Historical Society Museum

Stirling House
49 Broadway
Nedlands, WA 6009.
Ph: (08) 9386 3841 Fax: (08) 9386 3309
9.30a.m. – 3.30p.m. Monday to Friday.
1 quilt, a patchwork tablecloth and
small items of patchwork.

The Royal Western Australian Historical Society was founded in 1926. It has played a pioneer role in conserving and interpreting the state's social history. There is an extensive reference library for members and a monthly newsletter provides details of forthcoming activities. There is also a bookshop which is open to the public. The Society's Museum was

From the Country to the City. Made by members of the Mount Magnet Craft Group, 1996. 100cm x 120cm.
Collection West Australian Quilters' Association, Nedlands, W.A.

established to house the many records, photographs, paintings and other items of historical significance. The costume collection includes clothing owned by the earliest settlers of the state and some items date back to 1829. There are embroidered collars and cuffs, bed and table linen, samples of tatting and a large collection of lace.

✷ The patchwork is not on permanent display but may be seen by arrangement. Please contact the Museum one week in advance, if possible on a Tuesday when several members of the Society are available to speak to visitors.

✂ The collection includes a beautiful Log Cabin cloth with lace edging c.1890 (72cm x 72cm) of unknown maker. The pattern of light and dark concentric diamonds enclosing a dark central square is known as Barn Raising. The fabrics include brilliantly coloured silk, satin, and velvet with a dark pink backing. The double edging of wide cotton lace stitched around the outside of the patchwork suggests that it was intended for use in a Victorian drawing room.

A Crazy Patchwork quilt c.1890 (135cm x 115cm) is also of unknown provenance. Made from fabrics of silk, velvet, brocade and cotton, each patch has been outlined with feather and herringbone stitch. The quality of the sewing varies throughout the work suggesting that it may have been made by more than one person. It has been edged with braid and has a lining of unbleached calico.

A Crazy Patchwork tea cosy of unknown maker has been created from silk and brocade fabrics. Each patch has been embroidered with feather stitch and embellished with little motifs. The reverse side has been made from velvet patches over which gold thread work has been couched in wavy lines. Tiny pieces of gold silk fabric have been used to create a feathered edging around the outside.

All Saints Church

7 Liwara Place
Greenwood, WA 6024.
Ph: (08) 9447 6225 Fax: (08) 92462692
church office.
The church office is open between
10.00a.m. and 3.00p.m Monday,
Wednesday and Friday.
Services are held on Saturday at
6.30p.m. and Sunday at 7.30a.m.,
9.00a.m., and 10.30a.m.

The suburb of Greenwood is located approximately 10 minute's drive north of the city centre.

✷ The frontal is displayed in the presbytery and visitors are welcome to see it. Please contact the church office 24 hours in advance.

✂ This festal frontal (180cm x 90cm) was designed and made by Ivy O'Sullivan in 1997. It commemorates the 40th anniversary of the ordination of Father Pat Ahern. The shamrocks represent his Irish heritage, the wattle his Australian birth, and the Kangaroo Paws his home state. The large birds are New Holland Honeyeaters which are frequent visitors to gardens within the vicinity of the church. They were included as symbols of the faithful community feeding at the table of the Lord. *'Where two or three are gathered in my name, I shall be with them.'* (Matthew 18:20).

Each appliquéd piece was created individually and stitched in place to the hand painted background. More than 400 separate wattle flowers were made, each one created by wrapping yarn around a tap washer and securing the threads in the centre by machine. The threads were then cut to remove the washer and release the loops into pom-pom blossoms. Hand dyed fabric was used to create the Kangaroo Paws which were machine embroidered, padded, and hand stitched into position. The Honeyeaters were also machine embroidered and hand sewn in place. Their heads and bodies were padded, their wings wired and then manipulated to stand in relief from the background. While Father Ahern is no longer the parish priest at All Saints, his life and commitment to the church will long be remembered in this inspiring textile art work.

The Water Corporation

John Tonkin Water Centre
629 Newcastle Street
Leederville, WA 6007.
Ph: (08) 9420 2827 Fax: (08) 9420 2500
9.00a.m. – 1.00p.m. Fridays
by appointment.

The suburb of Leederville is located a few minutes drive north west of the city centre.

✷ The quilt is hung on permanent display in the Corporation's board room. The room is often in use but Friday mornings are usually free. Please fax or telephone a few days in advance to arrange a time. Contact the Secretary, Facilities Management.

✂ This quilt entitled *Undercurrents* (118cm x 150cm) was made in 1994 by Western Australian fibre artist Alison Schwabe. It was designed as an entry for the Water Corporation's Inaugural Art Award and depicts the flow of water

ABOVE: Detail of *Undercurrents.* Made by Alison Schwabe, 1994. 118cm x 150cm. The Water Corporation, Leederville, W.A.

currents in a river. Declared one of two joint winners, it was purchased for display in the company's Head Office. The background of the quilt consists of repeat blocks through which strips of fabric have been inserted to form random wavy lines. Cotton and cotton blend fabrics were used in colours of blue, brown, grey and green. Some were hand dyed. The work was quilted by machine using shiny metallic lamé thread.

Warwick Leisure Centre

Cnr. of Wanneroo and Warwick Roads
Warwick, WA 6027.
Ph: (08) 9342 4977 Fax: (08) 9342 8297
8.30a.m. – 10.00p.m. Monday to Friday.
8.00a.m. – 7.00p.m. Saturday and Sunday.

The suburb of Warwick is located 17 kilometres north of the city centre.

✷ The triptych is hung on permanent display in the foyer of the Centre and may be seen during opening hours.

✂ This magnificent mural entitled the *Wanneroo Fibre Triptych* (3.5m x 2m) was designed and directed by local textile artist Jennie Abbott. It was created during 1990 and its making involved more than 360 people. A full-sized colour design was prepared encompassing both the history and landscape of the region and using the theme 'Diversity of Life' in Wanneroo.'

Jennie encouraged the use of the widest possible range of textile crafts to represent the beautiful limestone reefs, the beaches, wetlands, city, rural areas and bush. The Lacemaking Guild created exquisite three dimensional wild flowers and gum leaves. The Weavers' Guild used hand spun and dyed woollen threads to represent the local tuart trees and banksia. Recognisable community figures were added by transferring photographic images to fabric using free machine stitching. Other techniques included spinning, hand and machine appliqué and embroidery, patchwork, felting, fabric dyeing and airbrushing.

Tranby House
Johnson Road
Maylands, WA 6051.
Ph: (08) 9272 2630
2.00p.m. – 5.00p.m. Tuesday to Saturday.
11.00a.m. – 5.00p.m. Sunday.
Closed Christmas Day, Good Friday, and the month of June.
2 quilts.

The Maylands peninsula is located approximately 6kms east of Perth.

The National Trust property of Tranby House sits on a rise above the banks of the Swan River. Originally known as Peninsula Farm, it was built in 1839 for Joseph Hardey. It has been furnished according to the style of the period from 1800 to 1850 and there are some fine examples of needlework to be seen.

✷ The quilts are permanently displayed on beds within the house and may be seen during opening hours.

✂ Two quilts have been made in recent years and donated to the National Trust as suitable coverings for the old beds at Tranby House. A hand pieced and quilted cot quilt of Bow Tie design was created in 1986 by Maureen Hart. The Bow Ties were made from multi-coloured cotton fabrics, the background squares from calico. An Autograph Cross quilt was made by members of the West Australian Quilters' Association in 1986. The work was hand pieced using the English method over paper templates in fabrics of blue cotton and calico. The names of the makers were hand embroidered to the central square of each block and the work was finished with hand quilting.

Also in Perth

A constantly changing display of member's work is to be seen at the headquarters of the Embroiderers' Guild of Western Australia. The building is located south of the city at 565 Canning Highway, Alfred Cove and visitors are always welcome. Postal address: PO Box 85, Applecross, W.A., 6153. Telephone (08) 9330 3065.

Also south of the city, at the Uniting Church, 16 Herald Avenue, Willetton, there are three beautiful quilts displayed on the walls of the octagonal-shaped chapel. Entitled *Southern Cross, Rainbow* and *Creation,* they were designed and made by members of the congregation. Visitors are welcome to see them. Please contact the parish office in advance. Telephone (08) 9354 5723.

Guildford

The historic town of Guildford is set in the picturesque Swan Valley, only a 30 minute drive east of Perth. The area was discovered and named by Captain James Stirling during an expedition in 1827 to find suitable land for a new settlement. Today, Guildford still retains the atmosphere and charm of an English country village and many of the original buildings remain from the colonial period. The Swan Valley is home to some of Australia's best known and most historic wineries and many of the vignerons welcome visitors to their cellars. There are art galleries, restaurants, antique and craft shops scattered throughout the region.

Guildford Grammar School, which had its beginnings at Woodbridge, has a magnificent chapel in which beautiful tapestry kneelers can be viewed by appointment. The school's *Centennial Quilt*, made by Margaret Lamb, wife of a former staff member, may also be seen. Contact the School Archivist. Telephone (08) 9377 9212.

Woodbridge Historic Home
Ford Street
West Midland
Guildford, WA 6055.
Ph: (08) 9274 2432 Woodbridge.
(08) 9321 6088 National Trust Headquarters.
1.00p.m. – 4.00p.m. Monday to Saturday.
Closed Wednesday.
11.00a.m. – 5.00p.m. Sunday and public holidays.
8 quilts.

The gracious Victorian mansion of Woodbridge is located on Captain Stirling's original property along the banks of the Swan River, just north east of Guildford. Built between 1883-'85, the home belonged to Charles Harper, a successful pastoralist, parliamentarian, and part owner of the West Australian newspaper. The school that was opened by Harper in the billiard room of the house was to form the beginning of Guildford Grammar.

Meticulously restored by the National Trust, Woodbridge reflects life during the late Victorian era and has been furnished with paintings, antiques, and memorabilia, some of which belonged to the Harper family.

✷ The collection is held in storage except for special exhibitions and short periods of display. The quilts may be seen by prior appointment. Please contact Sarah Murphy at Trust Headquarters.

✄ The collection comprises some very significant historical quilts including one of the oldest in the country. This large and magnificent quilt of appliquéd squares (226cm x 251cm) was made in England by Sarah Evans in 1806. An accomplished needlewoman, Sarah embroidered her name and the date in cross stitch on the back. The quilt was found in a box of oddments purchased from an auction held at Mentmore Towers, an English stately home.

The work is beautifully stitched in a naive and whimsical style. It features three rows containing large squares, each one having a central cameo of calico on which a fanciful motif has been sewn. The large squares have been framed and separated from each other by smaller squares appliquéd with lively designs. A wide border of red and blue printed triangles has been sewn around the outside of the quilt and every red triangle has a single leaf stitched to its centre.

Almost two hundred years old, the cotton fabrics in brown, pink, blue, orange, and green prints still hold their vivid colours. The appliquéd motifs include twigs, daisies, and vases of sunflowers and tulips. Smaller squares feature hearts, fans, circles, and single leaves. The work is a counterpane with no filling or quilting and has a backing of cream cotton twill. Ref.603

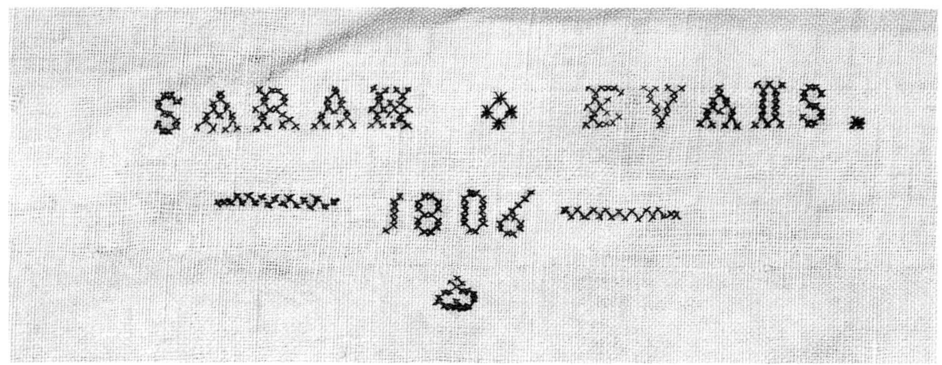

ABOVE: Detail of *Pieced and Appliquéd Quilt* and the embroidered signature of the maker, Sarah Evans, 1806. Collection National Trust of Australia (W.A.) – Woodbridge Historic Home, Guildford, W.A.

PHOTOGRAPHY PATRICK BAKER.

A medallion quilt (265cm x 218cm) of unknown maker dates from the mid 19th century. The central square has been made from four large triangles and surrounded by successive borders of Sawtooth triangles, Squares-on-point, and Four Patch blocks. The fabrics are printed cottons in colours of brown, pink and blue, with an outer border of brown and pink floral chintz. Ref. 83/156

A lovely quilt of large hexagon blocks was made in County Down, Ireland by Jane Pattern c.1850. It is believed to have been hand stitched by candlelight. Made from cotton fabrics, the hexagon blocks form three graphic rows which are separated from each other by sashing strips of multi-coloured rosettes. The colours are blue, brown, beige and pink. The work has no filling, is backed with heavy cream cotton, and every hexagon has been finely quilted. Ref. 76/27

A quilt of Grandmother's Flower Garden design is also attributed to Jane Pattern c.1850. The quilting has been finely stitched in an all-over chevron pattern typical of Irish quiltmakers of the time. The fabrics used for the rosettes are printed cottons of blue, pink, and brown with a background of cream calico. Ref. 76/27

A beautiful hexagon medallion quilt (205cm x 192cm) was made c.1860 by Mrs S. Morrison of Stornoway, a fishing port on the island of Lewis just off the coast of Scotland. The central square features a large hexagon created around a brown rosette. It has been framed by successive borders of triangles, strips formed from hexagons, and rosettes. The quilt has no filling and has been backed with plain cotton fabric. Ref. 86/54

Kalamunda

Kalamunda, its name derived from Aboriginal words meaning 'A Home in the Forest,' is nestled in the picturesque foothills of the Darling Range, about 25kms east of Perth. Surrounded by National Parks and State Forests, the town was first established as a timber settlement during the late 1860s. From the turn of the century it became a popular health resort and beautiful guest houses were built to which people from Perth and Fremantle could escape the stresses of city living. Many of the historic buildings still remain and much of the charm of the early years has been retained. Heritage trails have been designed to provide guides for visitors. There are charming open gardens and tea rooms dotted amongst the hills, and the many galleries and studios specialise in crafts ranging from wood turning to ceramics and glass.

Kalamunda History Village
56 Railway Road
Kalamunda, WA 6076.
Ph: (08) 9293 1371
History Village: 10.00a.m. – 3.00p.m.
Monday to Thursday.
10.00a.m. – 3.00p.m. Saturdays.
1.30p.m. – 4.30p.m. Sundays.
Stirk Cottage: 1.30p.m. – 4.30p.m.
Sundays or by special request.
Closed Fridays, Christmas Day, Boxing Day and Good Friday.
4 quilts.

The largest folk museum in Western Australia, Kalamunda History Village has been established on the site of the old Kalamunda Station yard built during the 1890s. The two original stations remain and have been listed by the National Trust. There are several other heritage buildings which have been relocated to the site and each one contains evocative displays portraying the diverse history of the Hills District. They depict the days of the pioneer timber industry, the development of the orchards and the growth of the guest houses. Stirk's Cottage, in which one of the four quilts is displayed, is a house of wattle and daub built c.1881 by Frederick and Elizabeth Stirk, the first permanent settlers. Located at 12 Kalamunda Road, it is also managed by the Kalamunda Historical Society.

✷ Two of the quilts are on permanent display – the patchwork quilt of cotton hexagons in McCullagh Cottage and the *Blue Bag Coverlet* in Stirk Cottage. They may be seen during the hours listed. The treasured *Milliner's Quilt* is only exhibited periodically. For advice regarding planned exhibitions please contact the Kalamunda History Village.

✂ A magnificent patchwork quilt of hexagons (265cm x 233cm) and the remarkable story of its origins were donated to the Village in 1972 by Mrs Laura Harrison of Wattle Grove, near Kalamunda. The quilt is believed to date from the early years of Queen Victoria's reign c.1837. It was made by Laura's great-great-aunt who was employed as the milliner to the Queen's court. The silks and velvets used in its creation were the dressmaking remnants from gowns worn by the Ladies of the court. These fabrics therefore present a rare collection of the very best materials of the period. The milliner gave the quilt to Laura's mother, Mrs Hode, who always treasured it and brought it with her when she emigrated to Western Australia in 1912.

OPPOSITE: *Pieced and Appliquéd Quilt.* Made by Sarah Evans, 1806. 226cm. x 251cm. National Trust of Australia (W.A.) – Woodbridge Historic Home, Guildford, W.A.

PHOTOGRAPHY PATRICK BAKER.

The quilt features a beautiful design of hexagon rosettes stitched together in successive rows around a central rosette of red velvet. This rich red fabric is believed to have been an upholstery remnant from the making of Queen Victoria's coronation foot stool. It has been finely embroidered with tiny petit-point roses and a peacock. The quilt has a backing of fine Irish linen and has been hand stitched in the traditional English method, the scrim-like templates still remaining in place. It is usually housed in climatically controlled storage at the Kalamunda History Village and is only displayed periodically.

A hand pieced patchwork quilt of hexagons (241cm x 239cm) is of unknown maker and was donated to the Village by Mrs Beautie Forrest of Kalamunda in 1981. Dating from the 1890s, it has been created from hexagon rosettes in the Grandmother's Flower Garden design, each rosette made from printed shirtings and recycled dress cottons.

A coverlet of white Suffolk Puffs (197cm x 195cm) and two matching pillow shams were donated to the History Village in 1989 by Mrs Denise Booth of Kalamunda. They had been given to Mrs Booth's mother by a neighbour, an old lady who had lived by the Swan River in Caversham, not far from Perth, and who is thought to have been the maker. The coverlet dates from the turn of the century and has been made from cotton fabric saved from *Reckitt's Blue Bags,* a laundry product used at the time for the whitening of linens.

A frail but lovely 19th century medallion quilt (196cm x 180cm) is of unknown provenance. It is believed to be of English origin and has been made in medallion style. The central square features an appliquéd design depicting a large red star with cut-out centre. Red diamonds have been stitched into each corner The medallion has been surrounded by successive borders of Turkey-red and white triangles and strips, a fabric combination that was especially popular in Britain during the Victorian era. The quilt has been hand sewn, possibly by more than one maker as the quality of the stitching varies throughout. Later additions have been made to the edge by machine and there are indications that the work may have been hung as a curtain at some stage. A current community project to celebrate the Centenary of Kalamunda involves the making a replica of this quilt which will be available for viewing when completed.

Also in Kalamunda

Four embroideries entitled the *Seasons Panels* were created by the Kalamunda community between 1983 and '84 and now hang on permanent display in the Public Library. The panels depict the beauty of the Hills District in each season of the year and were made by various groups under the guidance of local artist, Beryl Porter. There is also a magnificent stained glass Commemorative Window made by members of the community. The Kalamunda Library is located in William Street adjacent to Kalamunda History Village and is open weekdays between 9.00a.m. and 8.00p.m. and Saturdays between 9.00a.m. and 12 noon.

Armadale

The Armadale region is a 30 minute drive south east of Perth. It was one of the earliest to be established following the arrival of settlers to the Swan River Colony in 1829. Today, the timber logging and orchards of the past have made way for housing development and the area has become a pretty suburb on the southern fringe of the city.

History House
Jull Street
Armadale, WA 6112.
Ph: (08) 9399 6845
10.00a.m – 12.00 noon and
2.00p.m. – 4.00p.m. Monday to Friday.
2.00p.m. – 4.30p.m. Sunday and
public holidays.
Other times by arrangement.
2 quilts plus small items of patchwork.

History House is the repository of a large and fascinating collection recording the history of the Armadale-Kelmscott region. The museum was erected on land that originally formed part of the Brookside residence, owned by pioneer settler, Martin Edward Jull. The huge white gums to be seen near the building were planted by Jull around the turn of the century. In addition to the patchwork, there is a large collection of lace, embroidered linens and two sewing boxes dating from the colonial era.

✷ The *Settler's Quilt* is displayed as part of the 'Journey to a New Land' exhibit. Other items are not on display but may be seen by arrangement. Please contact the museum 24 hours in advance.

PHOTOGRAPHY JOHN LINTON.

PHOTOGRAPHY LES TAYLOR.

OPPOSITE, TOP: Details of *Patchwork Quilt of Hexagons* including central rosette of red velvet believed to be a remnant from Queen Victoria's coronation foot stool. Made by the milliner to Queen Victoria's court, c.1837. 265cm x 233cm. Collection Kalamunda History Village, Kalamunda, W.A. BELOW: Detail of *Patchwork Quilt of Hexagons.* Made by Francis Fretwell, c.1890. 190cm x 106cm. Collection History House, Armadale, W.A.

ABOVE AND BELOW: *Pieced and Appliquéd Tea Cosy.* Made by Mrs Lorraine Bracks, 1923. OPPOSITE: Detail of the *Settler's Quilt.* Believed to have been made by Mary Sowerby, c.1880. Collection History House, Armadale, W.A.

✂ An unfinished patchwork quilt of hexagon rosettes (190cm x 106cm) was made in England by Francis Fretwell. Francis was born in 1860 and it is believed that she made her quilt c.1890. Members of her family brought it with them when they emigrated to Western Australia to become pioneer settlers of the Armadale region. The work was cared for as a treasured heirloom for many years. It was donated to History House by the maker's granddaughter, Mrs Isobel Fretwell.

The patchwork was stitched by hand using the English method over templates of heavy white blotting paper. Many of these templates still remain and are clearly visible in the back of the work. The fabrics include plain, checked and striped silk, satin and taffeta, the pastel colours used for the rosettes illuminated by the black hexagons surrounding each one. Ref. AK701.84

A medallion quilt known as the *Settler's Quilt,* was also donated to the museum by Mrs Isobel Fretwell. It is believed to have been made by a relative of the Fretwell family, Mary Sowerby c.1880. The central square features four large triangles which have been separated from each other by diagonal strips of Squares-on-point. Successive hand pieced borders of strips frame the centre. The work has a thin filling of cotton and has been quilted in diagonal lines. Ref AKH 528.81

There are several small items in the collection. A charming pieced and appliquéd tea cosy was made by Mrs Lorraine Bracks in 1923. Mrs Bracks served as mayoress of North Fremantle in 1931 and the cosy was donated to the museum by her family. It has been made from richly coloured velvets and cottons, each patch outlined with hand embroidery. Appliquéd and embroidered motifs have been stitched to the work

PHOTOGRAPHY LES TAYLOR.

and the initials and date *'LMB 1923'* have been added along the base.

There is also a pillow sham of white Suffolk Puffs made from *Reckitt's Blue Bags* by an unknown maker c.1900. A cushion cover of multi-coloured Suffolk Puffs was made during the 1980s by Mrs Gwen Blackburn.

In the Nearby Region

The town of Mandurah overlooks the Peel Inlet approximately 50kms south of Armadale. A patchwork quilt of squares and rectangles is displayed in historic Hall's Cottage and is believed to date from the earliest days of the Swan River colony. The cottage was built in 1832 by pioneer settler Henry Edward Hall and is located in Leighton Road opposite Hall's Park. It is open every Sunday between 1.00p.m. and 4.00p.m. or by appointment. Telephone (08) 9581 4841.

Dardanup

At Dardanup, about 10kms south east of Bunbury, there are two quilts made by small groups of community quilters displayed in the Shire office. The first commemorates the centenary of local government, the second depicts the history of the nearby town of Wellington Mills. The Shire office is located in Little Street, Dardanup and is open between 9.00a.m. and 4.30p.m. Monday to Friday. Telephone (08)9728 1058.

Harvey

The rural town of Harvey lies in a rich pastoral and agricultural region approximately 50kms north of Bunbury. A pictorial quilt is hung on permanent display in the Harvey Tourist and Interpretive Centre, corner of South West Highway and James Stirling Place. It was made in 1997 by members of the Harvey Districts Creative Arts Centre Inc. and features appliquéd images designed to illustrate the many facets of life in the Shire. The Centre is open between 9.00a.m. and 5.00p.m. Monday to Saturday, and 9.30a.m. and 4.00.p.m. Sunday and public holidays.

Busselton

The charming seaside town of Busselton overlooks the Geographe Bay 50kms south of Bunbury. One of the oldest towns in the state, many of its heritage buildings have been restored for use as galleries, restaurants and tea rooms. The wooden jetty, 2km long, has been a focal point of Busselton for more than 130 years. Surrounding the town, the picturesque countryside is dotted with vineyards, cattle and dairy properties.

The Old Butter Factory Museum
Peel Terrace
Busselton, WA 6280.
Ph: (08) 9754 2166
2.00p.m. – 5.00p.m. daily except Tuesdays.

The Old Butter Factory Museum is home to many historical items from the pioneering years of the region. The eight rooms include a parlour, a display hall and a butter room. There is a collection of teapots of varying ages and numerous cosies to go with them. A sampler was made by Anne Samin in 1887 and a framed embroidery was worked on writing paper by E. Jeffries in 1806. There is also a fully furnished Group Settlement with humpy, house, dairy and one-room school. It provides a fascinating glimpse of the life of early 'Groupies' – pioneers who came to Western Australia filled with hope and enthusiasm inspired by promises made by the Government. Most had little or no farming experience and endured great hardships. Some, like the quiltmaker's family, battled on to create a dairy farm from virgin bush. Many failed, finally walking off the land with little more than the clothes they stood in.

✱ The quilt is permanently displayed in the upstairs bedroom of the Museum and may be seen during opening hours.

✂ A wholecloth quilt of pieced strips known as *Aunt Clara's Quilt* (230cm x 220cm) was made in England by Clara Staley's grandmother in 1863. Aunt Clara is remembered in Busselton as one of the earliest Groupies. She had come to Western Australia with her husband in 1920, bringing with her the quilt that had been made by her grandmother more than fifty years earlier.

Like other settlers, the Staleys had little farming experience and arrived in a strange country to face enormous hardship. During the early months, Clara and her husband lived in a hut with hessian walls and bark roof. Strange animals and snakes were a menace. They joined the Group Settlement in 1922, establishing a farm from virgin bushland. Determined to succeed, they spent thirty eight years on the farm and during World War II Clara ran it alone. She had a nine year old daughter to care for, twenty cows to milk by hand, horses and a bull to feed, and windmills to supervise.

It is incredible given this background that the quilt survived. The work had been stitched entirely by hand from delicate lawn fabrics, some of which now show signs of wear. The quilting pattern is similar to other English strippy quilts of the period and features a triple row cable design with flowers worked through the centre. Ref. 959.

Capel

The little town of Capel is located between Bunbury and Busselton. This picturesque area combines the pretty coast of nearby Peppermint Beach with a background of rolling hills and natural forest. Between July and October the area is ablaze with wild flowers. As a farming region, it is renowned for its wineries and orchards as well as for sheep, cattle and dairy properties.

Shire of Capel
Forrest Road
Capel, WA 6271.
Ph: (08) 9727 2030 Fax: (08) 9727 2603
9.00a.m. – 4.30p.m. Monday to Friday.

✷ The quilt is hung on permanent display in the foyer of the Shire building and may be seen during opening hours.

✄ This quilt (220cm x 160cm) depicting the history of Capel was made in 1993 to celebrate the Shire's 150th year of settlement. The project involved more than 2000 hours of work in research, planning and sewing. Designed by artist Denise Mercer, it was made by Caitlin Gordon, Anne-Marie Ward, Dellas Macdougall and Sheila Harvey.

The work features a central picture surrounded by scenes and buildings that explain the story of Capel's history and development. Coloured fabrics were used to illustrate the present day, soft brown and sepia tones for images of the past. A pioneer family dressed in clothing from the 1850s were shown looking across the Capel Bridge towards their future. Colour was introduced through the centre to depict the farmland, ploughed paddocks and diverse rural activities. An orange orchard and winery, sheep, beef and dairy cattle were stitched in hand appliqué with embroidered details. Much of the appliqué involved layering of materials in order to provide the depth of colour and texture. Some of the fabrics were reversed and some were tea dyed. The summer recreation area of Peppermint Beach was added in colourful strip piecing at the top. The quilting was done by hand with local flora and fauna worked around the border.

PHOTOGRAPHY PATRICK BAKER.

ABOVE: Detail of *Capel History Quilt.* Made by Caitlin Gordon, Anne-Marie Ward, Dellas Macdougall and Sheila Harvey, 1993. 220cm x 160cm. Shire of Capel, W.A.

Bunbury

The thriving port of Bunbury sits on a peninsula overlooking Koombana Bay. It is a two hour drive south of Perth and 50kms from Busselton. Settled by Europeans during the 1830s, today it is the major sea port of the south west. The renowned wineries of the Margaret River region are only a short drive away, and together with the pristine Indian Ocean coastline and picturesque hinterland, make the region one of the state's most popular tourist areas.

King Cottage Museum
77 Forest Avenue
Bunbury, WA 6230.
Ph: (08) 9721 7546 Museum.
(08) 9725 0473 Curator.
2.00p.m. – 4.00p.m. Tuesday and Sunday.
Other times by appointment.
2 quilts plus a patchwork cushion cover.

Henry King's cottage was built c.1880 and the family lived in it for forty years. Henry was a brick-layer by trade and he employed four ticket-of-leave men to help make the bricks for his house, using clay obtained on the property for the job. Today, the cottage is filled with Victorian mementoes reflecting the domestic history of Bunbury around the turn of the century. There are constantly changing exhibitions of linen, embroidery and 19th century clothing. A cross stitch sampler dated 1813 has been framed and is hung on permanent display.

✷ The quilts are not always on display. They may be seen by contacting the Historical Society three days in advance.

✄ This Crazy Patchwork quilt (150cm x 158cm) was made during the mid 19th century by Mrs Dodwell Brown of Ratines Castlebar in the County Mayo of Ireland. It was brought to Australia in 1867 by the maker's son, Dr Dodwell Brown, who practiced medicine in Bridgetown, south east of Bunbury, for many years.

The work features Crazy patches of silk, brocade, velvet and cotton, each one outlined in double herringbone stitch using yellow silk thread. The patches have been embellished with finely embroidered motifs including fuchsias, waterlilies, daisies, birds, and oriental designs. The quilt has a backing of polished black cotton and has been tied with yellow silk thread. The edge has been finished with black cording and there are two loops and a black fringed tassel in each corner. Ref. L80.159

A quilt of hexagons (206cm x 157cm) was made c.1897 by May Walker (nee Carey). May had spent her childhood years in Bunbury and later met and married John Walker. Her quilt is of Grandmother's Flower Garden design and was hand sewn over paper templates. The fabrics are printed dress cottons in colours of pink, blue and brown. Ref. L80.8

A unfinished cushion of Crazy Patchwork (50cm x 52cm) is believed to have been made by Mrs J. Daly who was born in Bunbury and lived there for many years. It has been created from random patches of silk, velvet, brocade and cotton and is hexagonal in shape. Some of the patches have been outlined with cream silk herringbone stitch, others with yellow and orange chenille thread. Ref. L80.13

ABOVE AND OPPOSITE: *Crazy Patchwork Quilt*. Made by Mrs Dodwell Brown, c.1850. 150cm x 158cm. Collection King Cottage Museum, Bunbury, W.A.

PHOTOGRAPHY MICHAEL WEBSTER.

ABOVE AND OPPOSITE: *Patchwork Cushion.* Unknown Maker, c.1890. Collection National Trust of Australia (W.A.) – Old Farm, Strawberry Hill, Albany.

Augusta

The west coast seaside fishing village of Augusta is set on the slopes of the Hardy Inlet 320kms south of Perth. This picturesque site overlooks both the Blackwood River and the Southern Ocean and has as its background the rural farmlands and densely forested national park. Augusta is the third oldest settlement in the state. The first group of English settlers to the district sailed from the Swan River Settlement in the *Emily Taylor*, landing with their families in 1830. The hardships endured by these early pioneers, along with stories of whaling rescues, the timber industry, the lighthouse and ship wrecks can be explored at the Augusta Museum.

Augusta Historical Museum

Blackwood Avenue
Augusta, WA 6290.
Ph: (08) 9758 1948 or (08) 9758 1795
10.00a.m. – 12.00 noon daily except Christmas Day.
2.00p.m. – 4.00p.m. between September and April, plus school and public holidays.
2 quilts plus small items of patchwork.

The Museum is housed in a specially constructed brick building. Its collection includes many examples of period clothing and trousseau items. There are handmade camisoles, nighties and christening gowns, as well as fans, shawls, embroidered linen, crochet work, and beaded evening bags.

✷ The Bicentennial Quilt is hung on permanent display and may be seen during opening hours. The old quilt is very fragile and may only be seen by special arrangement with the Museum.

✂ The *Augusta Bicentennial Quilt* (150cm x 130cm) was made by the Augusta Quilters in 1988. Designed and co-ordinated by Jen Johnson, it features pictorial blocks depicting the beauty of the region's natural environment as well as the history of the early pioneering days. The tall ship *Emily Taylor* is shown in the large central square. Surrounding images include the historic Cape Leeuwin Lighthouse, the old wooden water wheel and the original Augusta Hotel. This hotel is still operating today and

PHOTOGRAPHY MALCOLM HEBERLE

enjoys spectacular views of the river and Southern Ocean. The quilt was pieced by machine, appliquéd, embroidered and quilted by hand.

A fragile 19th century patchwork quilt is of unknown maker. It is believed to have originated in Ireland and was brought to Australia in 1923 by one of the early group settlers. It has been made from red and white cotton fabrics in a design of four pointed stars, each star formed from diamonds over paper templates. The fabrics have deteriorated over time but are supported by the rows of tiny quilting stitches.

There is also a collection of hexagon patchwork pieces remaining from the making of a late 19th century quilt. The paper templates cut from old letters are clearly visible behind each piece.

Augusta Centennial Hall
Allnut Terrace
Augusta, WA 6290.
Ph: (08) 9758 1403 or (08) 9758 1888

✷ The quilt is hung on permanent display in the Hall and may be seen by arrangement. Please telephone a day or two in advance.

✂ This quilt (120cm x 200cm) was made by the Augusta Quilters to commemorate the centenary of the building of the Cape Leeuwin Lighthouse in 1897. Designed and co-ordinated by Edith Williams, the work was completed in 1997. Cape Leeuwin is the most south westerly tip of Australia and the point at which the Southern and Indian Oceans meet. This area of notorious underground rips has been responsible for the sinking of numerous ships and claimed many lives. The quilt depicts the Lighthouse within a long central panel, the surrounding wooded countryside worked in hand embroidery in the foreground. A wide border made from pieced blocks of Ocean Waves pattern frames the Lighthouse. Appliquéd motifs of nautical symbols are stitched to the blocks. The work was machine pieced, hand appliquéd, embroidered and quilted.

Albany

The historic and picturesque Port of Albany overlooks the Princess Royal Harbour on the southern coast of Western Australia. It is about a five hour drive from Perth. Albany was the first settlement in the state, having been established as a penal outpost by Major Lockyer in 1826. A heritage trail provides walking tours and descriptions of many colonial buildings and historic sites.

The Old Farm, Strawberry Hill
Middleton Road
Albany, WA 6330.
Ph/Fax: (08) 9841 3735
10.00a.m. – 5.00p.m. everyday.
Closed Christmas Day, Good Friday and the month of June.
2 quilts and a patchwork cushion.

The pretty stone cottage known as the Old Farm, Strawberry Hill, is one of the oldest houses in the state and has been meticulously restored by the National Trust. It was built in 1836 on land originally developed as the first farm in Western Australia. Surrounded by a charming garden, the interior has been furnished to depict early colonial life. The collection includes several framed cross stitch samplers dating from 1794, a century-old hand made

PHOTOGRAPHY MALCOLM HEBERLE.

ABOVE AND OPPOSITE: Log Cabin Cushion featuring twenty five tiny blocks. Unknown Maker, c.1866. Patrick Taylor's Cottage, Albany, W.A.

candlewick coverlet, shawls, mittens, beaded purses and bags, and a small beaded screen made by Mrs Bird in 1879.

✱ The items are permanently displayed and may be seen during opening hours.

✄ A pieced quilt of Fruit Basket design was created by members of the West Australian Quilters' Association in 1986. It was made from cotton fabrics and was hand quilted. Ref.86/4

A tiny Crazy Patchwork quilt was made during the 1950s by Mrs Barnsley for the antique cradle in the nursery. It was created from brightly coloured cotton fabrics and each patch was outlined with feather stitch. Ref.78.011

A patchwork cushion of unknown maker dates from the Victorian era. It has been created from silk and velvet triangles and has a backing of silk. The patches have been outlined with feather stitch and embellished with lace motifs and pearl buttons. Ref. 72:210.

Patrick Taylor's Cottage

Duke Street
Albany, WA 6332.
Ph: (08) 9841 6174
1.00p.m. – 4.15p.m daily.

Patrick Taylor's Cottage was built of wattle and daub in 1832 and is the oldest house in the state. It is managed by the Albany Historical Society as a folk museum and contains an extensive collection of period costumes, old clocks, and silverware. There are embroidered tea cosies, doilies, table runners, and a white Signature cloth made in 1944.

✱ The cushion is permanently displayed and may be seen during opening hours or by arrangement with the Society.

✄ A cushion of Log Cabin design (41cm x 40cm) was created by an unknown maker c.1866. It was donated to the Society by Mrs Joyce of Albany and features twenty five tiny blocks, each one measuring only 8cm square. The blocks have been sewn by hand, twelve multi-coloured satin strips stitched around the little central square. The cushion has been edged with purple braid and has a backing of purple satin. Ref 91–1144.

Esperance

The south coast town of Esperance was named after the French ship *L'Esperance* which was forced into the bay by a fierce storm in 1792. During the 1890s Esperance prospered as a port for the nearby goldfields but today it is best known for its spectacular coastline, wonderful beaches and offshore islands.

Esperance Public Library
Windich Street
Esperance, WA 6450.
Ph: (08) 9071 0680
10.00a.m. – 6.00p.m. Monday, Wednesday, Thursday and Friday.
9.00a.m. – 12.00p.m. Saturday.

✷ The quilt is hung on permanent display in the Library and visitors are welcome during opening hours.

✄ This quilt was made in 1988 by members of the Esperance Patchwork Club to celebrate Australia's Bicentenary. The central medallion illustrates the *L'Esperance* from which the town derived its name. Pictorial blocks illustrate historic buildings and landmarks well known in the region. Pieced and appliquéd borders illustrating native flowers frame the quilt. The work was machine pieced, hand appliquéd, embroidered and quilted.

Narrogin

Narrogin is located on the Great Southern Highway approximately 200kms south east of Perth. First settled by Europeans during the 1860s, it was officially founded in 1892. It soon developed as an important railway junction as well as the centre of a prosperous agricultural region. The town's Centenary Pathway, initiated by the Narrogin Council and created by local artists, presents an overview of life during the past century. The project involved using 100 granite tiles on which historical events and local folklore were depicted. Narrogin is also renowned for its beautiful gardens, many of which are open to the public during Spring.

R.W. (Bob) Farr Memorial Regional Library
Fortune Street
Narrogin, WA 6312.
Ph: (08) 9881 1944 Fax: (08) 9881 3092
10.00a.m. – 6.00p.m Monday.
1.00p.m. – 6.00p.m. Tuesday.
10.00a.m. – 5.00p.m Wednesday and Friday.
1.00p.m. – 8.00p.m Thursday.
9a.m. – 12 noon Saturday.

✷ The panels are hung in a specially designed frame within the library and may be seen during the hours listed.

✄ This wonderful triptych (100cm x 200cm each panel) was made in 1992 as a community project to celebrate the centenary of local government in Narrogin. Inspired by Julie Sutton and designed by local artist Joy Rich, it illustrates the history and development of the region, its landscape, flora, and fauna.

The three panels depict the countryside during the seasons of Spring, Summer, and Autumn. The project began with a workshop held with textile artist Jennie Abbott and photographs were collected of buildings, people, flowers, animals and heritage sites. Cartoons were drawn to actual size by community artists and these

1892
NARROGIN
ROAD BOARD
OFFICE

THIS PAGE: *The Narrogin Triptych* (left) and details. Made by the community of Narrogin, 1992. 100cm x 200cm each panel. R.W. (Bob) Farr Memorial Regional Library, Narrogin, W.A.

formed the starting point for each maker. The background was created with paper templates cut to the exact shape of hills and paddocks. Some were made from hand or machine-knitted pieces, others strip pieced and appliquéd.

Fences, buildings, flowers and animals were created individually using a diverse range of techniques. The huge eucalypt, its branches spanning all three panels, was hand painted on silk and then machine stitched to the backing. Numerous leaves and flowers were machine embroidered. Many fabrics were dyed, painted, or printed. Silk embroidery threads were also dyed, and wool was felted. Fabric manipulation was used to achieve texture with many areas being hand padded and fine wire being incorporated into leaves and flowers. Caterpillars were tatted and kangaroos were made from lace.

The project gathered together people with diverse skills ranging from patchwork and embroidery to spinning, weaving and knitting. A strong sense of community spirit and enthusiasm was engendered as groups worked together on its creation.

York

York is nestled on the banks of the Avon River, 100kms east of Perth. Western Australia's oldest inland town, it was established during the 1830s and named because the countryside of the Avon Valley reminded early pioneers of Yorkshire.

Old Gaol and Courthouse
130 Avon Terrace
York, WA 6302.
Ph/Fax: (08) 9641 2072
10.00a.m. – 4.00p.m. everyday.
3 quilts.

There were constant problems between the white settlers, Aborigines and convicts during the early years and a strong police presence was vital to maintain peace. The Old Gaol and Courthouse were in use for more than one hundred years before being acquired by the National Trust in 1983. A tapestry depicting the history of the building is hung on display within the complex.

✷ The quilts are permanently displayed and may be seen during opening hours.

✂ Three quilts were made by the York Quilters and Patchworkers using designs and fabrics specially chosen to recreate the period of occupation by the troopers. A quilt of random hexagons and a baby's cot quilt of squares were made in 1993. A traditional Grandmother's Flower Garden quilt was completed in 1998.

The group also made two quilts entitled *Rolling Diamonds* and *Agricultural Show* for display in the York Tourist Bureau, corner of Avon Terrace and Joaquina Street. The Bureau is open daily between 10.00a.m. and 5.00p.m. Telephone (08) 9641 1301.

Also in York

One of the first workshops to teach patchwork in Australia took place in 1976 at the stately mansion of Faversham House, York. Inspired by the American Bicentennial and organised as part of the York Society Fair, it resulted in the creation of a patchwork quilt of hexagons which is now displayed at the Residency Museum. The workshop was also to lead to the establishment of the West Australian Quilters' Association, one of the earliest to be formed in Australia. The Residency Museum is located in Brook Street. It is open between 1.00p.m. and 3.00p.m. Tuesday to Thursday, 1.00p.m and 5.00p.m. Saturday and Sunday. Telephone (08) 9641 1751.

Nungarin

Nungarin is set in a rich pastoral region of wheat farms and sheep properties approximately 290kms east of Perth. Spring is a beautiful time to visit as there is a spectacular display of native wildflowers.

Mangowine Homestead
Karomin North Road
Nungarin, WA 6490.
Ph: (08) 9046 5149
1.00p.m. – 4.00p.m. Monday, Tuesday, Thursday and Friday.
10.00a.m. – 4.00p.m. Saturday and Sunday. Closed Wednesday.
Other times by appointment.
4 quilts plus patchwork cushions.

Mangowine Homestead was built in 1876 for pioneer settlers Charles and Jane Adams. It was constructed with massive stone and mud-brick walls to provide shelter from the blistering summer sun. When gold was discovered at nearby Yilgarn, the Adams built a wayside inn for the diggers. The homestead and inn have now been restored by the National Trust and furnished to recreate the original atmosphere.

✷ The quilts are permanently displayed and may be seen during the opening hours listed or by appointment. Please telephone Sarah Murphy at Trust Headquarters in advance.

✂ An unusual cot quilt made from strip pieced blocks and Suffolk Puffs was created by Mary Ann Coleman c.1890. It is believed that Mary Ann was in her mid seventies when she made the work. The centre features eight squares of multi-coloured strips which have been surrounded by printed cotton puffs. A wide border of strip pieced squares has been worked around the puffs and a pink lining is clearly visible behind them. Ref.249

A patchwork quilt of hexagon rosettes was made by Alicia Spencer c.1940. The rosettes were appliquéd to a blue cotton background and used to cover an old eiderdown. Ref. 78/35

Two quilts were created in 1987 by members of the West Australian Quilters' Association. Traditional styles were chosen to suit the era of the pioneer homestead. One is a Nine Patch design of cotton fabrics in Autumn coloured prints. The other is a cot quilt of Double Irish Chain design which features extensive hand quilting. Ref.86/4

Several cushions of patchwork and appliqué were also made by WAQA members and are displayed throughout the house.

Detail of *Cot Quilt of Suffolk Puffs and Strip Piecing*. Made by Mary Ann Coleman, c.1890. Collection National Trust of Australia (W.A.) – Mangowine Homestead, Nungarin.

Kalgoorlie

The town of Kalgoorlie is 600kms east of Perth. For more than one hundred years it has been the heart of Western Australia's gold mining region.

William Grundt Memorial Library

Roberts Street
Kalgoorlie, WA 6430.
Ph: (08) 9021 9802 Fax: (08) 9091 4009
10.00a.m. – 8.00p.m Monday to Friday.
9.00a.m. – 12 noon Saturday.
2.00p.m. – 5.00p.m. Sunday.

✷ The quilt is hung on permanent display in the Library and may be seen during opening hours.

✂ This quilt (180cm x 150cm) was made by the Patchwork Pollies in 1993 to commemorate the centenary of Kalgoorlie Boulder. The mining heritage of the town dominates the quilt, both in the buildings depicted as well as in the quilting design. The stately Post Office forms the focal point in the centre, the city's name and centenary dates embroidered in cross stitch beneath it. Upholstery, dress and curtain materials were used to create the quilt. Authentic colours were obtained by dyeing fabrics with rust, red oxide and yellow ochre. The work was appliquéd by hand and machine and quilted by hand.

Broome

The fascinating pearling town of Broome is located on the northern coast of Western Australia around the shores of the beautiful Roebuck Bay. This region, renowned for its long stretches of sandy white beaches, pristine water and beautiful shells, is 2,250kms from Perth. It is actually closer to Bali than it is to the state capital. Broome was founded during the 1880s following the discovery of the rich pearling grounds off the coast. Thousands of people flocked to the area in the hope of making their fortunes and today the town has one of the most cosmopolitan populations in Australia.

Broome Historical Society Museum

Saville Street
Broome, WA 6725.
Ph/Fax: (08) 9192 2075
10.00a.m. – 1.00p.m. everyday.

The Historical Society Museum is located in a building dating from the early 1900s which served first as a general store to the pearling fleet and then as the original Customs House. There is a large collection of photographs, files and historical items that piece together the fascinating history of the town, its pioneering pearl divers and their families.

✷ The cloth is hung on permanent display within the museum and may be seen during the opening hours listed.

✂ This Signature cloth is part of the Kennedy-Haynes family display. These two families were amongst the earliest settlers in Broome. It was Nita Kennedy, mother of the founder of the Historical Society, who made the cloth in 1916.

Nita embroidered the Union Jack into the centre of the work, surrounding it with more than 150 signatures from the local community. Despite the fact that we had our own Australian flag, the Union Jack was often used during this period as a token of loyalty to Britain. This is the likely reason that it was included on Nita's cloth, and it is probable that her work was made to raise funds for the War effort.

The signatures were written on cream fabric, cut out, and appliquéd to the background using feather stitch. The cloth was finished with an edging of hand made lace. Sadly Nita died in 1926 at the age of only thirty eight and her husband, a master pearler, sent their four young children to live with their grandmother in Melbourne.

Darwin Commemorative Quilt.
Made by Jenny Armour, 1992–'94.
Northern Territory Library,
Parliament House, Darwin.

QUILTS OF THE NORTHERN TERRITORY

Darwin

The capital of the Northern Territory, Darwin is Australia's gateway to Asia and the closest city to the world heritage-listed Kakadu National Park. In the early days, the town developed as the northern terminus of the Overland Telegraph Line. It was also a supply centre for the 1870s gold rush at nearby Pine Creek. Today the population is one of the most multicultural in Australia. The people, like those throughout the Territory, are endowed with an indomitable spirit as apparent in their quilts as in their ability to overcome adversity.

The Japanese attacked Darwin on February 19th, 1942, inflicting a bombing raid that killed more than 240 people and destroyed eight ships. In total there were sixty eight air attacks between 1942 and '43 and much of the city was destroyed or damaged. Shocking devastation occurred once again when Cyclone Tracy struck on Christmas Day, 1974. Remarkably, some heritage buildings still remain. A leaflet which outlines a walking tour of historic sites is available from the National Trust.

The Northern Territory Library
Parliament House, State Square
Darwin, NT 0800.
(08) 8999 7177
10.00a.m. – 6.00p.m. Monday to Friday.
1.00p.m. – 5.00p.m. Saturday and Sunday.

The new Parliament House building opened in 1994. It sits on one of Darwin's most historic sites and free tours provide both historical and architectural commentaries.

✷ The quilt is hung on permanent display inside the Library and may be seen during opening hours. Its position is significant because it hangs at the location of the bombed Post Office which has come to symbolise the tragedy of the War in the Northern Territory. Photography is not permitted but prints of the entire quilt or enlargements of specific patches can be ordered at the Library. Names appearing on the work have been listed on a data base to help pinpoint their location on a particular patch.

✄ This enormous and remarkable quilt (5m x 3m) was made by Jenny Armour between 1992 and '94. The signatures on the patches were contributed by 1600 people who visited the Northern Territory during 1992, the Year of Commemoration of the bombing of Darwin. Many others who had spent time in the Territory during the war years wrote from interstate and overseas. Some were civilians, others were defence personnel, evacuees, nurses or police.

The signature blocks were stitched together to resemble a typical porcellanite stone wall. Examples of these walls can still be seen today in old buildings throughout the city. Interspersed between the names were twenty-one appliquéd images of buildings and places that would have been familiar landmarks to people living in war-time Darwin. The illustrations were based on photographs taken during the war and now held in the collection of the Library, all of them sites of significance to military and civilian personnel.

One building of particular historical importance was the Post Office, destroyed during the first bombing raid on the city. This incursion was led by the same Japanese commander who had so successfully attacked Pearl Harbour two months previously. The main objective of the mission was to destroy communications so his attack concentrated on the area of town that contained the cable and telegraph offices as well as the Post Office. On this busy Monday morning at 10.00a.m. virtually all postal staff were killed instantly, together with one customer who had not left the building on hearing the air-raid siren. Many years later this site was chosen for the new Parliament House and Library and included in the foyer was a reconstructed piece of the original Post Office wall.

Another appliquéd picture showed the recently completed hospital which was bombed despite the Red Cross painted on its roof. Illustrations of the flying-boat base and the railway station were included because of their significance to departing evacuees. The image of Darwin Harbour was intended to pay homage to the thousands of sailors who drowned when their ships were sunk.

This powerful and evocative quilt took almost eighteen months to complete. The piecing, appliqué, embroidery and quilting were all done by machine. The work extended and obsessed its maker, both for its artistic value and for the poignant message it would leave for future generations.

Supreme Court
Court Room 5, State Square
Darwin, NT 0800.
(08) 8999 7953
9.00a.m. – 4.00p.m. Monday to Friday.

✷ The wall hanging is permanently displayed in Court Room 5 and may be seen during the hours listed.

✄ This hanging of the Northern Territory Coat of Arms (184cm x 158cm) was made by Jenny Armour in 1991. It was appliquéd by machine with details added in machine embroidery.

ABOVE: *Ghost of Harvests Past.* Made by Jan Irvine-Nealie, 1997. Wool blanket, wool filled, cotton backing. Airbrush dyed, hand stitched. 105cm x 200cm. Collection Museum and Art Gallery of the Northern Territory, Darwin.

Museum and Art Gallery of the Northern Territory

Conacher Street, Bullocky Point
Darwin, NT 0820.
Ph: (08) 8999 8201 Fax: (08) 8999 8289
9.00a.m. – 5.00p.m. Monday to Friday.
10.00a.m. – 5.00p.m. Weekends.
Closed Christmas Day and
Good Friday.
3 quilts plus other hangings.

The Museum stands on a beautiful site overlooking Darwin Harbour. Its holdings include a diverse range of fine textiles within three separate collections. The Craft Collection includes lengths of printed and dyed fabrics, rugs, several appliquéd, embroidered, and patchwork wall hangings, tapestries, and a quilt. The Southeast Asian and Pacific Collection includes hand woven cloths, traditional apparel and historical textiles. The Territory History Collection includes examples of lacework, tablecloths, doyleys, crochet, samplers, and a Signature cloth which features the names of miners from the early gold mining community of Brocks Creek.

✷ A gallery has recently been established to showcase works from the collection. To view textiles that are not on display requests can be made in writing one month in advance to the Collections Manager, MAGNT, GPO Box 4646, Darwin, NT 0801.

✂ The collection includes *Ghost of Harvests Past.* This quilt (105cm x 200cm) was designed and made in 1997 by textile artist Jan Irvine-Nealie. It depicts a huge corrugated-iron grain silo used in times past to store the crop following harvest in the Wimmera District of Victoria. Once a feat of bush architecture, it has now been superseded and stands neglected with sections missing from its sides, a ghost of harvests past. The enormity of the building is emphasised by the sharp perspective looking skyward and by the lone bird circling overhead. Made from a woollen blanket c.1950, the quilt was airbush dyed and hand quilted. It has a filling of wool and a backing of cotton.

A quilted 'lukisan batik' or batik painting (222cm x 172cm) entitled *Musim Buah* (the Fruit Season) was made in 1996 by Ardiyanto Pranata, one of Indonesia's leading textile designers. Ardiyanto used the quilted cotton fabric to provide an additional three dimensional effect.

The Red Bug (148cm x 198cm) was made in 1990 by Pacita Abad, a contemporary artist from Southeast Asia. Pacita describes her work as 'trapunto painting' as it is a combination of painting, embroidery, and textile collage on a quilted canvas support.

Details from
Distance and Diversity.
Made by Helen Buchanan,
1990. Northern Territory
House, Darwin.
CLOCKWISE,
FROM TOP LEFT:
Katherine Gorge;
Arnhem Land
escarpment country;
MacDonnell Ranges;
Devils Marbles; Uluru.
OPPOSITE, TOP: Kakadu.
OPPOSITE, BELOW:
Shoreline of
the Arafura Sea.

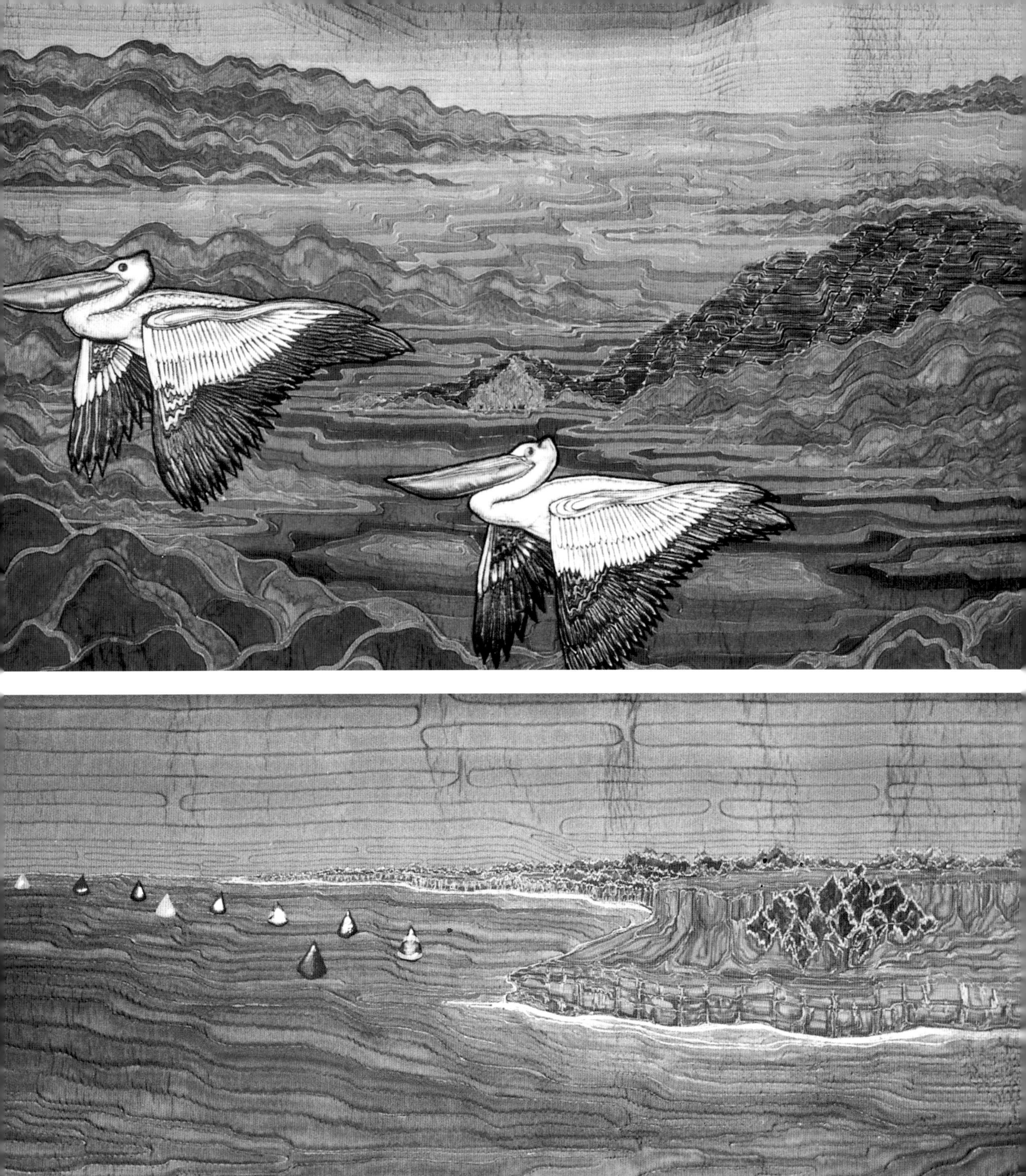

PHOTOGRAPHY MICHAEL MCROSTIE.

Department of the Chief Minister

Northern Territory House
Mitchell Street
Darwin, NT 0801.
Ph: (08) 8999 6653
9.00a.m. – 3.00p.m. Monday to Friday.
8 quilted panels.

✷ The panels are hung on permanent display in the reception lobby of the 9th floor and may be seen during the hours listed.

✂ This wonderful series of panels entitled *Distance and Diversity* was created by Helen Buchanan in 1990. Each work depicts a different view, all of them instantly recognisable as belonging to this part of Australia. The first four panels reflect the glowing colours of the tropics. They begin with the vivid turquoise water of the Arafura Sea and the flood plains that form the amazing landscape below the escarpment of Kakadu. Here the streams and lagoons create a paradise for birdlife and the large black and white storks illustrated by Helen are prevalent throughout the area.

The third mural depicts the freshwater billabongs, paperbark and monsoon forests of the Mary River wetlands. This region, 170 kilometres from Darwin, is home to hundreds of saltwater crocodiles. The final image of the tropical north shows the rugged escarpment country of Arnhem Land with its waterfalls cascading from sandstone plateau. Large groves of cyclads like those in the bottom corner are to be found by the falls and the spring fed creeks.

Dramatic changes in colour and landforms occur as the scenes progress from the wetlands of the Top End to the arid desert of the Centre. The spectacular river canyon of the Katherine Gorge is shown, its deep blue water in sharp contrast to the orange-red walls that tower above it. The huge granite boulders known as the Devils Marbles are found south of Tennant Creek and are said by Aboriginal people to be the eggs of the Rainbow Serpent. Much closer to Alice Springs, the MacDonnell Ranges with their gorges and waterholes are illustrated to perfection.

The final panel of the series depicts the most famous of all Australian landmarks, Uluru, its remarkable colour contrasted against the blue desert sky. Created from silk satin and Japanese silk habutai, the fabrics were specially dyed using wax resist and gutta resist techniques. They were appliquéd, machine embroidered and machine quilted.

Crafts Council of the Northern Territory

Darwin Division, Conacher Street
Fannie Bay, NT 0801.
Ph: (08) 8981 6615 Fax: (08) 8981 7175
9.00a.m. – 5.00p.m. Monday to Friday.

✷ The quilt is not permanently displayed but may be seen by arrangement. Please contact the Executive Officer, Leonie McNally, one week in advance.

ABOVE: *A Pictorial Survey of the Top End.* Made by members of the Crafts Council, 1982. Crafts Council of the Northern Territory, Darwin.
OPPOSITE: Details illustrate aspects of life in Darwin during the 1980s – the 'Beer Can Race,' the 'bloke' and his beer, crocodiles, and 'footy.'

SHELL

2K
CARLTON
LIGHT
DARWIN
DOWN THE TRACK

10

✂ This lively quilt entitled *A Pictorial Survey of the Top End* (200cm x 150cm) was created by members of the Crafts Council in 1982. It was designed and made during a workshop conducted by British textile artist Polly Hope and provides a wonderful glimpse of Darwin during the early 1980s. It captures in fabric the humour, the environment, the colour and the controversies of the day.

The cluster of buildings seen on the left had been recently constructed in the wake of the devastation caused by Cyclone Tracy. The casino had just opened and the new city car park was a great source of contention at the time. New legislation had just been passed requiring that no alcohol be consumed within a two kilometre radius of any licensed premises. One 'bloke' can be seen standing in shorts, leather thongs and red cap, his beer to hand just outside the '2 km' sign!

The great Aussie institution of 'footy' is also included with a player lining up for a shot at goal. Top Enders are fanatical sportsmen and play two different codes of football in the Wet season and two in the Dry.

Dotted throughout the quilt are tropical palms and flowers created from organza and tulle using a variety of three dimensional techniques. Many humorous details add to the charm of the work. Three ladies are rowing frantically in the annual 'Beer Can Regatta.' A street sign points towards Darwin in one direction and 'Down the Track' in the other. The number of crocodiles present could certainly make one nervous about the possibility of ending up as 'croc dinner'! The work was appliquéd and embroidered by hand and machine using a wide variety of fabrics.

Katherine

The town of Katherine is set in a region of rugged and spectacular wilderness approximately 300 kilometres south east of Darwin. Established in 1871 to service the Overland Telegraph Line, it has grown to become the third largest town in the Territory. It is the major centre for the region's rural and mining communities and as the gateway to the Katherine Gorge, it is also an important tourist destination.

A place of cultural diversity, Katherine has attracted many interesting and colourful characters. The old O'Keeffe Residence provides a fascinating insight into the pioneering days. It was used by several early families and occupied by military personnel during World War II. Built from timber, corrugated iron and flywire, it has now been opened to the public by the National Trust as a classic example of bush technology.

Crafts Council of the Northern Territory
Katherine Division, Second Street
Katherine, NT 0850.
Ph: (08) 8971 0740
9.00a.m. – 3.00p.m. Tuesdays
and Wednesdays.
2 wall hangings.

The Katherine River, red desert sands and lush tropical forest present an inspiring palette for artists and quiltmakers. The Katherine Division of the Crafts Council was established in the 1960s and has always been a very active community-based organisation. It provides rooms in which members can work, a library of craft books and periodicals, and a monthly newsletter detailing activities, forthcoming workshops and exhibitions. Diverse interests are catered for and tutors from both the Territory and interstate visit Katherine regularly to teach new skills. One of the pioneer members of the Crafts Council was Kathleen Short whose far-sighted proposal it was to initiate the tradition of creating a quilted wall hanging for every new public building in the town.

✷ The hangings are permanently displayed in the Crafts Council rooms and may be seen during opening hours or at other times by appointment with the Project Officer.

✂ The Crafts Council wall hangings (both 100cm x 100cm) were designed to reflect our heritage of embroidery. They were created by members during 1988 to commemorate Australia's Bicentenary. Each one was made from a series of blocks stitched on even-weave linen using a diverse range of techniques. There are examples of Assisi and black work, canvas and stumpwork, needle weaving, cross stitch, hardanger, pulled thread, smocking, crewel, appliqué and Log Cabin patchwork.

Katherine Civic Centre
Stuart Highway
Katherine, NT 0850.
Ph: (08) 8972 1322
8.00a.m. – 4.15p.m. Monday to Friday.

✷ The quilt is hung on permanent display in the entrance foyer of the Civic Centre and may be seen during the hours listed.

✂ This quilt entitled *Reflections of Katherine* (250cm x 180cm) was made by members of the Crafts Council in 1986. It was created during a machine embroidery workshop conducted by visiting textile artist Polly Hope. To plan the design, a large piece of calico was placed on the floor and divided into segments. This background was then completely covered with fabric pieces secured in place and embellished with machine embroidery. Each member of the group created her own impression of the region. The diverse images include the many faces and cultures of Katherine, the bright yellow school bus, the radio tower from the School of the Air and the colourful paddocks along the Gorge Road. The dark brooding skies of the Wet season with their lightning storms are shown in dramatic contrast to the pink and grey sunset of the Dry. The foreground depicts the trees, low shrubs, water-smoothed rocks and sandstone cliffs that make up the region's unique landscape.

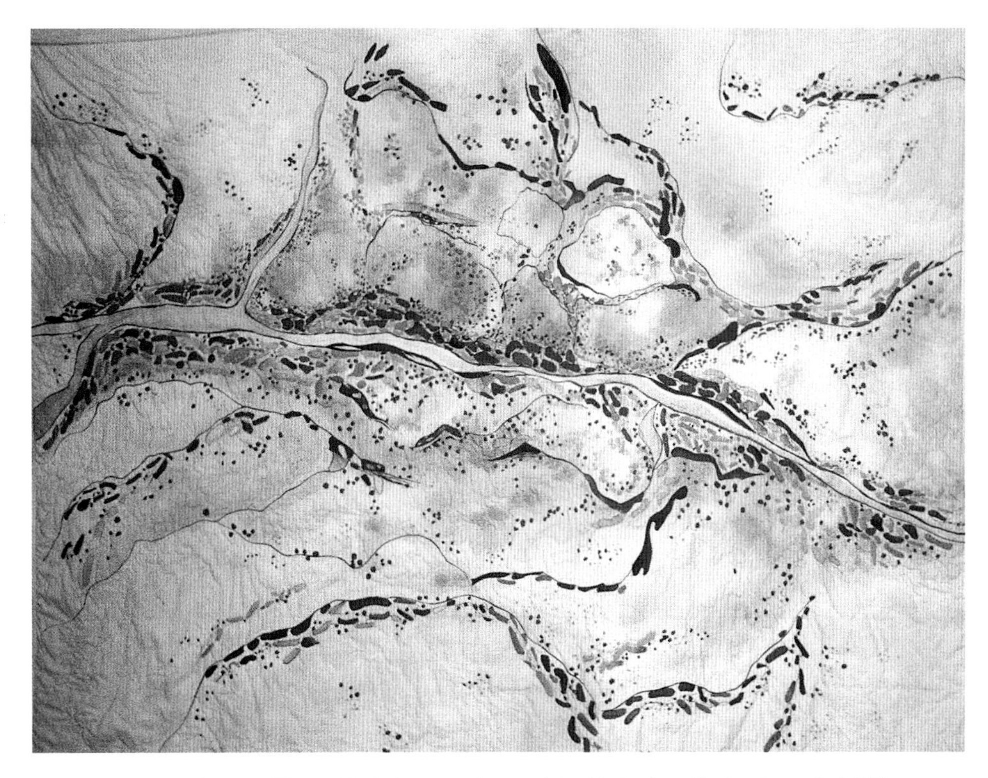

ABOVE: *Rivers of Time.* Made by members of the Katherine Crafts Council, 1995. 200cm x 180cm. Katherine Court House, Katherine.

Katherine Information Centre

Cnr. Katherine Tce and Lindsay Street
Katherine, NT 0850.
Ph: (08) 8972 2650 Fax: (08) 8972 2969
9.00a.m. – 5.00p.m. everyday between April and October. Closed weekends between November and March.

✷ The quilt is hung on permanent display in the Information Centre and may be seen during the hours listed.

✄ The most recent quilt to be created by members of the Crafts Council is entitled the *Katherine Region.* Made during 1997 and '98, the work features four distinct sections divided, as is the town itself, by the Stuart Highway and the Katherine River. The dividing lines mirror those of the logo of the Katherine Regional Tourist Association. Each section depicts a different view of the environment. There is the Timber Creek area with its escarpment and boab trees; the Roper River area with its palms and thermal springs; the Katherine Gorge with its river and sandstone cliffs; and finally the Borroloola region with a female dugong and her baby. The pictorial scenes were hand and machine appliquéd and overprinted with stencils. Fabrics were hand dyed and the work was finished with hand quilting.

Katherine Court House

Cnr. First Street and Giles Street
Katherine, NT 0850.
Ph: (08) 8973 8956
8.45a.m. – 4.00p.m. Monday to Friday.

✷ The quilt is hung in the foyer of the Court House and may be seen during the hours listed.

✄ This lovely quilt entitled *Rivers of Time* (200cm x 180cm) was made in 1995 by members of the Crafts Council. The previous year had marked the 100th anniversary of the Constitution Act Amendment giving the women of South Australia and the Northern Territory the right to vote and to stand for parliament. When the bill was given royal assent in 1895 it made these women among the first in the world to be granted the voting privileges formerly accorded only to men.

The anniversary coincided with the opening of the new Katherine Court House and a centenary of suffrage grant was awarded by the Northern Territory Government to assist the Crafts Council in making a commemorative quilt for the new building. The project began with a week-long work shop held with Western Australian textile artist Wendy Lugg. Members were taught new skills in the use of colour. They also learnt several embellishment techniques using fabric, paint, hand and machine embroidery.

The quilt design features an aerial perspective of the Katherine River and was painted by local artist John Smith. The background was hand painted and fabric pieces representing rocks and vegetation were then applied using a combination of hand and machine embroidery. The work was extensively hand quilted under Wendy's direction.

A message written in calligraphy explaining the history of the vote was screen printed to the back. This was its poignant conclusion:

'Due to the very harsh conditions in which they lived and their great strength of character, it is fitting the Territory women, together with those of South Australia, were the first in the world to receive this right.'

Clyde Fenton Primary School
Rapide Street
Katherine, NT 0850.
Ph: (08) 8972 1122
8.30a.m. – 3.00p.m. Monday to Friday during school terms.

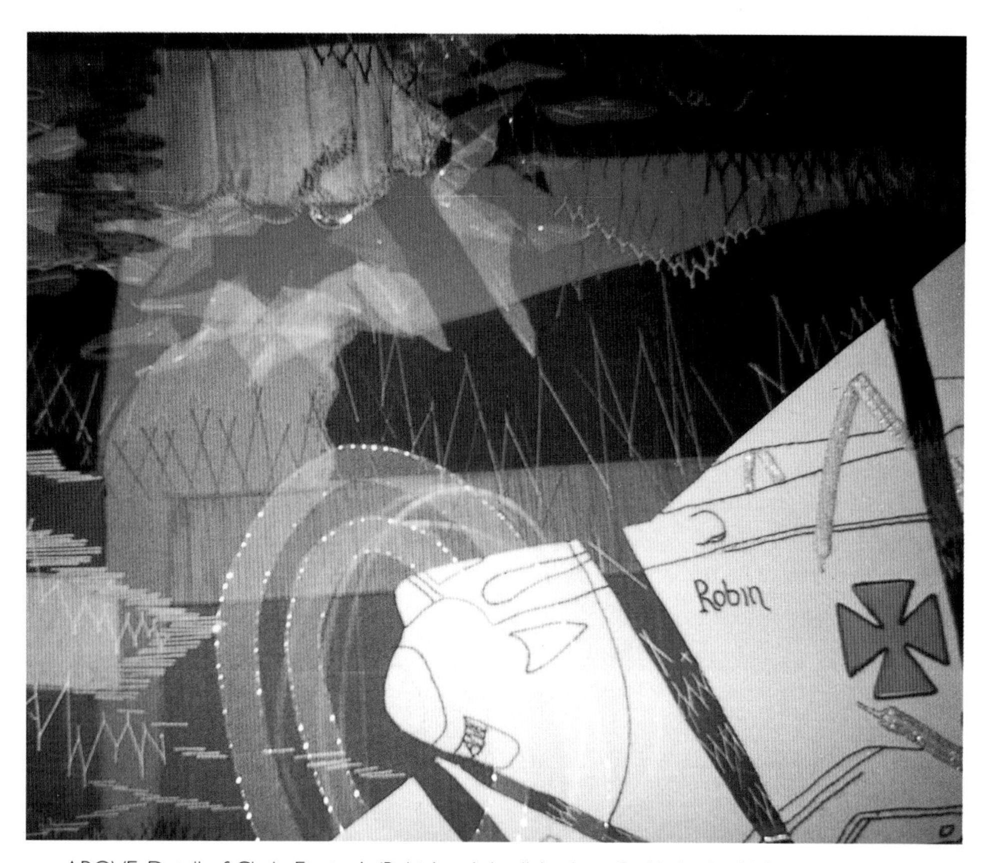

ABOVE: Detail of Clyde Fenton's *'Robin'* and the lightning of a Katherine Wet season storm.

✱ The quilt is hung on permanent display in the foyer of the building and may be seen during the hours listed.

✄ This spectacular pictorial quilt (200cm x 180cm) was initiated by Kathleen Short and made by members of the Embroiderers' Guild in 1977. Designed by local artist Gillian Banks, it commemorates the work of the first Flying Doctor in Katherine, the legendary Clyde Fenton.

The focal point of the quilt is the Gypsy Moth aircraft *'Robin'*, used by Doctor Fenton to bring medical help to patients in remote localities. The plane has been appliquéd to a dramatic aerial view of the region created from patchwork. Each piece has been stitched to the grey woollen army blanket used as a backing. The foreground depicts fields and paddocks along the banks of the Katherine River and has been embellished with chain stitch, running stitch and couched threads. The blue and purple sky has been shown slashed by the lightning of a Wet season storm and the dramatic effect has been enhanced by the use of giant fly and feather stitches. The plane's realistic propeller has been made from silk organza and edged with silver thread.

The quilt took six months to complete and was a true community project with Gillian's four children and Kathleen's husband all contributing to the stitching.

Clyde Fenton's original *'Robin'* may still be seen today in the local Katherine Museum. There is also a display of photographs and other memorabilia concerning the life of the famous doctor and his adventures.

Tennant Creek

The outback town of Tennant Creek is set in the red desert of Central Australia approximately 500 kilometres north of Alice Springs. Known as the *'Golden Heart of the Northern Territory,'* Australia's most recent gold rush occurred in the region during the 1930s and the mining of gold and copper are still important today. A National Trust Museum is housed in the original hospital building and its collection of memorabilia dates back to the pioneering days of the 1870s. A huge mural in the centre of town celebrates Aboriginal Dreaming as well as contemporary life in Tennant Creek. The spectacular landform known as the Devils Marbles are to be found a short drive south. These huge round granite boulders sit perched precariously, one on top of the other.

PHOTOGRAPHY COURTESY WENDY LUGG.

ABOVE: *The Clyde Fenton Quilt.* Made by members of the Embroiderers' Guild, 1977. 200cm x 280cm. Clyde Fenton Primary School, Katherine.

Tennant Creek Town Council
Peko Road
Tennant Creek, NT 0860.
Ph: (08) 8962 2401
Tennant Creek Town Council or
(08) 8962 4355 or (08) 8962 2754
Joan Carpenter, Crafts Council.
9.00a.m. – 4.00p.m. Monday to Friday.

✷ The quilt is hung on permanent display in the Civic Centre of the Council and may be seen during office hours. The quilters of Tennant Creek extend a warm welcome to visitors and in addition to the Commemorative Banner, they are happy to show you their own quilts. Please contact Joan Carpenter.

✂ This Commemorative Banner (120cm x 150cm) was made in 1992 by members of the Tennant Creek Crafts Council. The project was designed to celebrate the fiftieth anniversary since the Japanese bombing of Darwin during World War II. It also recorded a lasting history of Tennant Creek's involvement during the war years. Photographs from the 1940s were applied to silk fabric using the photocopy transfer method. Some of the older members of the Aboriginal community recalled the period vividly and their stories were transferred to fabric along with the photos. Each silk impression was hand painted by local artist Chris Elcoate and then hand stitched to the background.

Alice Springs

Alice Springs is one of the country's most famous and colourful towns, immortalised forever in Neville Shute's book *A Town like Alice.* Situated in the very heart of Central Australia, it is the major stopping point for tourists visiting the real outback and the giant rock formation of Uluru. Some of the history of the town can be discovered by taking one of the self-guided heritage walks which may be obtained from the National Trust Office in the Old Hartley Street School.

Despite the heat of the desert, quilting is immensely popular in Alice Springs. It is encouraged by the large number of American women living in the town because of the Joint Defence Facility at nearby Pine Gap. The local Quilting Club is very active, publishing a regular newsletter and holding an annual exhibition at the Araluen Arts Centre. Work by the famous Aboriginal artist Albert Namatjira is also to be enjoyed at Araluen and there are wonderful stained glass windows, mostly of Aboriginal design, reflecting the colours and themes of Central Australia.

ABOVE, FROM TOP: Details of Desert Roses, fluffy Acacia and tiny Poached Egg Daisies.

Alice Springs Desert Park
Larapinta Drive
Alice Springs, NT 0870.
Ph: (08) 8951 8788
7.30a.m. – 6.00p.m. daily.
Closed Christmas Day.

Set in the foothills of the spectacular MacDonnell Ranges, the Alice Springs Desert Park is just a ten minute drive from the centre of town. It has been planned to encompass the enormous diversity of landscapes, animals, and plants that are to be found within the Central Desert of Australia. A 1.6 kilometre walking path links the diverse habitats of Desert Rivers, Sand Country and Woodlands, and within each one the different species of flora and fauna can be seen in their own natural environment.

✷ The quilt is hung on permanent display in the Park Exhibition Centre and may be seen during opening hours.

✂ This lovely quilt entitled *Cycle of Life* (150cm x 95cm) was commissioned for the opening of the new Desert Park in March 1997. It was made by a group of eight Darwin quiltmakers and designed and co-ordinated by Jenny Armour. The intention of the work was to create a general impression of the region and its most distinguishing features. The design also focused on the sudden and brilliant transformation that takes place following rainfall when hundreds of plants explode into blossom.

The background of the quilt was made from horizontal sections and involved foundation and curved piecing, machine appliqué, fabric dyeing, spray-painting, embroidery and quilting. The trees and clumps of flowers blooming in proliferation across the desert were made individually by machine embroidery. Grasses were formed from frayed and distressed fabrics, each finished piece sewn in place by hand. Several species of glorious desert flowers were created using three dimensional techniques and are remarkable for their realism. On the right of the quilt is the intriguing orange Spade Flower, its weird three-pronged blooms like bright propellers. Each one was created by machine embroidering two layers of hand dyed fabric over thin batting. Fluffy yellow Acacia and large cream Grevillia were made using a mixture of wool, silk and rayon threads held in place with jewellery wire. Each flower required at least a day to complete.

Pale pink Desert Roses were created from translucent fabric, every petal made separately with a satin stitched edging. The centre of each rose was hand painted and wispy stamens were added with soft embroidery threads. Blue paper-like Cattlebush flowers were also made from layers of fabric over batting, the yellow stars in their centres formed with machine embroidery. In the foreground of the quilt, the brilliant red Sturt Desert Peas were created using stiffened fabric, each petal and leaf having a minute tuck sewn along its length. Tiny Poached Egg Daisies were made using yellow colonial knots for the centres and white silk ribbon for the petals. Each one was stitched onto a backing formed from a Suffolk Puff. The magnificent cream Spider Flower in the top corner, as well as most of the branches and stems, were made from wired rouleau.

This masterpiece of desert blooms was created by an innovative group of quiltmakers who combined some of the latest techniques of dying, painting, machine stitchery and use of fabric stabilisers, with traditional appliqué, beading and stuffed work.

PHOTOGRAPHY SUE HANSEN.

Alice Springs School of the Air
Head Street
Alice Springs, NT 0870.
Ph: (08) 8951 6834
8.30a.m. – 4.30p.m. Monday to Saturday.
1.30p.m. – 4.30p.m. Sunday.

The Alice Springs School of the Air was the first of its kind established in Australia. Today broadcasts are given directly from the school's own studios using a specially designed frequency to provide two way communication. The broadcast area served is enormous, taking in 1.3 million square kilometres and overlapping the borders of Western Australia, South Australia and Queensland. There are approximately 140 students enrolled. Many of them live on cattle stations, others come from Aboriginal communities, camel farms, national parks, mining and road work camps.

✷ The quilt is hung on permanent display in the Visitor Centre and may be seen during the opening hours listed.

✂ This quilt entitled *Opening Up the Centralian Outback* was made by students enrolled with the School of the Air at the time of the Australian Bicentennial in 1988. The project was initiated by Penny McConville, a teacher at the school, with the aim of depicting the heritage of outback children in a quilt to be made by the children themselves. It provided an opportunity for children who were separated from one another by great distances to work as a community group, and through their participation to engender a sense of school spirit.

Squares of calico were sent out to the stations and settlements on which the children lived and each participant was asked to depict some aspect of their life in pictorial form. Many of the children illustrated the day to day work

ABOVE: *Cycle of Life*. Made by a group of Darwin quiltmakers, 1997. 150cm x 95cm. Alice Springs Desert Park, Alice Springs.

PHOTOGRAPHY TERRY KNIGHT.

carried out on their properties, the mustering of animals and the tending to bores. Many included their homesteads, emus, kangaroos, camels and domestic pets. Most of the blocks were appliquéd by hand using whatever fabrics could be found at the time. They were assembled and sewn together by Penny before being hung on permanent display in the Visitor Centre, a unique insight into the life of outback children during this period.

Children at Braitling Primary School, located in the same grounds as the School of the Air, also created a quilt to celebrate the Bicentennial. Illustrations representing the past, present, and future of Australia were drawn by the students, then traced, painted, and sewn together by their teacher, Joan Simpson. The work may be seen in the front office of the school.

The Australian Broadcasting Corporation

Cnr. Gap Road and Speed Street
Alice Springs, NT 0870.
Ph: (08) 8952 3433
9.00a.m. – 5.00p.m Monday to Friday.

✷ The quilt is hung on permanent display in the foyer of the building and may be seen during office hours.

✂ A striking circular abstract quilt entitled *Know Your A.B.C.* was made by Jennifer Gray in 1988. Inspired by a photograph of a similar quilt, the design was chosen to fit harmoniously into its location in front of an arched feature wall. The mosaic design of triangles, squares and diamonds was pieced together by hand using plain cotton fabrics in tones of blue and apricot. It was hand quilted and enclosed within a circular frame measuring three metres in diameter. The frame had to be specially made in two parts so that it would fit within the orange circular casing bordering the pieced centre of the quilt. The finished work was suspended from the ceiling using invisible nylon fishing line so that it hangs high above the reception desk and forms an integral focal point within the arched wall behind.

National Pioneer Women's Hall of Fame

Old Courthouse
27 Hartley Street
Alice Springs, NT 0870.
Ph: (08) 8952 9006 Fax: (08) 8952 9406
10.00a.m. – 2.00p.m. daily or by appointment. Closed mid December to February and public holidays.

The Old Courthouse is a heritage listed stone building with a wide verandah and corrugated iron roof. It is located in the heart of town on the corner of Hartley and Parsons Streets, just near the Post Office. The National Pioneer Women's Hall of Fame is a unique museum founded in 1993 by Molly Clarke. A fascinating woman now in her mid '70s, Molly has spent most of her life at Old Andado Station, an isolated property some 350 kilometres from Alice Springs.

The aim of the museum is to commemorate the place of women in the history and development of Australia. The women recorded have come from many backgrounds, diverse locations, and from earliest days to present times. Their contribution to the country's heritage is preserved within collections of stories, photographs and artefacts.

There is a fascinating photographic exhibition entitled 'Ordinary Women, Extraordinary Lives: Women First in their Field.' It features more than one hundred photographs of women who were pioneers in largely male-dominated professions. A new exhibition of pictures and stories relating specifically to Central Australian women is currently being prepared. There is also a display of needlework and crafts, as well as domestic items used in the traditional 'women's work' of laundering, cooking and cleaning.

✷ The quilt is not on display but visitors are welcome to see it by appointment. The Curator is available on Wednesdays and Thursdays and the Museum is staffed by volunteers on other days. Please telephone or fax at least one week in advance.

✂ This beautiful quilt of Log Cabin design (225cm x 225cm) was made by Nicholes Wallace c.1895. Nicholes lived with her husband, Isaac, on a farm at Carlston in north east Victoria. She had originally married a Mr Brown and together they had four sons. Isaac Wallace was her second husband and the couple had a daughter named Elizabeth. Nicholes made at least one quilt for Elizabeth, as well as for all her daughters-in-law. Her son John married in 1902 and this quilt, believed to have been made some years before the wedding, was given to his wife, Alma. It was donated to the museum in 1995 by Alma's daughter, Pat Fleming of Alice Springs, and it is now referred to affectionately as *Mrs Fleming's Quilt.*

The work is a traditional Log Cabin design known as Light and Dark, each block having twenty-four tiny strips of fabric sewn together by hand. In an unusual variation, the square around which the strips are pieced has been placed in the corner rather than the centre.

A remarkable border frames the quilt. Made from three rows of hand pieced triangles, the cleverly alternating light and dark fabrics create a stunning design of elongated diamonds, broken in each corner by three squares. A narrow cream

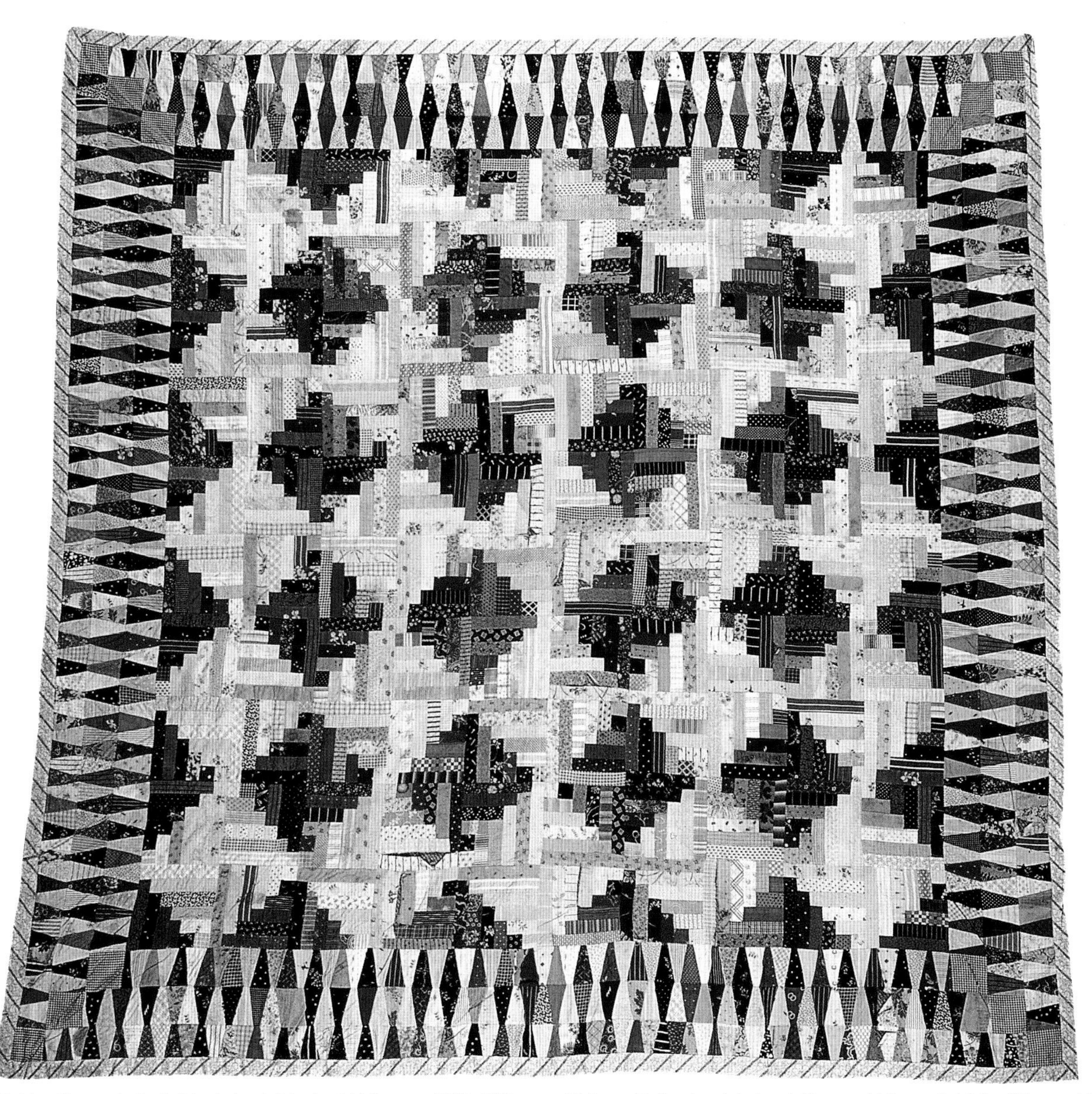

ABOVE: *Mrs Fleming's Quilt.* Made by Nicholes Wallace, c.1895. 225cm x 225cm. Collection National Pioneer Women's Hall of Fame, Alice Springs.

PHOTOGRAPHY STEVE STRIKE.

striped binding has been sewn around the outside edge, the only example of machine stitching to appear on the quilt. The fabrics are printed cottons and include paisley, florals, checks, spots and stripes. This treasured work is considered to be the oldest and most precious item in the collection of the National Pioneer Women's Hall of Fame.

Also in Alice Springs

A small pictorial quilt (60cm x 90cm) was made in 1987 by members of the Alice Springs Quilting Club to celebrate the Bicentennial. The design was inspired by a photograph depicting a desert waterhole with spinifex grass emerging from its edges, pigeons circling above. The work was hand pieced, appliquéd and quilted using fabrics of cotton, rayon, silk and satin. It is hung on permanent display at the Alice Springs Town Council, corner of Todd and Gregory Terrace, and may be seen between 8.00a.m. and 5.00p.m. Monday to Friday. It is advisable to ring before visiting to ensure the Chambers are not in use. Telephone (08) 8950 0500.

The Alice Springs Quilting Club also made a cot quilt in 1986 to display on the old iron cot at the historic Telegraph Station. The quilt is a simple chequerboard design made from squares of calico and printed cottons. The Station is situated in the Historical Reserve on the Stuart Highway. It presents a fascinating glimpse of the isolation and loneliness endured by those who established Australia's telegraphic lifeline to the world. It is open daily from 8.00a.m. to 7.00p.m. between May and September, and 8.00a.m. to 9.00p.m. during other months. Telephone (08) 8952 1013.

Detail of *Essence of Maroochy*. Made by a local community group, 1989–'90. 6m x 2m. Nambour Civic Centre, Nambour, Queensland.

QUILTS OF QUEENSLAND

PHOTOGRAPHY MARK LEE.

LEFT: Detail showing the central medallion of Mrs Kent's quilt with its Egyptian motifs. RIGHT: Detail of *Quilt of Hexagon Diamonds.* Made by Mrs Lawless, c.1850-'60. OPPOSITE: *Medallion Quilt.* Made by Mrs Kent, c.1820. Collection Miegunyah Pioneer Women's Memorial House Museum, Bowen Hills, Queensland.

Miegunyah Pioneer Women's Memorial House Museum

35 Jordan Terrace
Bowen Hills, QLD 4006.
Ph: (07) 3252 2979
10.30a.m. – 3.00p.m. Wednesday, Saturday and Sunday.
Open Tuesday and Thursday by prior arrangement. Closed Monday, Friday and the months of December and January.
Approximately 20 quilts.

Bowen Hills is an inner suburb of Brisbane located just a few minutes drive north of the city centre.

Miegunyah is a family house museum run by the Queensland Women's Historical Association as a memorial to the pioneer women of the state. A beautiful Victorian residence built in 1884, Miegunyah was purchased by the Association in 1967. Over the years it has been restored and furnished as a family home of the period 1880 to 1900 and the furniture, china, silver and other possessions are typical of the late 19th century. The collection of clothing includes items as early as 1760 and extends to the present day. In addition to the patchwork quilts, there are hand crocheted and hand embroidered coverlets of exceptional beauty. There are also many wonderful examples of white work, cut work, lace and embroidery.

✷ There will always be some quilts and other textile items on display in Miegunyah. The remainder of the collection may be seen by appointment. Please contact the Museum at least one week in advance so that a volunteer who is familiar with the textiles can arrange a viewing time.

✂ The collection includes a frail but beautiful medallion quilt brought to Australia from England by Major John Kent c.1832. The quilt had been made by his mother and contains fabrics dating from the early 19th century. The central square features an octagon of printed chintz with cotton triangles in each corner. The surrounding border of squares contains fabrics printed with Egyptian motifs. Such motifs were especially popular during this period following successful archaeological excavations resulting in the uncovering of ancient Egyptian cities. Successive borders of plain strips, diamonds, Squares-on-point, and herringbone strips have been used to frame the medallion. The work has a backing of cream cotton, a filling of carded wool and has been quilted by hand in a diamond pattern. Metal rings sewn to one end indicate that it may have been hung as a curtain, possibly to keep out draughts.

A quilt of hexagon diamonds was made c.1850-'60 by Mrs Lawless who had emigrated to Australia from Wales. The

Lawless family established a property called 'Boobyjan Station' near Goomeri and were amongst the earliest settlers in the district. The hexagon diamonds have been separated from each other by a plain white background and the work has been finely hand stitched over papers. The templates cut from old letters are still clearly visible behind each patch.

A quilt of large printed cotton hexagons and squares is of English origin and was presented to the Queensland Women's Historical Association by Mrs K. Foote. It had been made by an aunt of Mrs Foote's husband at the family's ancestral home of 'Syston Court,' near Bristol. The work was pieced over papers and finely quilted by hand.

A single bed quilt of white gathered hexagons dates from the early 20th century and is of unknown maker. A tiny flower has been hand embroidered into the centre of each hexagon and a gathered frill has been sewn around the sides.

LEFT: *Fraser Island*. Made by Judy-Ann Moule, 1998. Marriott Hotel, Brisbane.

✷ The quilts are displayed occasionally. They may also be seen by appointment. Requests should be made in advance to the Curator of Decorative Arts.

✄ The Gallery has three quilts by Ruth Stoneley. Included is a pieced work entitled *Eternity* (135cm x 140cm) which was made in 1990 from black cottons and silks. It was quilted with metallic thread and embellished with beads and touches of paint.

Barbara Macey's *Wave 7* was made in 1981. Based on the traditional Log Cabin design, the work was created entirely from one fabric, a crisp black cotton lawn. Some of the strips were cut parallel and some at right angles to the selvage, the variance in grain direction governing the light reflection of the fabric and creating some light strips and some dark.

Sarah Crowest's quilt *After Okayama* (230cm x 174cm) was made in 1993. It recorded special memories of her trip to Okayama Prefecture by using souvenir fabrics purchased in Japan as well as prints that she created herself. The work was machine pieced using dyed, screen printed and painted cottons.

Biri Dancers was made in 1989 by Aboriginal quiltmaker Coralie Wason. Commercial dyes were used in a batik technique which was then quilted.

Queensland Art Gallery
Queensland Cultural Centre
South Bank, QLD 4101.
Ph: (07) 3840 7333
Fax: (07) 3844 8865
10.00a.m. – 5.00p.m. Monday to Sunday.
Open until 8.00p.m. Wednesday.
8 quilts.

The Gallery only had one quilted panel in its collection before the 1982 'Survey of Contemporary Australian Craft.' Quilts by several Australian textile artists were acquired at this time. Since then quilts have been added to the collection when considered of importance in the context of Queensland crafts or when manifesting Australia's connections with Asia.

The Embroiderers' Guild, Queensland
149 Brunswick Street
Fortitude Valley, QLD 4006.
Ph: (07) 3252 8629
9.00a.m. – 1.00p.m. Thursdays.
1.00p.m. – 4.00p.m. Saturdays
or by arrangement.
6 quilts.

RIGHT: *Moreton Bay.* Made by Judy-Ann Moule, 1998. Marriott Hotel, Brisbane.

Fortitude Valley is an inner suburb of Brisbane located just a few minutes drive north of the city centre. It is the heart of the Chinatown district.

The Embroiderers' Guild was established in 1968 to promote and encourage the art of fine embroidery within the state. The property in Brunswick Street was purchased as a permanent home in 1982. The Guild's textile collection represents many different cultures. They include Eastern Europe, Hungary, China, and India. There are two white work coverlets c.1915, a hand knitted bedspread, a cross stitch sampler dated 1754, and an English waistcoat c.1770.

✷ There are always items from the collection on display in the Guild Rooms and sometimes these will include quilts. Quilts held in storage may be seen by prior arrangement. Please telephone the Guild several days in advance.

✂ The collection includes quilts made by members over the years as well as others donated to the Guild as historical examples. A Crazy quilt (180cm x 130cm) was made by Anne Humphreys in 1978. The fabrics include silk, satin, brocade, velvet and corduroy. The work features a diverse range of embroidery stitches and is framed by a border of burgundy silk.

A sampler quilt entitled *Medley of Memories* (138cm x 114cm) was made by the Guild's night group in 1996. The twenty blocks were created using a variety of techniques including appliqué, piecing, Crazy Patchwork, screen printing, ribbon embroidery, cross stitch and tatting. The blocks were joined with burgundy sashing and framed with floral chintz.

A wagga (162cm x 100cm) was made by Nell Wilcox of Mt Gravatt, Queensland during the 1940s. Nell spent the war years working in a Brisbane clothing factory and it was from this source that she obtained her woollen offcuts. The top and backing were made from rectangles of plaid dressing gown fabric, the filling from sheeting. The wagga was in use until 1988 and some patches are now very worn.

Brisbane Marriott Hotel

515 Queen Street
Brisbane, QLD 4000.
Ph: (07) 3303 8000 Fax: (07) 3303 8088
24 hours a day.

✷ The wall hangings are displayed on the second floor outside the ballroom and visitors are welcome to see them.

✂ These stunning contemporary wall hangings entitled *Moreton Bay* and *Fraser Island* (80cm x 100cm each) were created by textile artist Judy-Ann Moule in 1998. They depict aerial views of the coast and present the environments of Moreton Bay and Fraser Island as jewels that must be treasured and preserved.

Judy-Ann uses colour and texture to capture and explore her emotional response to the sea. The depth of colour in these fabric collages is achieved by the multiple layering of silk, organza, and hand dyed fabrics. Many of the fabrics are constructed by cutting out a palette of colours and sandwiching them between tulle. Judy-Ann achieves the extraordinary realism of finely painted watercolours using layering and machine stitchery as an artist's brush to paint delicate lines, shapes, and textures.

In the Nearby Region

The suburb of Coorparoo is located approximately 10 minutes drive south east of the city. An inspiring series of ecclesiastical textiles has been created over a period of years for the Coorparoo Uniting Church by Betty Rees and Olwyn Beech. The symbolic images were designed to enhance both the beauty and spiritual ambience of the church and to portray clear Christian messages. The church is located on the corner of Cavendish Road and York Street and the collection may be seen by making an appointment a few days in advance. Telephone (07) 3397 4377.

Betty Rees also created two little quilted pictures depicting the Queen Alexandra Home and the adjacent building of Hatherton. The work was made with hand and machine appliqué, embroidery and quilting and is displayed in the Memorabilia Room of the Queen Alexandra Home Community Centre, 347 Old Cleveland Road, Coorparoo. Please telephone in advance (07) 3244 6602.

The bayside area of Cleveland is approximately 30 kilometres south east of the city. Two *Bread and Wine* hangings were created in 1995 by Ruth Fleming for the Uniting Church, Passage Street, Cleveland. The works were made by hand using the Stained Glass appliqué technique. They are hung on permanent display within the church and visitors are welcome to see them. Please telephone in advance (07) 3286 5627.

Ruth also created a hanging entitled the *Word Made Flesh* for the chapel of the Department of Community Service, 166 Baroona Road, Rosalie. It is hung on permanent display and may be seen between 8.30a.m. and 5.00p.m. Monday to Friday. Telephone (07) 3367 3840.

Brookfield and Kenmore

The picturesque community of Brookfield is located approximately 14 kilometres west of Brisbane. It is a peaceful semi-rural region despite its close proximity to the city. The Kenmore Village Shopping Centre is located on the Brisbane side of the Shire.

Kenmore Village Shopping Centre

Cnr. Moggill and Brookfield Roads
Kenmore, QLD 4069.
Ph: (07) 3378 7722
9.00a.m.– 5.00p.m. Monday to Friday.
Open until 9.00p.m. Thursday.
9.00a.m.– 4.00p.m. Saturday.

✱ The quilt is displayed within the Centre. If entering by the main door on the ground floor, it is to be found on the left side towards the Mitre 10 store.

✂ The beautiful *History of Brookfield Quilt* (200cm x 150cm) was made in 1988 as part of 'Greetings from Brisbane,' a project initiated by Brisbane City Council's Community Arts Unit. This scheme involved many local communities in the production of 'textile postcards' which were exhibited in Brisbane before being returned to their own municipalities. The quilt was designed by mixed media artist Sharyn Hall. It was made by a talented group of fourteen women who worked with Sharyn as artist-in-charge. The design focused on the history of the region which for more than a century had been centred around the logging industry. The background depicts Mt Elphinstone and the surrounding green hills. It was strip pieced in separate sections for ease of sewing. Fabrics included furnishing materials, velvets, wools, hessian, vinyl, silk, cotton and chintz. The sky was created from a single piece of hand painted and quilted cotton. The heritage sites of the 'Brookfield Precinct' were grouped in the centre, each building made separately using free machine stitchery with hand embroidered and quilted details. The magnificent trunks of Red Cedar, Hoop Pine and Grey Gum which frame each side of the quilt were created with manipulated fabrics and overlays of organza.

Wool couching, trapunto, quilting, and graduated padding were all used to produce the three-dimensional effect. Softly curled and twisting leaves were made from chintz, dyed silk and organza, and finished with leather stems. The timber wagon was formed from rouleau and shadow quilting, the logs from padded and painted fabric. Hundreds of hours were spent on the creation of the work. It was finished with detailed hand and machine quilting.

ABOVE: *History of Brookfield Quilt.* Made by a community group with Sharyn Hall as artist-in-charge, 1988. 200cm x 150cm. Kenmore Village Shopping Centre, Kenmore, Queensland.

Brookfield Uniting Church
2 Upper Brookfield Road
Brookfield, QLD 4069.
Ph: (07) 3378 4505 parish office.
The parish office is open between
9.00a.m. and noon weekdays.
Services are held each Sunday morning
at 8.30a.m.

The Brookfield Uniting Church is more than 125 years old and is one of several historic buildings in the area known locally as the 'Brookfield Precinct.' The Hoop Pine which is depicted on the left side of the quilt was planted during the later part of the 19th century and can still be seen today in the church grounds.

✱ The quilt is not on permanent display but is hung every Sunday for the service and visitors are welcome to attend. It may also be seen at other times by prior arrangement. Please contact the office.

✄ This pictorial and symbolic quilt (250cm x 150cm) was made in 1989 by Sharyn Hall. It was commissioned by the church as a memorial to a former parish member. The design was created by Sharyn in consultation with the church elders and was inspired by both religious symbolism as well as the *History of Brookfield Quilt.* The background depicts Mt Elphinstone with the little church nestled into the green hills of the valley. It was strip pieced using a wide variety of fabrics. They included furnishing materials, silks, velvets, wool, cotton and chintz. The nine doves flying overhead symbolise the nine gifts of the Spirit and were appliquéd by hand to the pieced background. The enormous tree framing the left side of the work represents the Tree of Life as well as the century old Hoop Pine that stands in the church grounds. Beneath it, children look out across the quilt and symbolise the beginnings of creation. This is reiterated in the blood of the lamb slain at the base of the cross.

Each symbol was made separately using free machine stitchery with details added in hand embroidery and quilting. Much of the work was padded. Trapunto and fabric manipulation were also used to bring the quilt to life. Tulle and organza were applied as over-lay fabrics to achieve shadowing and shading, and wool, silk and metallic embroidery threads were added for embellishment.

PHOTOGRAPHY PETER WILLIAMS.

ABOVE: *Patchwork Quilt.* Unknown Maker, mid to late 19th century. Caboolture Historical Village, Caboolture, Queensland. OPPOSITE: Details of the central medallion and border.

The Gold Coast

The Gold Coast stretches from Southport to Coolangatta. Its perfect climate, beaches and major family attractions make it the most popular holiday destination in Australia.

Parkroyal Hotel
2807 Gold Coast Highway
Surfers Paradise
Gold Coast, QLD 4217.
Ph: (07) 5592 9900
24 hours a day.

✷ The mural is hung on permanent display in the entrance lobby of the hotel and visitors are welcome to see it.

✄ This large mural (6m x 180cm) was made by Margaret Scott in 1991. It depicts the Norfolk Island Pines growing along the sandy stretch of coastal Broadbeach, the ocean in the distance. The work was appliquéd, embroidered and quilted by machine. Six triangular protrusions run longitudinally through the centre. When viewed slightly to one side, they create a fascinating illusion of movement in the undulating dunes.

A fabric sculpture entitled *Red Gums* was also created by Margaret and may be seen in the hotel coffee shop. The work symbolises the peeling bark of the beautiful Australian eucalypt and was made from appliquéd and embroidered materials wrapped tightly over batting-covered rods.

Belle Maison
129 Surfers Parade
Broadbeach
Gold Coast, QLD 4218
Ph: (07) 5570 9200
9.00a.m. – 5.00p.m. Monday to Friday.
2 murals.

✷ The murals are hung on permanent display in the main reception area of the building. Visitors are welcome during office hours.

✄ These two fabric murals were created by Margaret Scott in 1992 and were designed to compliment the Art Nouveau style of the building's interior. Entitled *Moon Garden* and *Sun Garden,* the flowers were machine appliquéd onto a background of natural linen. Both murals were embellished with machine embroidery and beading and *Moon Garden* was finished with hand tying.

Caboolture

Caboolture has retained its rural atmosphere despite its close proximity to Brisbane which is only 45 kilometres to the south. It is surrounded by a thriving region of dairy properties, tropical fruit orchards and mixed farms. Nearby are the beautiful beaches of the Sunshine Coast and it is only a short drive to the bridge that crosses Pumicestone Passage to Bribie Island.

Caboolture Historical Village
Beerburrum Road
Caboolture, QLD 4510.
Ph: (07) 5495 4581
Fax: (07) 5495 8746
(07) 5496 8774 after hours.
9.30a.m. – 3.30p.m. daily.
Closed Good Friday, December 24th and Christmas Day.

The Village is located two kilometres north of the town. It includes more than fifty buildings of historical significance which have been relocated from other sites within the shire. They range from the original post office, police station, general store and grocer's shop, to a morgue and chook house. One small cottage contains hundreds of jugs dating from the 1890s. A Linen Museum is housed in another cottage and its collection includes numerous examples of needlework.

✱ The quilt is displayed behind glass in the entrance building and may be seen any day during opening hours.

✄ This patchwork quilt of English origin dates from the mid to late 19th century. The maker is unknown but the work is believed to have originated in the County of Cumberland. It was purchased by Barbara Gash in 1945 at a farm auction in the small town of Calbeck, near Carlisle. Mrs Gash lived in Caboolture and treasured the work for many years before donating it to the Historical Village.

The centre of the quilt features a large hexagon-shaped medallion formed by stitching together successive rows around a central rosette. The print design in each hexagon has been meticulously matched so that each one features the same leaves, the identical dusky roses, daisies, or geometric shapes. Cotton prints in colours of cream, brown and pink have been used for the medallion, with printed dress fabrics for the random hexagons surrounding it. The work has been edged with a strip border of printed cotton and backed with a paisley cotton. It has been made by hand over paper templates and every hexagon has been hand quilted.

Redcliffe

The historic coastal suburb of Redcliffe overlooks Moreton Bay, approximately 35 kilometres north of Brisbane.

Redcliffe Entertainment Centre
Downs Street
Redcliffe, QLD 4020.
Ph: (07) 3889 5388
9.00a.m. – 4.00p.m. Monday to Friday.
12 noon – 4.00p.m. Saturday.
6.00p.m. – 9.00p.m. Tuesday, Wednesday, Friday and Saturday evening.

✱ The quilt is hung on permanent display within the Centre and may be seen during opening hours.

✄ The *Redcliffe Bicentennial Quilt* (300cm x 300cm) was made by the Henzell Street Quilters in 1988. The work was designed and co-ordinated by Jenny Riley, and local artist Fiona Ward drew the pictorial blocks. The central square depicts the landing at Redcliffe Point in 1824 by John Oxley in the tall ship *'Amity.'* Surrounding blocks illustrate buildings and features of significance. The quilt was appliquéd by hand and machine and finished with hand embroidery and quilting. It was mounted using a special suspension system devised to ensure sufficient air circulated around it.

Caloundra

The seaside City of Caloundra is the most southerly resort on the Sunshine Coast and within an hour's drive north of Brisbane. The idyllic beaches and beautiful hinterland have made the region a popular holiday destination since the 1880s.

Caloundra Arts and Crafts Association
North Street, Golden Beach
Caloundra, QLD 4551.
Ph: (07) 5492 6993 or (07) 5492 8498
Caloundra Quilters.
9.00a.m. – 4.00p.m. weekdays except public holidays.

✱ The quilt is hung on permanent display in the Crafty Pelican Room of the Centre. The rooms are open most days of the week with a variety of groups using them. The Caloundra Quilters meet here on Friday mornings and Tuesday evenings and visitors are always welcome.

✄ This Bicentennial quilt (195cm x 254cm) was made by the Caloundra Quilters in 1988. Appliquéd scenes depict the sun, sea and water sports for which the region is renowned. Depicted in the centre is the Arts and Crafts building as well as the lighthouse, used by the quilters as their logo. Other blocks represent native fauna and flora, historical events and the pineapple industry of the hinterland.

Nambour

Nambour is found in the rich hinterland behind the Sunshine Coast, less than a half hour drive from Caloundra. Sugar has been the major rural industry here since the late 19th century and between July and December the cane trains wind their way through the main street of the town. A painted mural in Bury Street depicts the history of the region.

PHOTOGRAPHY ERROL LARKAN.

OPPOSITE: Detail of *Essence of Maroochy.* Made by a community group, 1989-'90. 6m x 2m. Nambour Civic Centre, Nambour, Queensland. The two large eucalypts were padded to create dimension and the different shades of their bark were mimicked with fabric overlays.

Nambour Civic Centre
Currie Street
Nambour, QLD 4560.
Ph: (07) 5430 9333 Fax: (07) 5441 7400.
9.00a.m. – 5.00p.m. Monday to Friday.
Weekend hours vary according to scheduled functions and entertainment.

✷ The quilt is hung on permanent display in the foyer of the Centre and may be seen during opening hours.

✄ This magnificent wall hanging entitled the *Essence of Maroochy* (6m x 2m) was created between 1989 and '90 by a community group. It was inspired by the theatre curtain made by the community of Griffith in western New South Wales which had been seen by one of the makers during a holiday. The design depicts a sweeping view of the Shire and was prepared by local graphic designer Hugh Anderson. Robin Dunn co-ordinated the project and textile artist Rose Halliday-Smith provided invaluable assistance in interpreting the work into fabric. The pieced background was divided into sections along the natural contours of the landscape, each one being created by a different group of makers. The diverse range of techniques included fabric dyeing, hand and machine appliqué, embroidery and quilting. Tiny details, including the butterflies hovering over flowers and the cane frog resting on a rock, were machine embroidered separately and then hand stitched to the background. Thousands of individual banksia, blackbean, grevillea, eucalypt, and melaleuca leaves were created by machine, some of them requiring several layers of fabric to realistically mirror the colours of nature. Countless stems were made from rouleau. The two large eucalypts featured in the foreground were lightly padded, the different shades of their bark mimicked with fabric overlays. This beautiful quilt took almost two years to make. It provided a wonderful focus for quilters and textile artists within the region and resulted in the creation of a lasting treasure for the entire community.

In the Nearby Region

The town of Gympie is a short drive north of Nambour. At the Gympie and District Historical and Mining Museum there is a coverlet of Suffolk Puffs c.1920. The puffs were made from plain and printed cottons and crepes and joined together by hand at six different points around their edges, thereby creating hexagon shapes. There is also a simple patchwork quilt of squares and triangles made during the 1970s by a small community group. The one hundred year old timber cottage in which the quilts are displayed was once the home of Andrew Fisher, the first Labour Prime Minister of Australia. The museum is located at 215 Brisbane Road, Monkland and is open between 9.00a.m. and 5.00p.m. daily except Good Friday and Christmas Day. Telephone (07) 5482 1625.

Crows Nest

The little town of Crows Nest sits on the crest of the Great Dividing Range, approximately a half hour drive north of Toowoomba. The undulating countryside surrounding the town is covered with rich fields of grain crops and lush pasture land. A statue in the picturesque village green commemorates the local folk hero, Jimmy Crow, after whom the town was named. Jimmy was an Aborigine who lived in the hollow of a tree near the police station and provided help to travellers during the early days. The local Carbethon Folk Museum has a fascinating collection of memorabilia. Included is a hand crocheted counterpane, examples of tatting, Battenberg lace and embroidery. There is even a picture made from silver chocolate-paper wrappers and a doyley made with hair pins c.1890. The Museum is open Thursday and Sunday afternoons or by appointment. Telephone (07) 4698 1776. Another landmark in the town is Salt's Antiques, housed in an enormous and beautiful Edwardian building.

Crows Nest Shire Council
25 Emu Creek Road
Crows Nest, QLD 4355.
Ph: (07) 4698 1155 Fax: (07) 4698 1717
8.30a.m. – 5.00p.m. Monday to Friday.
2 quilts.

✷ The quilts are hung on permanent display within the Council building and may be seen during office hours. Occasionally they are sent for short exhibition periods to nearby towns so it is advisable to ring in advance.

✄ A beautiful community quilt was designed by Janece King and made by the Crows Nest Quilters in 1996. The work was divided into four separate panels (150cm x 150cm each) which were joined together in the final stages to create a banner shape. Each panel

PHOTOGRAPHY ERROL LARKAN.

OPPOSITE: Detail of *Essence of Maroochy*. Made by a local community group, 1989-'90. 6m x 2m. Nambour Civic Centre, Nambour, Queensland. Thousands of individual banksia, blackbean, grevillea, eucalypt and melaleuca leaves were created by machine and hand stitched in place.

concentrated on a separate theme – the vast forests of Hoop Pine and Red Cedar that attracted the early settlers, the farms that quickly developed and which sustain the region today, the town itself, and finally the magnificent waterfall cascading over rocks in nearby Crows Nest National Park. The background presents an impressionist view of the sky, hills, fields, timber, dams and waterfalls. It was created using the colour wash technique and involved the machine piecing of thousands of tiny squares of fabric set on the diagonal. The foreground of each scene tells its own unique story. There are buildings, trees, animals and birds created individually using hand and machine appliqué and embroidery. The work was completed with machine quilting.

ABOVE: *Crows Nest Heritage Quilt.* Made by the Crows Nest Quilters, 1996. 150cm x 150cm. Crows Nest Shire Council, Crows Nest, Queensland.

A quilt entitled *Window into Tomorrow* (120cm x 180cm) was designed by Dorothy Parton and made by the Crows Nest Quilters in 1996. It depicts a huge stained glass window floating in a starry night sky and surrounded by a wide border of planets. The view through the window looks towards 'Tomorrow,' the brilliant sun providing a symbol of our

ABOVE: *Dalby Bicentennial Quilt.* Made by the Dalby Quilters, 1988. Dalby Town Council, Dalby, Queensland.

future and reflecting a myriad of colours. Everything is bright and beautiful and the pessimism and negativity of today have completely vanished. The quilt was made using the Stained Glass appliqué technique with luminous fabrics of velvet, satin, silk and metallics. Grey poly cotton was used for the bias in order to mirror the lead of a window. The work was pieced, appliquéd and quilted entirely by hand.

Dalby

The large and prosperous town of Dalby lies in the heart of the Darling Downs, a one hour drive north west of Toowoomba. The wide main thoroughfare of Cunningham Street dates from the early pioneering days, its width designed to allow the bullock teams adequate space to turn with ease. The rich farming land surrounding Dalby is among the most productive in Australia with flourishing wheat, cereal and cotton farms, and numerous sheep and cattle properties. In summer the fields of sun flowers create brilliant yellow stripes between the paddocks of green and brown. Only a short drive north is the historic home of Jimbour House, originally owned by prominent early settler, Thomas Bell. The extensive gardens are open to the public daily except in wet weather.

TOP: Juliane and Edward Jensen on their wedding day, November 24th 1920. ABOVE: *Patchwork Quilt.* Made by Juliane Jensen, c.1920. 195cm x 195cm. Gatton Historical Museum, Gatton, Queensland.

Dalby Town Council
107 Drayton Street
Dalby, QLD 4405.
Ph: (07) 4660 6100 Fax: (07) 4660 6199
8.00a.m. – 5.00p.m. Monday to Friday.

✷ The quilt is displayed in the upstairs hallway of the Council building and may be seen during opening hours.

✄ This beautiful quilt was created by the Dalby Quilters as a Bicentennial gift to the community. It was designed by local artist Jenny Maher together with quilting tutor Pauline Rogers. A drawing was prepared to full scale, its central picture illustrating the undulating hills of the Darling Downs with their patchwork of cultivated fields and grazing properties. The rich fabric colours were chosen to realistically portray the diversity of the rural area. Hand quilting was used to create the furrowed rows, to add direction and dimension.

The piecing of the picture was done entirely by machine. The oval border was padded to create a depth of view looking back to the distant horizon. The details in each field – the sunflowers, wheat, cotton, sheep and cattle, were all hand embroidered. Corner pictures depict some of the oldest buildings in the Dalby region with Jimbour House included on the lower left side. Each building was appliquéd, the templates made from enlarged photographs and the details added in hand embroidery.

The wonderful quilting design was transferred to the background using templates and all the quilting was done by hand. It included huge wheat silos, a water tower, local monuments and rural industries. St John's Anglican Church, established in 1866 and the oldest in the town, even had the finely quilted details of its stained glass rose window.

Gatton

One of the earliest settlements in Queensland, Gatton is nestled in the Lockyer Valley midway between Ipswich and Toowoomba. First settled during the 1840s, it became a changeover point for horses pulling the Royal Mail coaches and a resting place for weary travellers making their way from the coast to the Darling Downs. Today the town is the centre of a rich and diverse region of vegetable farms, orchards, beef and dairy cattle stations.

Gatton Historical Museum
Freemans Road
Gatton, QLD 4343.
Ph: (07) 5462 1580 or (07) 5462 2868
2.00p.m. to 5.00p.m. Sunday or other times by appointment.

The Historical Museum is housed in the old Caffey Dance Hall and provides a fascinating glimpse of life in Gatton from the mid 19th century. There are many items of needlework including lace, embroidered linens, cross stitch samplers and period clothing. There are also two pieces of satin formerly belonging to a Gatton dressmaker and dating from the turn of the century. They are still enclosed in their original folders complete with price tag of 2 shillings and 6 pence.

✷ The quilt is not permanently displayed but visitors are welcome to see it by prior arrangement. Please contact the Museum in advance.

✄ A patchwork quilt (195cm x 195cm) of pieced squares and triangles was made by Juliane Jensen of Gatton during the 1920s. Mrs Jensen lived in a cottage in the town and was renowned for her beautiful needlework. She was a member of the Country Women's Association and the Show Society and always contributed to the annual art and craft exhibitions. The quilt was made when she was a young woman. It was used by the family for many years before being donated to the museum.

The work was made from dress cottons, silks and crepes with a backing of cretonne. It was hand pieced in a Nine Patch design with each block made from Squares-on-point. A secondary pattern of orange crosses was created by the clever placement of blocks around the outside. At some later stage the quilt was altered to encase a worn pink paisley eiderdown. It is believed that Mrs Jensen probably made this change during the Depression years of the 1930s, using her patchwork over the tattered cover in the Australian tradition of 'making do.' It was only recently that the back seam was gently unpicked by local quilter Gwen Crozier to reveal the original work.

Gatton Shire Library
Railway Street
Gatton, QLD 4343.
Ph: (07) 5462 0370 Fax: (07) 5462 3269
10.00a.m. – 6.00p.m. Monday to Friday.
9.00a.m. – 11.30a.m. Saturday.
2 quilts.

✷ The quilts are hung on permanent display and may be seen during the opening hours listed.

✄ A pictorial quilt (210cm x 190cm) was designed and made by the Gatton Quilters in 1988 to commemorate the Bicentennial. A large central *'G'* of appliquéd blocks depicts important buildings, some historic and some more recent additions to the town. Images of Aboriginal carvings were based on those appearing in caves a few kilometres south of Gatton and were included as a tribute to the tribe that once inhabited the region. A view of Railway Street illustrates this main thoroughfare as it was during the 19th century. The background of the quilt is a rural scene of farms and orchards, a crop duster flying overhead and hot air balloons drifting above the countryside. The work was made from cotton fabrics. It was pieced, appliquéd, embroidered and quilted by hand.

The *Gatton History Quilt* (165cm x 120cm) was made in 1998 by Gwen Crozier to commemorate the centenary of Federation. It depicts photographs of heritage buildings taken at the turn of the century, each image applied to fabric using the photocopy transfer method. The pictures are framed by a border of strips and Nine Patch blocks and an early Coat of Arms is featured at the top. The quilt presents a valuable record of the past, and of a heritage which sadly has all but disappeared. The work was machine pieced and hand quilted.

Goondiwindi

Goondiwindi is located at the junction of five major highways approximately 200 kilometres south west of Toowoomba. The McIntyre River meanders through the town and forms part of the state border between Queensland and New South Wales. The region was first settled by graziers during the 1830s and developed as an important stopping point for teamsters. The quaint timber Customs House which is now home to the local folk museum was built in 1859 to prevent illegal trading between the colonies. Today the town is an important commercial centre for the thriving rural district surrounding it.

The Goondiwindi Waggamba Community Cultural Centre
Russell Street
Goondiwindi, QLD 4390.
Ph: (07) 4671 1122 Fax: (07) 4671 3013
Goondiwindi Town Council.
7.00a.m. – 12 noon and
1.00p.m. – 4.00p.m. Monday to Friday.

✷ The triptych is hung on permanent display within the Centre and may be seen during the opening hours listed or at weekends by prior arrangement with the Goondiwindi Town Council.

✄ This multi-media quilted wall installation is entitled *Moods of the McIntyre* (350cm x 215cm). It was created by more than 250 local people between 1991 and '93. The inspiration of Jenepher Wilson, the work was specially designed to hang in the new Community Centre. Textile artists Robyn White and Wendy Wright worked with the many community groups, Robyn as co-ordinator, Wendy as tutor and consultant.

Local artists were invited to submit contemporary paintings suitable for translation into a multi-media hanging. Jocelyn Cameron's beautiful abstract painting of the river was selected for the design. It takes the form of a triptych, the top depicting the foliage on the far bank of the McIntyre, the middle representing the river flow itself, and the base illustrating the reflections to be seen in the water.

The project began with the original painting being increased in size sixteen times. This was then copied and the copy painted for reference. Brilliant fabrics in many different textures were used – silk, velvet, voile, corduroy, muslin, leather, and cotton. The cotton had been grown and hand spun in Goondiwindi. The myriad of techniques included spinning, weaving, dyeing, hand and machine embroidery, and quilting. The spaces between the panels were embellished with mobiles designed to represent the flotsam on the water. These were made from pottery, stained glass, and copper enamelling. This magnificent art work took almost two years to complete and now hangs on permanent display, a tribute to the dedication and diversity of talent of the rural community that created it.

Ipswich

The oldest provincial city in Queensland, Ipswich is located forty kilometres south west of Brisbane. A wonderful legacy of fine historic buildings remain in the town as a testament to its early prosperity as a busy inland port and commercial centre. Heritage walking and driving trails guide visitors past many sites from grand mansions to humble turn of the century workers' cottages.

Ipswich City Council
South Street
Ipswich, QLD 4305.
Ph: (07) 3810 6652 Fax: (07) 3810 6741
Cultural Development Officer.
9.00a.m. – 4.30p.m Monday to Friday.
2 quilts.

✷ The quilts are hung next to each other on the second floor of the Council building and may be seen during office hours. Please contact the Cultural Development Officer with any inquiries.

✂ The *Ipswich Bicentennial Quilt* (274cm x 220cm) was designed and made by Joan McKenzie in 1988 as a commemorative project. The work illustrates the early history of the city in sepia coloured images mounted onto the pages of an old photograph album. Each one has been reproduced onto fabric using the photocopy transfer method and held in place with little black corners like those used in albums years ago. Many of the city's heritage buildings are depicted. The pieced background depicts the rural countryside. Appliquéd and quilted details provide further hints to the region's past history. The work was appliquéd, embroidered, pieced and quilted by machine.

The *Ipswich Heritage Quilt* (220cm x 180cm) was designed and made in 1994 by a local community group. The project was co-ordinated by Adriana Rodriquez using the theme 'Community – embracing cultures and drawing people together.' The quilt depicts Ipswich viewed from above and encircled by a graphic purple and black railway line. Groups representing different community cultures stand in the foreground gazing out over their city. Techniques used in creating the work included fabric dyeing, embroidery, piecing, hand and machine appliqué and quilting.

Miles

The little town of Miles is found on the western slopes of the Darling Downs approximately 150 kilometres north west of Toowoomba. Every year the region is transformed by thousands of wildflowers which burst into bloom following the first Spring rains. A wildflower festival is held in September with activities centred around the Historical Village.

Miles Historical Village
Murilla Street
Miles, QLD 4415.
Ph/Fax: (07) 4627 1492
8.00a.m. – 5.00p.m. daily except
Christmas Day.
3 quilts.

The Miles Historical Village comprises more than 30 buildings clustered around Pioneer Street to depict a typical Queensland country town at the turn of the century. The collection of textiles includes tatting, hand made lace, embroidered linen, christening gowns, a wedding dress c.1870, and an embroidered sampler that won first prize in the Miles Show of 1920.

✷ The quilts are permanently displayed in the Slab Hut and may be seen during opening hours.

✂ A Crazy Patchwork quilt (152cm x 226cm) was made in 1951 by Mrs W. H. Goodfellow of Bilinga, a town on the Gold Coast. The work was hand stitched using a range of plain and printed cottons, velvets, silks, and satins, and each patch was outlined and joined to the calico backing with herringbone stitch. It won first prize at the Gold Coast Show in year it was made.

A tube shaped hexagon quilt (200cm x 150cm) c.1960 is of unknown maker. It features colourful rosettes of printed dress cottons and crimplenes of the period.

A patchwork coverlet of multi-coloured squares was made during the late 1960s by Joyce Campbell, Evelyn Mundell and Edith Robinson of Miles. Cotton dress fabrics were hand sewn over paper templates to create the work especially for the antique bed at the village.

PHOTOGRAPHY DANIELLE LANCASTER.

OPPOSITE: *Moods of the McIntyre.* Made by more than 250 members of the local community, 1991-'93. 350cm x 215cm. Goondiwindi Waggamba Community Cultural Centre, Goondiwindi, Queensland.

PHOTOGRAPH JEAN HARSLETT.

TOP: Detail of *Sesquicentennial Quilt*. Made by the Balonne Creative Arts Group, 1996. 262cm x 122cm. St George Library, St George, Queensland. ABOVE: Detail showing back of *Patchwork Quilt of Hexagons* with templates cut from school exercise books. Made by Eileen Ward, c.1920. Collection Stanthorpe Heritage Museum, Stanthorpe, Queensland.

In the Nearby Region

The little town of Meandarra is about an hour's drive south of Miles. Displayed at the Library in Sara Street is a wall hanging created during 1995 and '96 by the Hannaford Patchwork Club. It depicts scenes and buildings within the region and was made as part of the stress relief programme introduced because of the long running drought. The library is open between 10.00a.m. and 3.00p.m. Tuesday and Thursday. Telephone (07) 4665 6147

Charleville

The outback town of Charleville is set on the banks of the Warrego River in the heart of mulga tree country, approximately 760 kilometres west of Brisbane. Established in the 1860s, the town is surrounded by a rich pastoral district and sheep and cattle have flourished here since pioneer days.

Historic House Museum
Alfred Street
Charleville, QLD 4470.
Ph: (07) 4654 3349
9.00a.m. – 4.00p.m. daily.

The textile collection of the Museum includes examples of lace, crochet, and embroidered linen. Framed cross stitch postcards date from World War I and there are several beaded costumes c1920.

✱ The quilt is hung on permanent display and may be seen during opening hours or by appointment. It is advisable to ring before visiting.

✂ This quilt was made as a Bicentennial gift to the town between 1988 and '89 by members of the Charleville Craft Group. The design was created by Reece Campbell and depicts the history and rural industries of the region. Historic House is shown in the lower corner with an old Cobb & Co. coach on the opposite side. A border of Flying Geese in the colours of the outback separate the blocks. The work was appliquéd and quilted by hand.

St George

St George has a picturesque setting on the banks of the Balonne River, a 2 hour drive north west of Goondiwindi. Named by the explorer, Sir Thomas Mitchell on St George's Day, April 23, 1846, the town commemorates this occasion each year with wonderful country activities such as wheelbarrow races, gum boot throwing, billy boiling and damper competitions. Murals depicting the history of cotton and transport have been hand painted by regional artists and may be seen in Balonne and Scott Streets. Only a short drive south at Nindigully is the historic 'Gully Pub.' Built in 1864 on the banks of the Moonie River, it was a Cobb & Co change-over station for many years and has been featured in several commercials as well as the film *Paperback Hero*.

St George Library
118 Victoria Street
St George, QLD 4487.
Ph: (07) 4625 3375 Fax: (07) 4625 4194
2.00p.m. – 5.30p.m. Monday.
1.30p.m. – 4.00p.m. Tuesday and Thursday.
2.00p.m. – 6.00p.m. Wednesday.
10.30a.m. – 5.30p.m. Friday.

✱ The quilt is hung on permanent display within the Library and may be seen during the opening hours listed.

✄ A *Sesquicentennial Quilt* (262cm x 122cm) depicting St George and its rural setting was made by members of the Balonne Creative Arts Group to celebrate the 150th anniversary of the foundation of the town. The project began with several workshops held under the guidance of Pauline Rogers. The quilt was created in four separate panels, each one concentrating on a different theme. They depict the region prior to the arrival of Europeans, the days of early white settlement, the development of the town and growth of the district, and the crops and industries that have flourished over the years. The Balonne River meanders across the quilt providing continuity. The background was hand painted by Pam Kilroy, many of its features further highlighted with hand embroidery. Techniques included hand and machine piecing, embroidery, appliqué, and a variety of three dimensional effects.

Stanthorpe

The pretty rural town of Stanthorpe is set in the highlands of south east Queensland, not far from the state border with New South Wales. Renowned as a region producing fine wool, the fertile slopes surrounding the town are also dotted with thriving orchards and vineyards. Many of the wineries are open to the public. The area is especially beautiful during Spring when the hundreds of fruit trees are in blossom.

Stanthorpe Regional Art Gallery
Weeroona Park
Locke Street
Stanthorpe, QLD 4380.
Ph: (07) 4681 1874 Fax: (07) 4681 4021
10.00a.m. – 4.00p.m. Monday to Friday.
1.00p.m. – 4.00p.m. weekends.
7 quilts.

ABOVE: *Still Life with Blue Jug*. Made by Judy Hooworth, 1992. 123cm x 123cm. Collection Stanthorpe Regional Gallery, Stanthorpe, Queensland.

The Stanthorpe Art Gallery is housed in a purpose designed building constructed in 1987. It consists of an upper and lower gallery divided by a glass fronted display case. There is also a library area which is used for smaller exhibitions. The collection includes paintings, sculpture, fibre and ceramic works. Fibre has been acquired since 1976 and includes both traditional and contemporary works created from a wide variety of materials.

✷ The quilts are not permanently displayed but are included in exhibitions throughout the year. Works held in storage may be seen by prior appointment. To guarantee access please contact the Gallery in writing 6 weeks in advance. You are welcome to telephone Stanthorpe with less notice, though access may not always be possible.

✄ The collection includes *Still Life with Blue Jug* (123cm x 123cm) made by textile artist Judy Hooworth in 1992. Judy returned to her background in painting to create this work which is based on a domestic theme. It depicts an abstract jug on a patterned cloth, a flat Matisse-like design of simple shapes and striking patterns. The centre is surrounded by borders of yellow and red check, crazy zig zag and a curving vine. The work was

LEFT: Detail of *Aussie Bush III*. Made by Fiona Gavens, 1988. 220cm x 240cm. RIGHT AND OPPOSITE: *Ruminative Nuances*. Made by Wendy Holland, 1996. 103cm x 146cm. Collection Stanthorpe Regional Gallery, Stanthorpe, Queensland.

machine pieced, appliquéd and quilted.

Ruminative Nuances (103cm x 146cm) was made by textile artist Wendy Holland in 1996. This quilt was one of a series in which Wendy used the sewing machine to 'draw' onto layered pieces. Old and new silks and old Japanese kimono fragments were appliquéd to painted cotton netting with coloured and gold machine satin stitch. The netting started out as a firm base under the soft and slippery silks but ended up as an integral part of the overall colour and texture. The work includes references to old documents, messages, samplers, symbols and talismans, but Wendy says it was really *'an excuse to play with this particular collection of fabric scraps.'*

Aussie Bush III (220cm x 240cm) was made by Fiona Gavens in 1988. This quilt was one of a series in which Fiona recorded her impressions of the bush – the layers of grass, bushland and trees, the tall straight trunks, the regular structure overlaid with infinite variety. The work also depicts the beauty of drought colours within a bush setting. No matter how dry and brown, there are always some spots of green as well as the glimpse of blue sky through the trees. The quilt was machine pieced and quilted from cotton and polycotton fabrics.

The collection also includes works by Sharyn Hall, Rose Marie Szulc and Tori de Mestre. A community quilt entitled a *Textile Tale* was made as part of the Bicentennial celebrations during 1988.

Stanthorpe Heritage Museum

12 High Street
Stanthorpe, QLD 4380.
Ph: (07) 4681 1711
10.00a.m. – 4.00p.m. Wednesday to Friday.
1.00p.m. – 4.00p.m. Saturday.
9.00a.m. – 1.00p.m. Sunday.

Many heritage buildings from the local area have been relocated to the museum site, each one restored and furnished to depict the life of pioneering settlers of the district. The large textile collection includes wedding and cocktail dresses from the 1930s, heirloom stitched night gowns, one of which includes the embroidered date '1908,' and a large number of embroidered and appliquéd vestments. A beautiful set of sheets and pillowslips came to Australia from Italy c.1930 and features white-on-white appliqué. A sewing bee is held at the museum each Friday afternoon to conserve items from the collection.

✷ The quilt is permanently displayed within the Museum and may be seen during opening hours.

✂ A small patchwork quilt of hexagons was made as a school sampler by Eileen Ward during the 1920s. The work was sewn in the English method over paper templates using printed cotton dress fabrics. The templates were cut from old school exercise and copy books and are still clearly visible behind the hexagons.

Toowoomba

Toowoomba is situated on the edge of the fertile Darling Downs approximately 130 kilometres west of Brisbane. It was established during the 1840s as a stopping point for squatters and teamsters travelling from Moreton Bay to the pastoral region of the west. Earliest settlement was at Drayton, once a separate village but now a suburb just a few kilometres south of Toowoomba. Much of the city's early colonial architecture has been preserved and it is also renowned for its beautiful gardens and wide streets lined with flowering trees.

Toowoomba Community Baptist Church
100 Glenvale Road
Toowoomba, QLD 4350.
Ph: (07) 4633 3173 Church office.
(07) 4635 1356 Robyn Ginn.
The Church office is open between 9.00a.m. – 3.00p.m. Monday to Friday.
Services are held on Sundays at 10.00a.m. and 6.30p.m.

Robyn Ginn, who designed and made this quilt for the church, is well known to many quiltmakers throughout Australia. In 1994 she published a book entitled 'That Quilt has a Story' and it is these stories that have particularly endeared her to many people. Behind her quilt 'And Then There was my Garden' is the beautiful thought that 'There will always be days filled with happiness and days full of shadow, but most days are a mixture of both. This quilt reminds me that there will always be a garden.'

✷ The quilt is hung on permanent display in the Sanctuary of the Church and visitors are welcome during office hours. Robyn Ginn has offered to share the lovely story quilts in her home with interested quiltmakers travelling through Toowoomba. Please contact her by telephone several days in advance.

✄ This inspirational quilt (300cm x 300cm) was designed by Robyn in 1996. It was made by Robyn with help from some of her friends and tells a story of celebration, cultivation, caring and communicating.

A dramatic cross of deep red fabric is the focal point, dividing the background into four separate pictures. Each one has a message. The two figures at the top with arms raised to Heaven are symbols of celebration. In the next quarter, the huge blue rain drops fall to earth, their moisture essential to cultivation and growth. Tears, highlighted as crystal beads on these drops, come with the bent knees and dirty hands that are part of cultivating and nurturing others. Below the cross, one figure holds his arm behind the other in a gesture of caring. The group of three symbolise communication. One holds the cross outstretched to others, while another communicates love with fresh bread. The road in the foreground is crossed to indicate that choice must be made. The stones that lie on it are the stumbling blocks of life. A square in the centre of the cross holds the crown of thorns illuminated against a dark background. Nails point towards the crown, their evil intent highlighted by the black triangles behind them. Two huge drops of blood flow from the crown, the blood of God that brought forgiveness.

The quilt was hand appliquéd, embroidered and quilted. The quilting pattern was designed to emphasise each message and to reproduce the people so that there are not just two or three, but many.

The Royal Bull's Head Inn
Brisbane Street
Drayton
Toowoomba, QLD 4350.
Ph: (07) 4630 1869
10.00a.m. – 4.00p.m. Thursday, Friday, Saturday and Sunday.
5 quilts.

The Royal Bull's Head is one of Queensland's earliest surviving inns. It was built in 1847 and named in honour of 'Champion,' a notable bull from the nearby Cecil Plains Station. The property is owned by the National Trust and provides a unique glimpse of accommodation offered to travellers on the Darling Downs during the 1860s. In addition to the quilts, there is an embroidered coverlet, a collection of period costumes, and a wide variety of embroidered linen and needlework.

✷ The cot quilt is the only work on permanent display. The other quilts are kept in storage but visitors are welcome to see them by prior arrangement.

✄ The collection includes a large quilt of silk diamonds c.1880 of unknown maker and origin. It has been pieced by hand using the English method over paper templates, the silk fabrics providing insights into the fashions of the era and the glorious colours that were available. The quilt has a central square featuring rows of Tumbling Block design surrounded by silk stars. The stars have been pieced from diamonds of light coloured fabric and illuminated by a black background. The work has no filling, a backing of satin, and has not been quilted.

A strippy cot quilt is also of unknown maker and origin. It has been created from alternating strips of white and blue striped cotton, pieced by machine and quilted by hand in a zig zag design.

PHOTOGRAPHY DAVID SEETO.

ABOVE: *Patchwork Quilt.* Made by Robyn Ginn and friends, 1996. 300cm x 300cm. Toowoomba Community Baptist Church, Toowoomba, Queensland.

University of Southern Queensland
West Street
Toowoomba, QLD 4350.
Ph: (07) 4631 2149
9.00a.m. – 5.00p.m. Monday to Friday.

✷ Visitors are welcome to see the quilt but because its location varies throughout the campus it is necessary to make an appointment. Please contact the curator a few days in advance.

✄ This quilt entitled *After the Ball* (138cm x 138cm) was made by Ruth Stoneley in 1989 and purchased by the University in 1995. It was one of a series of black quilts and was made by random piecing from cotton, cotton blends and silks, all of them black. It was quilted by hand and features a central slit with a sequined red heart beneath it.

Bundaberg

The coastal city of Bundaberg is set on the banks of the Burnett River about an hour's drive north of Maryborough. Numerous heritage buildings remain in the town from the early days and a walking tour prepared by the Council explains the history of the most important sites. An historical tapestry is hung on permanent display within the Council Administration Centre, Bourbong Street. It was made in 1967 to commemorate the centenary of Bundaberg by members of E.S.A., an international women's leadership and service organisation.

Fairymead House
Thornhill Street
Bundaberg, QLD 4670.
Ph: (07) 4153 6786 Fax: (07) 4152 4056
10.00a.m. – 4.00p.m. everyday.
3 quilts.

ABOVE: Detail of *World Quilt.* Made by Marguerite Vuichoud between 1927-'33. 200cm x 200cm. Bundaberg Historical Museum, Bundaberg, Queensland.

Fairymead House was built in 1890. It was presented to the city as a Bicentennial gift from the Bundaberg Sugar Company and has since been restored and opened as a museum of the sugar industry.

✷ The quilts are hung on permanent display within the house and may be seen during opening hours.

✄ A pieced heritage quilt of calico hexagons and Nine Patch blocks was made by the Bundaberg Quilters in 1990. Each hexagon features an image worked by hand in rust coloured quilting thread, some of heritage sites, others of pioneers, sea turtles and a casket of rum representing the world famous Bundaberg Rum Distillery. The work was made from cotton fabrics, pieced by machine and quilted by hand.

The *Toft Quilt* is a commemorative work depicting the life and history of the pioneering Toft Family. Harold and Colin Toft invented a cane harvester that was to revolutionise the sugar industry. The quilt was designed by Harold's daughter, Caroline Toft, and made by Joan Finlay in 1994.

A floral appliquéd quilt entitled *Australian Flowers of Yesterday and Today* was made in 1988 as a Bicentennial project by the Queensland State Council of E.S.A. The work was appliquéd, embroidered and quilted by hand.

Bundaberg Historical Museum
Young Street
Bundaberg, QLD 4670.
Ph: (07) 4152 0101
10.00a.m. – 4.00p.m. daily. Closed Christmas Day, Good Friday and Anzac Day.
1 Signature quilt and 2 Signature cloths.

The museum is set in the lovely grounds of the Botanic Gardens. The collection includes a wealth of hand work made by the women of the district from the 1880s onwards. There are examples of lace, cut work, crochet, tatting, appliquéd and embroidered doyleys, drawn thread work and beaded tea pot covers. Displayed in a frame is a panel of 12 embroidered squares collected from the cigarette packets of 1912. A glass panelled room houses a treasured collection of taffeta and brocade dresses and wedding gowns, some of them complete with bustles.

✷ The quilt is permanently displayed within the Museum and may be seen during the opening hours listed above.

✄ A delightful quilt was made by Marguerite Vuichoud between 1927 and '33. Entitled *World Quilt,* Marguerite embroidered her name, her home of Bundaberg, and the year in which she finished the work beneath a simple map of the world. In the tradition of Friendship quilts she posted small squares of green linen to favourite actors, authors, sportsmen and other famous people. Many of them returned autographed signatures written in ink. Marguerite used lemon juice to remove ink splotches before embroidering the names in stem stitch.

Little illustrations were added to the squares, each one drawn by her father. The autographs of cricketers Sir Donald Bradman and Archie Jackson included a bat, ball, and stumps worked in simple stitches. The word *'Hollywood'* was sewn above Will Roger's name, highlighting Marguerite's admiration for movie stars. She also stitched the words *'Mother'* and *'Dad'* above the Crest of Bundaberg. Among the many other signatures are the names of Amy Johnson, Charles Kingsford Smith, Gladys Moncrieff, Mary Grant Bruce, Maurice Chevalier and Mary Pickford.

There are two other Signature cloths in the collection. The first, embroidered in red thread, was made in 1906 and donated to the Museum by the Buss family. It contains the signatures of many of Bundaberg's prominent citizens of the day. The second cloth was worked in multi-coloured threads and made by Rose Sharp in 1920 to commemorate her wedding day.

Childers

The lovely old town of Childers lies in the rolling hills between Bundaberg and Maryborough, a three and a half hour drive north of Brisbane. The lush green fields of sugar cane growing in the surrounding countryside contrast vividly with the rich red volcanic soil that is a distinctive feature of this part of Queensland. Although the town suffered a disastrous fire in 1902 many buildings of historical significance still

PHOTOGRAPHY RON WILSON.

ABOVE: Details of the *Childers Bicentennial Quilt* showing the Anglican Church (top) and the Federal Hotel (below). Made by the Childers Quilters, 1988. 250cm x 200cm. Isis Shire Council, Childers, Queensland.

remain and Childers has been declared a National Trust town. A walking tour takes visitors past landmarks and heritage sites and the quilt is included on its list.

Isis Shire Council
45 Churchill Street
Childers, QLD 4660.
Ph: (07) 4126 1355 Fax: (07) 4126 1604
8.45a.m. – 4.30p.m. Monday to Friday.

✷ The quilt is hung in a glass case in the foyer of the Isis Shire Council and may be seen during business hours.

✂ This pictorial quilt (250cm x 200cm) was made by the Childers Quilters to celebrate the Bicentennial in 1988. A huge sun, symbol of the state, is the focal point of the work, the town's heritage buildings and rural industries depicted within its rays.

The Old Butcher Shop c.1896 which survived the fire unscathed is appliquéd next to cultivated farmlands. This quaint building has been sewn complete with striped awnings and iron lacework made from dyed guipure lace. The Federal Hotel with its original swinging doors and decorative balustrade is also included, its roof cleverly quilted to mimic the undulations of the iron. The town's beautiful Anglican Church can be seen in the centre. Built at the turn of the century, it is renowned for its stained glass windows depicting the life of Christ. Textured cotton was used reverse side up to create the weather-boards, paisley fabric for the windows.

The red border fabric was chosen to represent the colour of the region's soil. The work was appliquéd, embroidered and quilted by hand, the quilting pattern around the border designed to depict the many fruits and vegetables grown throughout the region.

ABOVE: The maker of the quilt, Ellen Jane Griffin (centre left) with six of her children. Aunt Winnie is seated next to Ellen. (centre right). OPPOSITE: Details of *Aunt Winnie's Quilt.* Made by Ellen Jane Griffin, c.1890. Collection Childers Historical Complex, Childers, Queensland.

Childers Historical Complex
Taylor Street
Childers, QLD 4660
Ph: (07) 4126 1522 President, Childers Historical Society.
(07) 4126 1994 Childers Tourist Information Centre.
9.00a.m. – 12 noon weekdays.

The Childers Historical Complex has a picturesque setting within shady parkland just off the main highway. Fascinating relics and treasures from early times are displayed in heritage buildings and include many examples of antique needlework. There is an exquisite white cotton christening gown, its pin-tucking, hem stitching and embroidery worked entirely by hand. A cream wedding dress c.1900 has also been hand stitched. A 'Childers Bazaar Autograph Cloth 1897' features hundreds of signatures embroidered in red silk thread around its border. There are also rag rugs, tapestry cushions and a white hand knitted coverlet.

✷ The quilt is displayed on a beautiful iron bed formerly owned by Dame Annabelle Rankin's family. It may be seen during opening hours or by appointment. The skin rug is not permanently displayed but may be seen by request.

✂ *Aunt Winnie's Quilt* was one of two embroidered coverlets made in the late 19th century by Ellen Jane Griffin who lived on a farm at Abingdon, just east of Childers. She later moved to Taylor Street and her home may still be seen opposite the Historic Complex. Ellen died in 1946 just before her 90th birthday. She had been the mother of eight children and her daughter Winnifred owned this quilt for many years. Like Ellen, Winnifred was also a wonderful needlewoman. She worked as a dressmaker at the Taylor Street house during the 1950s and her beautiful embroidery is still remembered. She never married and obviously treasured her mother's quilt, probably keeping it only 'for best.' It is still in perfect condition after one hundred years. Family members living in Childers today remember it as *Aunt Winnie's Quilt.*

Worked on heavy white linen, the embroidery has been stitched by hand using thick white cotton. In the centre, a cluster of lilies has been surrounded by a twining rose. An oval of hand made lace separates the lilies and roses from beautiful three dimensional sunflowers, some in full bloom, others just beginning to open. The stitches include stem stitch, buttonhole, huge colonial knots and densely padded satin stitch. The work has no backing and the meticulous stitching is clearly visible on the reverse.

A rug of Chinchilla Rabbit skin was donated to the museum by Eric Bryant. It was made in 1931 for Eric's grandfather, Oscar who was known affectionately by the family as 'Ossie.' During the Depression years of the 1930s Ossie lived in the Sydney suburb of Belmore. He kept

PHOTOGRAPHY RON WILSON.

approximately a dozen Chinchilla rabbits at a time, maintaining them in hutches in his back garden and using them as a source of fresh meat for his family. The pelts were saved and eventually sewn together into a warm grey rug and finished with a lining of checked feltex.

Gladstone

Gladstone is situated just south of the Tropic of Capricorn on the shores of Port Curtis. A prosperous city, it is a major industrial centre and port for Central Queensland. It is also a departure point for the Great Barrier Reef and safe harbour for competitors in the annual Brisbane to Gladstone yacht race.

Gladstone Regional Art Gallery and Museum

Cnr Goondoon and Bramston Streets
Gladstone, QLD 4680.
Ph: (07) 4970 1242 Fax: (07) 4972 9097
10.00a.m. – 5.00p.m. Monday to Friday.
10.00a.m. – 4.00p.m. Saturday and public holidays. Closed Sunday.
2 quilts.

The Gladstone Regional Art Gallery and Museum is housed in the heritage listed old Town Hall. It is a focal point for the preservation and display of the region's history and cultural heritage. There are three display areas – a museum room, front and main gallery. The diverse and innovative programme of events includes collection-based and interstate exhibitions. The Gallery works to foster local arts in addition to developing art, craft and social history collections pertaining to the region.

✷ The quilts are not on permanent display but may be seen by appointment. Please contact the Director by letter or fax one week in advance.

PHOTOGRAPHY STEPHEN MILLS.

ABOVE: Detail of *How Much Rain Did You Get Last Night?* Made by Rosemary Anderson and Jenny Whitehead, 1994. 389cm x 119cm. Collection Gladstone Regional Art Gallery and Museum, Gladstone, Queensland.

✂ A Crazy quilt entitled *Mama Taught Me Sewing* (170cm x 170cm) was made by Marguerita Dobrinin in 1992. The quilt, created as a tribute to Marguerita's mother Emily, tells her family's story. Born in Siberia, Emily grew up in Manchuria after fleeing the Russian Revolution. Ousted from China by the Communist Government in 1952, the family settled near Gladstone. The quilt features photographs of family members surrounded by rich and colourful fabrics, some from her mother Emily, and others from relatives and friends. Pieces of Chinese satin, scraps of lace, ribbons, buttons, and doyleys dating from the 1920s have been included. Each patch has been heavily embroidered using a multitude of stitches, many of them learned from Emily.

A wall hanging and installation piece entitled *How Much Rain Did You Get Last Night?* (389cm x 119cm) was made in 1994 by Rosemary Anderson and Jenny Whitehead. The work embodies the feelings of people living in Central Queensland during the long running drought – a time when the common-place greeting of *'G'day'* was frequently replaced by *How much rain did you get last night?*

The drama of an electric storm is captured by the intermingling of purple and blue dyes, gold hand-couched threads of lighting, and dark clouds made from overlaid silk-chiffon which partly obscure a silvery brocade moon. The bulbous silhouettes of the ubiquitous bottle trees were made from layered tulle, the stylised leaves and grasses from silk-chiffon and tulle. Three weathered fence posts stand in front of the hanging and support an optimistic array of rain gauges.

Maryborough

One of Queensland's oldest towns, Maryborough is set on the banks of the Mary River, a three hour drive north of Brisbane. It has retained much of its 19th century charm and is renowned for its beautiful colonial architecture. Many of the houses have been built from local timber with ornate use of lattice and decorative ironwork.

Maryborough City Library

Bazaar Street
Maryborough, QLD 4650.
Ph: (07) 4123 8892 or (07) 4123 8892
9.30a.m. – 4.45p.m. Monday, Wednesday and Friday.
12.00noon – 4.45p.m. Tuesday.
9.30a.m. – 8.00p.m. Thursday.
9.00a.m. – 11.30a.m. Saturday.

✷ The quilt is hung on permanent display upstairs in the library and may be seen during opening hours.

✄ This pictorial quilt was made by the Ms Stitches Needlework Group to celebrate the Bicentennial in 1988. A large central block depicts the stately Maryborough City Hall, built in 1908 in American colonial style. Green and red borders surround images of other historic buildings – a heritage cottage, the Customs House, War Memorial and band rotunda. The cultural interests of the town, the beautiful beaches of nearby Hervey Bay and the lucrative timber industry have also been included. The work was appliquéd by hand and machine, machine pieced and hand quilted.

In the Nearby Region

Displayed at the Hervey Bay Council Chambers, just a short drive from Maryborough, is a Coat of Arms made by the Hervey Bay Quilters in 1996. The work captures the essence of the Bay region with its emphasis on holiday fun, sailing, fishing, and whale watching. It was hand appliquéd, embroidered and quilted. The Council is open between 8.30a.m. and 4.30p.m. Monday to Friday and located at 77 Tavistock Street, Torquay. Telephone (07) 4125 0255.

Goomeri and Kilkivan

The rural towns of Goomeri and Kilkivan are located on the eastern slopes of the Great Dividing Range in the heart of the Burnett region, a short distance north east of Kingaroy. Goomeri is known as the 'Clock Town'

PHOTOGRAPHY STEPHEN MILLS.

ABOVE: *Mama Taught Me Sewing.* Made by Marguerita Dobrinin, 1992. 170cm x 170cm. Collection Gladstone Regional Art Gallery and Museum, Gladstone, Queensland.

because of its unique memorial clock. Dedicated to soldiers from the district, letters replace numbers on the four faces to spell out the words 'Lest we Forget.' The small township of Kilkivan is nestled in the hills 25 kilometres east of Goomeri.

Kilkivan Historical Museum
12 Bligh Street
Kilkivan, QLD 4600.
Ph: (07) 5484 1140 or (07) 5484 1191
12 noon – 3.00p.m. Tuesday and Saturday
or by arrangement.
1 quilt plus appliquéd quilt cover of net.

This little folk museum contains many items reflecting the colourful past of the district. The main building is the Rise and Shine Cottage in which rooms have been furnished to depict a parlour, bedroom and general store. The collection includes hand made underwear from the 19th century, two christening gowns c.1900, a rag rug and a school sampler of embroidery stitches dated 1912.

✷ Both items are permanently displayed within the Museum and may be seen during the hours listed.

✄ A rare and beautiful appliquéd quilt cover of net (250cm x 250cm) was hand made more than a century ago by Lil Woods of Gympie. Lil was a very skilled needlewoman and created the cover for her glory box. It is believed she may have had help with the sewing from her sister.

Appliqué on net had long been popular in England and instructions were included in publications such as Caulfeild's *Dictionary of Needlework* in 1882. Such work was extremely practical in the warm Australian climate. Designed to encase an old quilt or eiderdown, the filling could easily be changed from light to heavy for the different seasons. Lil appliquéd her design to a strong net background using various widths of white cotton braid. Her pattern would have been drawn onto a background of fabric or brown paper and tacked to the net before stitching began. Eight beautiful baskets of flowers with trailing bows have been appliquéd around the sides. The centre of each flower has a 'wheel' or eyelet made from buttonhole stitch worked closely over a thick thread. The leaves have been made from folded braid, the stems and tendrils from finely rolled cylinders. The outer edge of the net has been trimmed with braid and little fabric covered buttons have been spaced evenly along one end to encase the filling.

Lil died almost fifty years ago and the cover was left to her relative, Ita Brady. Ita treasured it for more than forty years before donating it to the Museum.

A quilt of Grandmother's Flower Garden design (106cm x 95cm) was made in 1991 by a group of local quiltmakers. The rosettes were created from a variety of floral prints and surrounded by a background of plain blue hexagons. The work was quilted by hand and the date and signature of each maker was embroidered to the back.

Kilkivan Shire Council Library
Moore Street
Goomeri, QLD 4601.
Ph: (07) 4168 4340 Library.
(07) 4168 4284 Librarian.
2.00p.m. – 5.00p.m. Monday and Thursday.
9.00a.m. – 12 noon Tuesday
and Wednesday.

✷ The quilt is hung in a glass case within the library and may be seen during opening hours or at other times by prior arrangement with the Librarian.

✄ This heritage quilt (210cm x 225cm) was designed by Margaret Green and made by Margaret and the Goomeri Quilters in 1990. It features a large central *'G'* of appliquéd blocks depicting unique features and heritage buildings. Many of the images were inspired by photographs from Dulcie Logan's book *Where Two Rivers Run*. The background of the quilt reflects the agricultural diversity of the region with its lucerne, sorghum, soya beans, dairy cattle and pigs. Boonara Homestead, depicted in the centre, was the sight of the first white settlement in the region. The quilt was appliquéd, embroidered and quilted by hand.

Kingaroy

Kingaroy is a thriving business and rural centre within the rich agricultural area of South Burnett. Home of former Queensland Premier, Joh Bjelke-Peterson, it is known as the Peanut Capital of Australia and lush green peanut crops cover the fertile red paddocks surrounding the town.

Kingaroy Bicentennial Heritage Museum
Haly Street
Kingaroy, QLD 4610.
Ph: (07) 4162 4953
9.00a.m. – 4.00p.m. Monday to Friday.
9.00a.m. – 2.00p.m. Saturday.
and Sunday.

The Museum preserves the history of Kingaroy and depicts the development of the peanut industry from the pioneering days of the 1870s when it was first grown by Chinese fossickers. The collection includes embroidered linen, a hand crocheted coverlet c.1900, and a century old beaded cape.

PHOTOGRAPHY BERNIE CRAWFORD.

OPPOSITE: Detail of *Appliquéd Quilt Cover of Net.* Made by Lil Woods, c.1890. 250cm x 250cm. Collection Kilkivan Historical Museum, Kilkivan, Queensland.

✷ The quilt is hung on permanent display within the Museum and may be seen during opening hours.

✂ This quilt (210cm x 270cm) was made in 1988 by members of the Kingaroy Bicentennial Quilting Group. It features pictorial blocks illustrating historic buildings, local industries, native birds and flowers. It was hand appliquéd, machine pieced and hand quilted.

Wondai

The South Burnett town of Wondai lies midway between Kingaroy and Goomeri. The spectacular native bottle tree may be seen growing in large stands in two areas of the Shire.

Shire of Wondai Museum
MacKenzie Street (behind the library)
Wondai, QLD 4606.
Ph: (07) 4168 5402 Fax: (07) 4168 5808
Museum and
(07) 4168 5675 or (07) 4168 5647
after hours.
10.00a.m. – 12.30p.m. and
1.30p.m – 4.00p.m. Monday to Friday.
Weekends by arrangement.

The collection of the Museum includes hand embroidered, crocheted and painted articles dating from the early 1900s.

✷ The coverlet is displayed on an iron bed may be seen during opening hours.

✂ This patchwork coverlet (165cm x 228cm) was made c.1940 by Mrs Moore of Armidale. It features a pattern of stars created from triangles, diamonds and hexagons. It was hand stitched over paper templates using fabrics of printed cotton. The edge of the pieced work was machine stitched to the cream cotton background.

There are also several hospital basinet and cot coverlets. They were made during the 1930s by the night staff who embroidered the work during periods when the wards were quiet.

Sarina

The little town of Sarina is set in the foothills of the Connors Ranges in the region of northern Queensland known as the Sugar Coast. The beautiful bay of the Sarina Inlet is close by and the Great Barrier Reef is also within easy access. It is the incredible diversity of the region that is reflected in the naming of the quilt *Sarina Surprise.*

Sarina Shire Library
65 Broad Street
Sarina, QLD 4737.
Ph: (07) 4943 1730 Fax: (07) 4943 1814
9.00a.m. – 5.00p.m. Monday, Tuesday,
Wednesday, Friday.
10.00a.m. – 4.00p.m. Thursday.
9.00a.m. – 12.00 noon Saturday.

✷ The quilt is framed and hangs on permanent display in the Library. It may be seen during opening hours.

✂ This lovely quilt entitled *Sarina Surprise* (350cm x 250cm) was made between 1993 and '95 by the Sarina Fibre Arts Group. Several workshops were held with Pauline Rogers and members were taught new techniques and design skills. Photographs of buildings were enlarged and traced and fabrics of suitable colour and texture were chosen.

One of the most special inclusions was the Diner, shown at the centre top of the quilt. Also known as the Pie Cart, it was originally on wheels and meandered from site to site around the town. It was purchased by Bob Ellis for two pounds during the Depression and he was given two years to pay the sum. Pies cost threepence each at the time. The Pie Cart was to develop a very special place in the hearts of the battlers of the community – it served as information bureau, travel centre, employment agency, social and spiritual home for the jobless, the hungry, the destitute and the stranger. Over the years the Diner has been threatened with closure. Each time it has survived and meals are still being served to this day.

Also depicted is St Michael's Catholic Church, the quaint Sarina Railway Station, the bomb shelter built during World War II and the commemorative sun dial. In the foreground, the region's picturesque beaches, the Plane Creek Mill, and sugar cane being fired to remove the snakes and undergrowth before harvesting.

Each building was made by hand, some requiring up to thirty five individual pieces. The large tree weaving its branches between the buildings represents the many old figs shading the town's main street. It was appliquéd, machine and hand embroidered into place. Fabric for the background was specially hand painted and dyed. The leaves and flowers of the eucalypt framing the left side were machine embroidered. Wire was encased in each one so that they could be sculpted into shape. The quilt was finished with fine hand quilting, more than two thousand hours of stitching involved in its creation.

OPPOSITE: *Sarina Surprise.* Made by the Sarina Fibre Arts Group, 1993-'95. 350cm x 250cm. Sarina Shire Library, Sarina, Queensland. (clockwise from top left) the Sarina Railway Station; the flowering gum tree with wired flowers and leaves; the Plane Creek Mill and cane fields; the Diner.

SARINA
LEST WE
FORGET

BRUCE HIGHWAY
ROCKHAMPTON 1 MACK

Charters Towers

The historic city of Charters Towers lies in the fertile countryside of the Burdekin River Valley, approximately 130 kilometres inland from Townsville. The discovery of gold in the nearby hills in 1871 was to lead to rapid development and many of the elaborate Victorian buildings remaining today reflect the prosperity of the 1880s and '90s. The town is the hub of a thriving rural area and has also become an important educational centre.

All Souls' and St Gabriel's School
Flinders Highway
Charters Towers, QLD 4820.
Ph: (07) 4787 1433 Fax: (07) 4787 3049
8.30a.m. – 3.00p.m. Monday to Friday.
Closed school holidays.

✷ The quilt is hung on permanent display in the school library. It can be seen during school hours or at other times by appointment with the Librarian. Groups are asked to telephone in advance.

✄ This lovely quilt of Stained Glass appliqué (190cm x 240cm) was made by members of the school community to commemorate the 75th Anniversary of All Souls' and St Gabriel's. The large central window depicts the Phoenix rising from the flames of World War 1. The cornerstones are the emblems of the founding orders, the Brotherhood of St Barnabas for All Souls, and the Society of the Sacred Advent for St Gabriel's. Framing the sides are the crests of the various houses, the Phoenix Palm of the school crest at the top. Brocade and cotton fabrics were used to produce the varied texture and colour combinations and the background fabric was tie dyed to achieve the effect of a cloudy blue sky.

Zara Clarke Transport and Folk Museum
Mosman Street
Charters Towers, QLD 4820.
Ph: (07) 4787 4161
10.00a.m. – 3.00p.m. daily.
2 quilts.

The Museum is housed in a fine 19th century commercial property which formerly served as a general merchant's store. The large collection of textiles includes costumes, heirloom nighties and christening robes. There are examples of embroidery, tatting, hand made lace and crochet. Several cross stitch samplers were made by school children around the turn of the century.

✷ The patchwork quilt is permanently displayed and may be seen during opening hours. The wagga is not always on display but may be seen by request.

✄ A delicate hand pieced patchwork quilt in subdued colours of pale pink and white was made by Zara Clarke c.1910-'20. Zara had been born in 1885, one of ten children. Her parents, William and Mary Clarke, had immigrated to Australia from Antrim, Ireland. The family lived just outside Charters Towers on a grazing property named 'Mirtna,' a name taken from their Irish home town spelt backwards. A water colour painting done by Zara of the homestead is also held by the museum. Zara never married and it is believed that she had only a limited education. She was very artistic however, and a fine needlewoman.

Ireland had a long tradition of quilt making and there is little doubt that Zara would have been taught these skills by her mother. Her quilt was made from pieced Nine Patch blocks placed on-point and alternated with plain squares of white cotton. It has a thick and heavy filling and has been finely quilted in a pattern of concentric squares. The work remains as a rare example of an early Australian quilt made in a repeating block design and quilted. Zara died in 1974 at the age of 89. Her will provided a legacy which enabled the establishment of the museum.

The collection also includes a wagga made in 1946 by Mrs Nielsen who lived in the little gold mining town of Pandanus, just east of Charters Towers. The wagga was used by the maker's family for many years. It is extremely heavy with a top and backing created from recycled blankets and a filling of corn feed bags. A few machine stitches placed every 30cm hold the three layers together.

Thursday Island

Thursday Island is the most northerly point in Australia. Situated in Torres Strait off the tip of Cape York Peninsula, this tiny tropical island has a fascinating history. Years ago it was a vital area for the pearling industry and adventurers came from all over the world to hunt for bech-de-mer, the sea cucumber eaten as a delicacy in China. Many people stayed and today the population of around 4000 is extraordinarily diverse.

All Souls' and St Bartholomew's Cathedral
Douglas Street
Thursday Island, QLD 4875.
Ph/Fax: (07) 4069 2499 Church or
Ph: (07) 4069 1551 Fax: (07) 4069 1365
Christine Conner, Peddell's Ferry and Tour Service.
The Cathedral is open most of the time. Services are held at 7.30a.m. and 5.30p.m. Monday to Saturday and 10.00a.m. Sunday.

LEFT: *All Souls' and St Gabriel's 75th Anniversary Quilt.* Made by the school community, 1995. 190cm x 240cm. All Souls' and St Gabriel's School, Charters Towers, Queensland. RIGHT: *Quetta Memorial Quilt.* Made by the Cammeray Quilters, 1990. 114cm x 182cm. All Souls' and St Bartholomew's Cathedral, Thursday Island, Queensland.

The Cathedral was built as a lasting memorial to those who lost their lives when the RMS Quetta struck an uncharted rock and sank near Mt Adolphus Island on a serene moonlit night in 1890. Many of the relics from the shipwreck are displayed within the church. There is a very multi-cultural congregation and music is an important part of services. Hymns are sung in English as well as the Island languages of Merium Mer and Kala La Gawa.

✷ The quilt is hung on permanent display in the side chapel of the Cathedral and visitors are always welcome.

✂ The *Quetta Memorial Quilt* (114cm x 182cm) was commissioned by members of the Cathedral Ladies Guild on Thursday Island and made by the Cammeray Quilters in 1990. Research information used as a basis for the design came from a book entitled the *Wreck of the Quetta* by John Bayton, as well as from Bishop and Mrs Hall Matthews.

The quilt depicts the terrible moments following the collision as the ship lurches, tilts and begins to sink into the ocean. Jets of steam and a large oil slick can be seen emerging from the stricken vessel as the terrified survivors watch helplessly from the ocean. The appliquéd people represent crew and passengers who actually survived the disaster. The top border depicts the Cathedral, quilted rays of light linking its cross to the Quetta as a symbol of the Lord's love to those in distress. The work was hand appliquéd, embroidered and quilted and the stars and rock were tied. The shark circling beneath the survivors, as well as the partly immersed ship, were covered with turquoise organza to give the impression of being underwater. Most of the fabrics used were synthetic to resist fading as well as the dampness and mould of a humid climate.

INDEX

Page numbers in italics indicate illustrations.

FIRST PUBLISHED IN AUSTRALIA IN 1999 BY AQD PRESS
PO Box 202, Hunters Hill NSW 2110, Australia

ISBN 0-646-36164-3

Designed by Elisa Wood
Printed and bound in Hong Kong by Everbest Printing Co. Ltd.

COVER: ***Nursery Rhyme Quilt*****. Made by Amy Amelia Earl, 1925.**
Collection Tasmanian Museum and Art Gallery, Hobart, Tasmania.

PAGE ONE: Detail of ***The Wedding Quilt*****. Made by Mary Jane Hannaford.**
Collection National Gallery of Australia, Canberra.

PAGE TWO: ***Yarns Artwork in Silk*****. (Summer panel).**
Made by the community of Deloraine, 1992-'95.
Deloraine Community Complex, Deloraine, Tasmania.

PAGE FOUR: : Details of ***Durham Quilt of Yellow and White Cotton Sateen*****.**
Made by Matilda Clish, 1913.
Collection Embroiderers' Guild of South Australia, Mile End, S.A.

PAGE SIX: Details of ***Pieced and Appliqued Quilt*****. Made by Sarah Evans, c.1806.**
National Trust of Australia (W.A.) – Woodbridge Historic Home, Guildford, W.A.

PAGE NINE: Detail of ***Patchwork Quilt*****. Made by Elizabeth Keen, 1879.**
Collection Queenscliffe Historical Museum, Queenscliff, Victoria.

PAGE ELEVEN: Detail of ***Crazy Patchwork Quilt*****. Unknown Maker, c.1898.**
Collection Eskbank House, Lithgow, New South Wales.

THIS PAGE: Detail of ***Pieced Woollen Quilt*****. Said to have been made by freed Texan slaves, c.1865. Collection Powerhouse Museum, Ultimo, Sydney.**

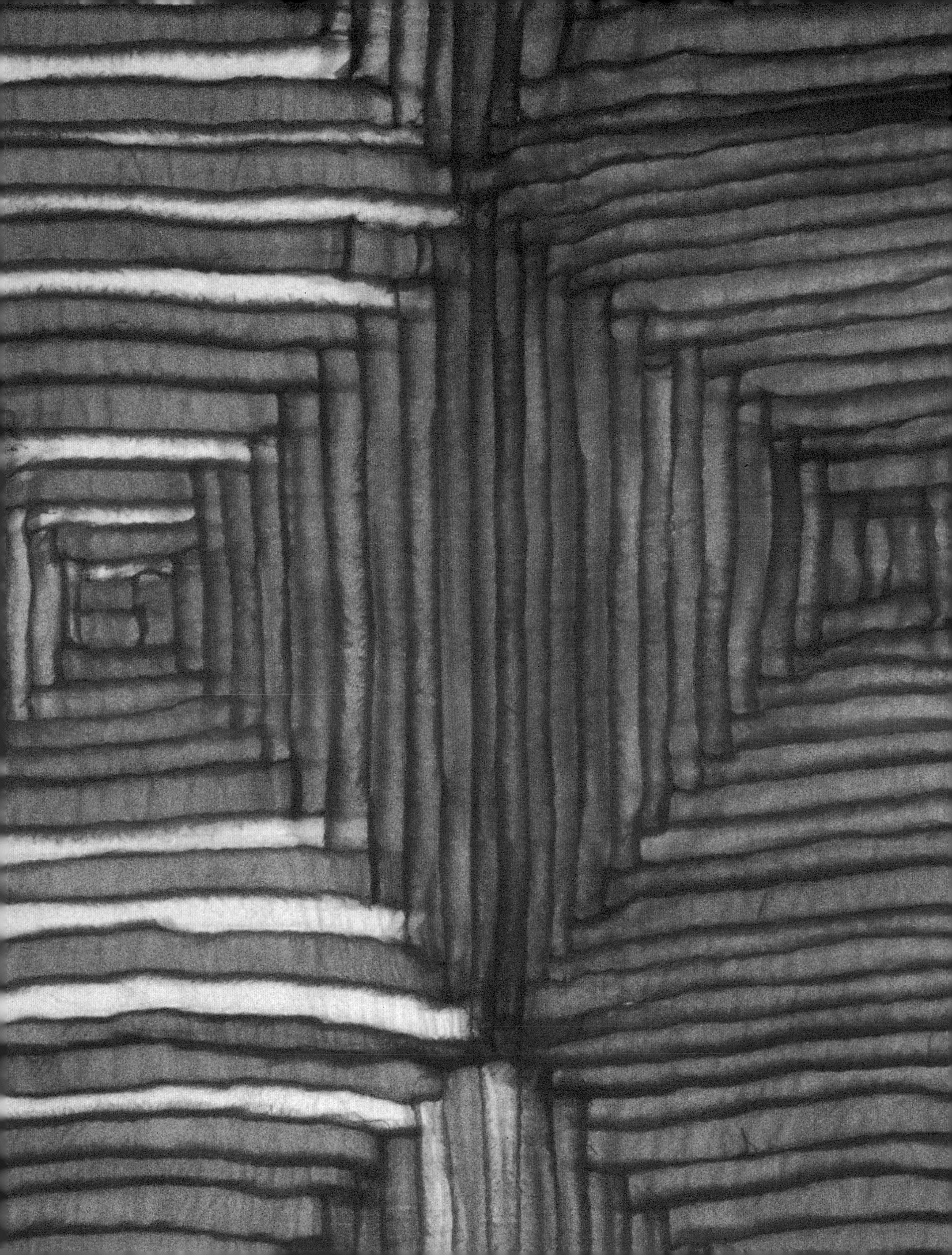